Elements of Soil Mechanics for Civil and Mining Engineers

G. N. SMITH, M.Sc., M.I.C.E., M.I.Struct.E., M.Am.Soc.C.E.

Third edition

Crosby Lockwood Staples   London

Granada Publishing Limited
First published in Great Britain 1968 by Crosby Lockwood & Son Ltd
Second edition 1971

Third edition published 1974 by Crosby Lockwood Staples
Frogmore St Albans Herts and 3 Upper James Street London W1R 4BP

ISBN 0 258 96948 2 hardback
     0 258 96949 0 paperback

Reproduced and printed by photolithography and bound in
Great Britain at The Pitman Press, Bath

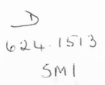

Preface

In this third edition of *Elements of Soil Mechanics* I have revised the text so that force and stress are now expressed exclusively in SI units. This revision has also given me the opportunity to include new material on subjects such as soil suction and partial saturation, and soil mechanics aspects of highway design, which are now finding their way into most undergraduate courses in soil mechanics.

I should like to express my thanks to Whatlings (Foundations) Ltd for their preparation of Figure 13.5, and also to the friends, and strangers, in the general field of soil mechanics who have written to me with comments on earlier editions. I trust that this new version may prove equally useful, if not more so.

G. N. SMITH

December, 1973

Contents

Notation Index

The following is a list of the more important symbols used in the text.

A	Area, pore pressure coefficient
A_b	Area of base of pile
A_r	Area ratio
A_s	Area of surface of embedded length of pile shaft
B	Width, pore pressure coefficient
C	Cohesive force, constant
C_c	Compression index, soil compressibility
C_r	Static cone resistance
C_s	Constant of compressibility
C_v	Coefficient of consolidation, void fluid compressibility
D	Diameter, depth factor, depth of pile
D_{10}	Effective particle size
E	Modulus of elasticity, efficiency of pile group
F	Factor of safety
G	Particle specific gravity, centre of gravity
H	Thickness, height
I	Index, moment of inertia
I_L	Liquidity index
K	Factor, ratio of σ_3/σ_1
K_a	Coefficient of active earth pressure
K_o	Coefficient of earth pressure at rest
K_p	Coefficient of passive earth pressure
K_s	Pile constant
L	Length
L.L.	Liquid limit
M	Moment
N	Number, stability number
N_c, N_q, N_γ	Bearing capacity coefficients
P	Force
P_a	Thrust due to active earth pressure
P_p	Thrust due to passive earth pressure
P.I.	Plasticity index
P.L.	Plastic limit
Q	Total quantity of flow in time t

Q_b	Ultimate strength of pile base
Q_s	Ultimate strength of pile shaft
Q_u	Ultimate strength of pile
R	Radius, residual, reaction, residual factor
R.D.	Relative density
S	Degree of saturation, settlement
S_t	Sensitivity
S.L.	Shrinkage limit
T	Time factor, tangential force, surface tension
U	Average degree of consolidation
U_z	Degree of consolidation at a point at depth z
V	Volume
V_a	Volume of air
V_s	Volume of solids
V_v	Volume of voids
V_w	Volume of water
W	Weight
W_s	Weight of solids
W_w	Weight of water
Z	Section modulus
a	Area
b	Width
c	Unit cohesion with respect to total stresses
c'	Unit cohesion with respect to effective stresses
c_b	Undisturbed shear strength of soil at pile base
$\bar{c}$	Average undisturbed shear strength of soil adjoining pile
c_w	Cohesion between wall and soil
d	Pile penetration depth, pile diameter
e	Void ratio, eccentricity
f	Ultimate unit skin friction for piles
g	Gravitational acceleration
h	Hydrostatic head
h_c	Capillary rise, tension crack depth
i	Hydraulic gradient
k	Coefficient of permeability
l	Length
m	Moisture content, stability coefficient
m_v	Coefficient of volume compressibility
n	Porosity, stability coefficient
p	Pressure
p_a	Active earth pressure
p_c	Preconsolidation pressure, cell pressure
p_o	Earth pressure at rest, overburden pressure
p_o'	Effective overburden pressure

p_p	Passive earth pressure
q	Unit quantity of flow, ultimate load
r	Radius, radial distance
r_u	Pore pressure ratio
t	Time
u	Pore water pressure
u_i	Initial pore water pressure
v	Velocity
x	Horizontal distance
y	Horizontal, vertical distance
z	Vertical distance, depth
α	Angle, adhesion factor for piles
β	Angle
γ	Unit weight
γ_b	Bulk unit weight of soil
γ_d	Dry unit weight of soil
γ_{sat}	Saturated unit weight of soil
γ_{sub}	Submerged unit weight of soil
γ_w	Unit weight of water
δ	Angle of friction between soil and wall
ϵ	Strain
θ	Angle
μ	Coefficient, one micron
ν	Poisson's ratio
ρ	Settlement, density
ρ_b	Bulk density of soil
ρ_d	Dry density of soil
ρ_{sat}	Saturated density of soil
ρ_{sub}	Submerged density of soil
ρ_w	Density of water
σ_n	Normal stress
σ'	Effective stress
$\sigma_1, \sigma_2, \sigma_3$	Major, intermediate and minor principal stresses
τ	Shear stress
ϕ	Angle of internal friction, with respect to total stresses, potential function
ϕ'	Angle of internal friction with respect to effective stresses
χ	Saturation parameter
ψ	Stress function

1. Classification and Identification Properties of Soil

AGRICULTURAL AND ENGINEERING SOIL

If an excavation is made through previously undisturbed ground the following materials are usually encountered (Fig. 1.1):

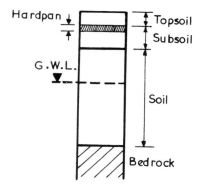

Fig. 1.1 Materials encountered during excavation

Topsoil
A layer of organic soil, usually not more than 500 mm thick, in which humus (highly organic partly decomposed vegetable matter) is often found.
Subsoil
The weathered portion of the Earth's crust lying between the topsoil and the unweathered soil below.
Hardpan
In humid climates humic acid can be formed by rain water causing decomposition of humus. This acid leaches out iron and alumina oxides down into the lower layers where they act as cementation agents to form a hard, rock-like material. Hardpan is difficult to excavate and, as it does not soften when wet, has a high resistance to normal soil drilling methods. A hardpan layer is sometimes found at the junction of the topsoil and the subsoil.

1

Soil
The soft geological deposits extending from the subsoil to bedrock. In some soils there is a certain amount of cementation between the grains which affects the physical properties of the soil. If this cementation is such that a rock-hard material has been produced then the material must be described as rock. A rough rule is that if the material can be excavated by hand or hand tools it is a soil.

Ground water
A reservoir of underground water. The upper surface of this water may occur at any depth and is known as the water table or ground water level (G.W.L.).

Engineering definitions

Geologists class all items of the Earth's crust as rock, whether hard or soft deposits. Civil engineers use the following definitions:

Rock
Igneous, metamorphic, or sedimentary.

Soil
The actions of frost, temperature, gravity, wind and rain are continually forming rock particles that eventually become soils. There are three types of soil when considering modes of formation.

(i) *Transported soil* (gravels, sands, silts and clays). Most soils have been transported by water. As a stream or river loses its velocity it tends to deposit some of the particles that it is carrying, dropping the larger, heavier particles first. Hence, on the higher reaches of a river, gravel and sand are found whilst on the lower or older parts, silts and clays predominate, especially where the river enters the sea or a lake and loses its velocity. Ice has been another important transportation agent, and large deposits of boulder clay and moraine are often encountered.

In arid parts of the world wind is continually forming sand deposits in the form of ridges. The sand particles in these ridges have been more or less rolled along and are invariably rounded and fairly uniform in size. Light brown, wind-blown deposits of silt-size particles, known as loess, are often encountered in thin layers, the particles having sometimes travelled considerable distances.

(ii) *Residual soil* (topsoil, laterites). These soils are found on level rock surfaces where the action of the elements has produced a soil with little tendency to move. Residual soils can also occur whenever the rate of break up of the rock exceeds the rate of removal. If the parent rock is igneous or metamorphic the resulting soil sizes range from silt to gravel.

Laterites are formed from limestones when the rain water leaches out the soluble rock material leaving behind the insoluble hydroxides of iron and aluminium.

(iii) *Organic soil* (topsoil, peat). The upper part of a soil layer at ground level usually contains organic matter. Peat (i.e. humus) deposits are sometimes encountered and can be extremely troublesome.

THE MINERAL CONTENT OF SOIL

It is generally believed that rock fragments can be reduced by mechanical means to a limiting size of about 0.002 mm, so that for soils containing particles above this size the mineral content is similar to that of the parent rock.

For the production of particles smaller than 0.002 mm some form of chemical action is necessary before breakdown can be achieved. Such particles, although having a chemical content similar to the rock, will have a different crystalline structure and are known as clay particles. An exception is rock flour: rock grains smaller than 0.002 mm, produced by the glacial action of rocks grinding against each other.

Classes of clay minerals

The minerals comprising a clay are hydrated aluminium, iron or magnesium silicates combined in complicated crystalline structures which can be divided into three basic types to give a means of classification. The structures are built up from two basic units, the silica tetrahedron and the octahedral hydroxide of aluminium (or of iron or magnesium). These molecules form sheets which in turn stack together to form clay minerals.

The three main classes of clay minerals are:

Kaolinite

Consisting of one sheet of silicate and one of aluminium hydroxide, the layers being tightly stacked together.

Montmorillonite

Two sheets of silicate and one of aluminium hydroxide loosely stacked together.

Illite

Of similar structure to montmorillonite except that the bondage between the adjacent silicate layers is affected by potassium ions resulting in greater strength and a tighter stacking.

Readers interested in this subject are referred to Grim (1953) and, for recent developments, to the publication *Clay minerals*.

COMMON TYPES OF SOIL

Soils are usually a mixture, e.g. silty clay, sandy silt, etc. Boulder clay is unstratified clay or sandy clay of glacial origin containing a scatter of stones of irregular sizes, moraines are gravel and sand deposits of glacial origin, and loam is a soft deposit consisting of a mixture of sand, silt and clay in approximately equal quantities.

'Fill' or 'made ground' describes all refuse and excavated ground used for filling a depression or raising the level of the ground.

SOIL CLASSIFICATION

In the field

Gravels, sands and peats are easily recognisable, but difficulty arises in deciding when a soil is a fine sand or a coarse silt or when it is a fine silt or a clay. The following rules may, however, help:

Fine Sand	Silt	Clay
Individual particles visible	Some particles visible	No particles visible
Exhibits dilatancy	Exhibits dilatancy	No dilatancy
Easy to crumble when dry	Easy to crumble when dry	Hard to crumble when dry
Feels gritty	Feels rough	Feels smooth
No plasticity	Some plasticity	Plasticity

The dilatancy test consists in moulding a small amount of soil in the palm of the hand; if water is seen to recede when the soil is pressed, then it is either a sand or a silt.

In the laboratory

A standardized system of classification helps to eliminate human error. The usual method is based on the determination of the particle size distribution by shaking a dried sample of the soil (usually after washing) through a set of sieves and recording the weight retained on each sieve. The classification system adopted by the British Standards Institution is the M.I.T. (Massachusett's Institute of Technology) system. The boundaries defined by this system can be seen on the particle size distribution sheet in Figure 1.7. The results of the sieve analysis are plotted with the particle sizes horizontal and the summation percentages vertical. As soil particles vary in size from molecular to boulder it is necessary to use a log scale for the horizontal plot so that the full range can be shown on the one sheet.

The smallest aperture generally used in soils work is that of the 0.075 mm size sieve. Below this size (i.e. silt sizes) the distribution curve must be obtained by sedimentation (pipette or hydrometer). Unless a centrifuge is used, it is not possible to determine the range of clay sizes in a soil, and all that can be done is to obtain the total percentage of clay sizes present. A full description of these tests is given in BS 1377.

It should be noted that these tests merely classify a soil with regard to its particle size, but they do not indicate whether the fine grained particles will exhibit the plasticity generally associated with fine grained soils. Usually this plasticity will be present, but there can be exceptions, e.g. a rock flour. Hence although a particle size distribution will completely define a sand or a gravel it is necessary to carry out consistency limit tests for a clay sized soil.

Consistency limit tests (or index tests)

As an introduction to these tests consider the effect on the strength of a soil as the water within it varies in amount (the definition of moisture content is given on page 15). In cohesionless soils (gravels and sands) there is little effect, but in cohesive soils (silts and clays) the variation in moisture can produce significant changes because as a clay dries it tends to become stronger and less compressible.

If we consider such a cohesive soil, first with an extremely high water content, i.e. a suspension of soil particles in water, the soil behaves as a liquid. In other words if a shear stress were applied to it there would be a continual deformation with no sign of a failure stress value. As the soil is slowly dried out a point is reached when the soil just begins to exhibit a small shear resistance. If this stress is removed it is found that the soil has experienced a permanent deformation: it is acting as a plastic solid and not as a liquid. The moisture content at which the soil stops acting as a liquid and starts acting as a plastic solid is known as the *liquid limit* (L.L.) (Fig. 1.2C).

As further moisture is driven from the soil resistance to large shearing stresses becomes possible. Eventually the soil exhibits no permanent deformation and simply fractures with no plastic deformation, i.e. it acts as a brittle solid. The limit between plastic and brittle failure is known as the *plastic limit* (P.L.) (Fig. 1.2A).

The *plasticity index* is the range of moisture content in which a soil is plastic; the finer the soil, the greater its plasticity index.

$$\text{Plasticity index} \quad = \quad \text{liquid limit} - \text{plastic limit}$$
$$\text{P.I.} \quad = \quad \text{L.L.} - \text{P.L.}$$

The shearing strength to deformation relationship within the plasticity range is illustrated in Fig. 1.2B.

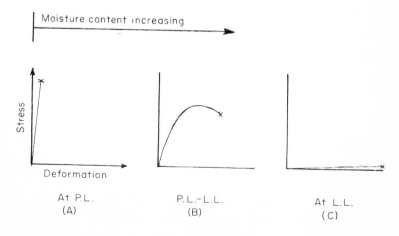

| At P.L. | P.L.-L.L. | At L.L. |
| (A) | (B) | (C) |

The *liquidity index* enables one to compare a soil's plasticity with its natural moisture content (m).

$$I_L = \frac{m-\text{P.L.}}{\text{P.I.}}$$

If I_L = 100 per cent the soil is at its liquid limit; if I_L = 0 per cent the soil is at its plastic limit.

Shrinkage limit

If the drying process is prolonged after the plastic limit has been reached the soil will continue to decrease in volume until a certain value of moisture content is reached. This value is known as the shrinkage limit and at values of moisture content below this level the soil is partially saturated. In other words, below the shrinkage limit the volume of the soil remains constant with further drying, but the weight of the soil decreases until the soil is fully dried.

In Fig. 1.3 the variation of the total volume of a soil with its moisture content is plotted, showing the positions of the liquid, plastic and shrinkage limits.

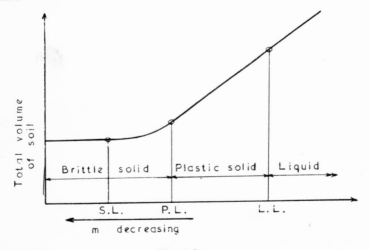

Fig. 1.3

Determination of liquid and plastic limits

Details of the liquid limit apparatus are given in Fig. 1.4

Liquid limit test. The soil is air dried and thoroughly mixed, and about 120 g are sieved through a 0.42 mm sieve. The soil is placed on a glass sheet

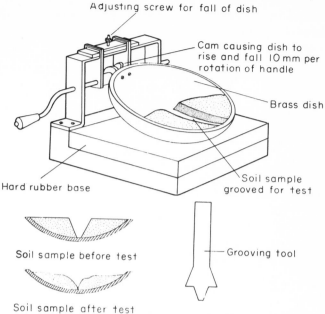

Adjusting screw for fall of dish

Cam causing dish to rise and fall 10 mm per rotation of handle

Brass dish

Soil sample grooved for test

Hard rubber base

Soil sample before test

Grooving tool

Soil sample after test

Fig. 1.4 Liquid limit apparatus

and mixed with a little distilled water. The cup of the apparatus is half filled with the wet soil and the top levelled off. A 2 mm groove is then cut in the soil by means of the grooving tool.

The handle of the apparatus is rotated at 2 revolutions per second. This actuates the cam which causes the cup to lift 10 mm and then to fall on to the rubber base. The number of blows required to close the gap over 12.5 mm is recorded and a portion of the soil just tested is removed for moisture content determination.

The test is repeated, usually three or four more times, employing a little more water for each test.

To obtain the liquid limit the moisture content is plotted vertically to a natural scale, and the number of blows is plotted horizontally to a logarithmic scale. The moisture content corresponding to 25 blows is taken as the liquid limit.

Plastic limit test. Fifteen grams of soil prepared as in the liquid limit test are used. The soil is mixed on the glass plate with just enough water to make it sufficiently plastic for rolling into a ball, which is then rolled out between the hand and the glass to form a thread. The soil is said to be at its plastic limit when it just begins to crumble at a thread diameter of 3 mm. At this stage a section of the thread is removed for moisture content determination. The test should be repeated at least once more.

The Casagrande classification system

This system was introduced in 1947 and the extended version evolved by A. Casagrande has been adopted by the British Standards Institution for use in Great Britain. With the Casagrande system the coarse grained soils are classified on the basis of their particle size (using the M.I.T. system). The fine grained soils are classified on the basis of a plasticity chart (see Fig. 1.5). The fibrous soils are identified by visual inspection.

The main soil types are designated by a letter and correspond to the M.I.T. classification:

Gravel	G	Clay		C
Sand	S	Organic silts and clays		O
Silt	M	Peat		Pt

A suffix is added to denote the subdivisions of each type. The suffices most often used are:

W — well graded, little or no fines
U — uniformly graded, little or no fines
P — poorly graded, little or no fines.

These suffices have the following meanings:

Well graded — having a particle size distribution extending evenly over a wide range of particle sizes, without excess or deficiency of any particle size. (U.C. greater than 5.)

Uniformly graded — having a particle size distribution extending over a very limited range, i.e. all particles in the soil are more or less of the same size. (U.C. 1.0 to 5.0.)

Poorly graded — having a particle size distribution containing an excess of some particle sizes and a deficiency of others.

The fine grained soils are divided into three subgroups:

L   (L.L. $<$ 35%)   — low compressibility
I   (L.L. 35–50%)   — medium (or intermediate) compressibility
H   (L.L. $>$ 50%)   — high compressibility.

The compressibility of a soil may be defined as the volumetric strain per unit pressure increase.

To use the plasticity chart of Fig. 1.5 it is necessary to plot a point whose coordinates are the L.L. and the P.I. of the soil to be identified. The soil can then be classified by observing the position of the point relative to the A line.

The A line is an empirical boundary that has been established after extensive observations of many tests on different soil types. The line goes through the base line at P.I. = 0, L.L. = 20 per cent. It also goes through the point L.L. = 50 per cent, P.I. = 22 per cent. The equation of the A line is therefore:

$$P.I. = 0.73 (L.L. - 20\%)$$

The A line represents the boundary between inorganic clays, CL to CH, which lie above the line, and organic silts and clays, OL to OH, which lie below it.

For soils with L.L. values less than 25 per cent there is a considerable amount of overlapping (as shown by the dotted area on the chart). For example, a soil with L.L. = 20 per cent and P.I. = 8 per cent could be either a sandy clay (CL), a very clayey sand (SP) or a well graded sand and clay mixture (SC). In such cases the soil could be classified as CL–SC, but an experienced engineer would be able to determine the correct classification by examination.

The position of the point on the chart gives an indication of the physical properties of the soil it represents. Comparing soils with the same value of L.L., it is seen that, as P.I. increases, cohesion (i.e. strength) increases whilst permeability decreases. The converse also applies.

There are no rigid boundaries between soil groups in the Casagrande system and boundary cases can be expressed by such designations as GW–SW, which indicates a fairly even distribution of sand and gravel sizes in the soil.

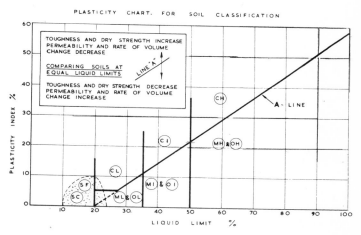

Fig. 1.5

Further information is available in BS Code of Practice CP2001, *Site Investigations,* and in the H.M.S.O. publication, *Soil Mechanics for Road Engineers.*

SOIL PROPERTIES

From the foregoing it is seen that soil consists of a mass of solid particles separated by spaces or voids. A cross section through a granular soil may have an appearance similar to that shown in Fig. 1.6A.

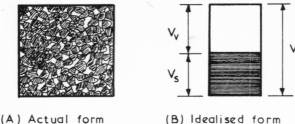

(A) Actual form   (B) Idealised form

Fig. 1.6 Cross-section through a granular soil

In order to study the properties of such a soil mass it is advantageous to adopt an idealized form of the diagram as shown in Fig. 1.6B. The soil mass has a total volume V and a volume of solid particles that summates to V_s. The volume of the voids, V_v, is obviously equal to $V-V_s$.

From a study of Fig. 1.6 the following may be defined:

Void ratio

$$e = \frac{\text{volume of voids}}{\text{volume of solids}} = \frac{V_v}{V_s}$$

Porosity

$$n = \frac{\text{volume of voids}}{\text{total volume}}$$

$$n = \frac{V_v}{V} = \frac{V_v}{V_v + V_s} = \frac{e}{1 + e}$$

Degree of saturation (S)

The voids of a soil may be filled with air or water or both. If only air is present the soil is dry, whereas if only water is present the soil is saturated. When both air and water are present the soil is said to be partially saturated

These three conditions are represented in Figs 1.7A, B and C.

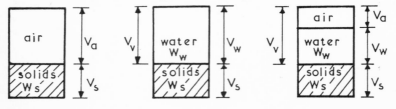

(A) Dry soil   (B) Saturated soil   (C) Partially saturated soil

Fig. 1.7 Water and air contents in a soil

The degree of saturation is simply:

$$S = \frac{\text{volume of water}}{\text{volume of voids}} = \frac{V_w}{V_v} \text{ (usually expressed as a percentage).}$$

Particle specific gravity (G)

The specific gravity of a material is the ratio of the weight or mass of a volume of the material to the weight or mass of an equal volume of water. In soil mechanics the most important specific gravity is that of the actual soil grains and is given the symbol G.

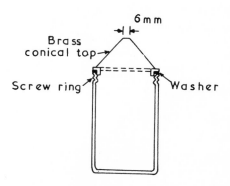

Fig. 1.8 The Pycnometer

From the above definition it is seen that, for a soil sample with volume of solids V_s and weight of solids W_s,

$$G = \frac{W_s}{V_s \gamma_w}$$

Where γ_w = unit weight of water and, if the sample has a mass of solids M_s

$$G = \frac{M_s}{V_s \rho_w}$$

where ρ_w = density of water

i.e. $$G = \frac{M_s}{V_s \rho_w} = \frac{W_s}{V_s \gamma_w}$$

Soil contains particles of different minerals with consequently different specific gravities: G therefore represents an average value for the particles and is determined from tests carried out on a representative soil sample.

The laboratory test on a fine grained soil is usually carried out using a 50 ml density bottle. For coarse-grained soils either a 500 ml flask or a pycnometer (a fruit preserving jar fitted with a conical top, Fig. 1.8) is used. Reasonably accurate results can be obtained for most soils with the pycnometer (see BS 1377).

Generally sands have an average $G = 2.65$ whilst clays have an average $G = 2.75$. For coal spoil heaps G can vary from about 2.0 for an unburnt shale with a high coal content, to about 2.7 for a burnt shale.

DENSITY AND UNIT WEIGHT

In a system of properly chosen units:

$$\text{Force} = \text{Mass} \times \text{Acceleration} \tag{1}$$

In the SI system of units the basic units are:

$$
\begin{array}{lll}
\text{Mass} & - \text{ the kilogramme} & \text{(kg)} \\
\text{Length} & - \text{ the metre} & \text{(m)} \\
\text{Time} & - \text{ the second} & \text{(s)}
\end{array}
$$

The derived force unit (the newton) is obtained by putting unit values into the right-hand side of equation (1). It is given the symbol N.

$$1 \text{ N} = 1 \text{ kg} \times 1 \text{ m/s}^2 \tag{2}$$

From equation (2) it is seen that the newton is that force which, when acting on a mass of one kilogramme, produces an acceleration of one metre per second per second.

In soils we are mainly interested in the gravitational force exerted by masses (i.e. their weights). The acceleration term in equation (1) therefore is g, the symbol used to denote the acceleration due to the earth's gravitational field. The average value for g, at the earth's surface, is 9.806 m/s^2.

The gravitational force which acts on a one-kilogramme mass is therefore $1 \times 9.806 = 9.806$ N. The weight of a one-kilogramme mass is 9.806 newtons.

We can therefore express the amount of material in a given volume, V, in two ways:

the amount of mass, M, in the volume, or
the amount of weight, W, in the volume.

If we consider unit volume, the two systems give the density and the unit weight of the material.

$$\text{Density, } \rho, \quad = \frac{\text{mass}}{\text{volume}} = \frac{M}{V}$$

$$\text{Unit weight, } \gamma = \frac{\text{weight}}{\text{volume}} = \frac{W}{V}$$

As an example, consider water at 20°C.

$$\text{Density of water, } \rho_w = 1000 \text{ kg/m}^3$$

The weight of a 1000 kg mass is 1000 × 9.806 N = 9806 N.
Hence the unit weight of water, γ_w, is 9806 N/m^3 = 9.81 kN/m^3.
In soils work it is generally more convenient to work in unit weights than in densities.

Unit weight of soil

The unit weight of a material is its weight per unit volume. In soils work the most important unit weights are as follows.

Bulk unit weight (γ_b)

This is the natural in-situ unit weight of the soil:

$$\gamma_b = \frac{\text{Total weight}}{\text{Total volume}} = \frac{W}{V} = \frac{W_s + W_w}{V_s + V_v}$$

$$= \frac{GV_s\,\gamma_w + V_v\,\gamma_w S}{V_s + V_v} = \gamma_w \frac{(G + eS)}{1 + e}$$

Saturated unit weight ($\gamma_{sat.}$)

$$= \frac{\text{Saturated weight}}{\text{Total volume}}$$

When soil is saturated S = 100 per cent (1)

$$\therefore \gamma_{sat.} = \gamma_w \frac{G + e}{1 + e}$$

Dry unit weight (γ_d)

$$= \frac{\text{Dry weight}}{\text{Total volume}}$$

$$= \frac{\gamma_w\,G}{1 + e} \text{(as S = 0)}$$

Submerged unit weight ($\gamma_{sub.}$)

When a soil is below the water table part of its weight is balanced by the buoyant effect of the water. This upthrust equals the weight of the volume of water displaced.

Hence, considering unit volume,

submerged unit weight = saturated unit weight − unit weight of water

$$= \gamma_w \frac{G + e}{1 + e} - \gamma_w = \gamma_w \frac{G - 1}{1 + e}$$

Similar expressions can be obtained for densities:

bulk density ρ_b $\qquad = \rho_w \frac{(G + eS)}{1 + e}$

saturated density ρ_{sat} $\qquad = \rho_w \frac{(G + e)}{1 + e}$

dry density ρ_d $\qquad = \rho_w \frac{G}{1 + e}$

submerged density ρ_{sub} $\qquad = \rho_w \frac{G - 1}{1 + e}$

Relationship between density and unit weight values

In the above expressions, G, e, S and the number 1 are all dimensionless. Hence a particular unit weight = γ_w times a constant. The corresponding density $\quad = \rho_w$ times the same constant.

Example

A soil has a dry density of 1900 kg/m³. What is its dry unit weight?

$$\rho_d = 1900 \text{ kg/m}^3 = \rho_w \times 1.9$$

Now $\qquad \gamma_d = \gamma_w \times 1.9 \quad = 18.64 \text{ kN/m}^3$

Similarly, if $\qquad \gamma_d = 18.64 \text{ kN/m}^3$

then $\qquad \rho_d = \frac{18.64}{9.81} \times 1000 = 1900 \text{ kg/m}^3$

Quick approximation

If we assume the engineering approximation that $\gamma_w = 10 \text{ kN/m}^3$ (instead of 9.81), then in the previous example:

$$\rho_d = 1900 \text{ kg/m}^3 \text{ and } \gamma_d = 1.9 \times 10 = 19 \text{ kN/m}^3$$

Hence, given a density in kg/m³, the unit weight (in kN/m³) is found by moving the decimal point two places.

Example

Saturated density $\quad = 2400 \text{ kg/m}^3$
Saturated unit weight $= 24 \text{ kN/m}^3$

(The more exact value for the unit weight is, of course, 2.4 × 9.81 = 23.54 kN/m³, but few engineers would hesitate to use the rounded-off figure of 24 kN/m³ as soil is in any case so variable a material.)

Relative density (R.D.)

A granular soil generally has a large range into which the value of its void ratio may be fitted. If the soil is vibrated and compacted the particles are pressed close together and a minimum value of void ratio is obtained, but if the soil is loosely poured a maximum value of void ratio is obtained.

These maximum and minimum values can be obtained from laboratory tests and it is often convenient to relate them to the naturally occurring void ratio of the soil. This relationship is expressed as the relative density of the soil:

$$\text{R.D.} = \frac{e_{max.} - e}{e_{max.} - e_{min.}} \text{ expressed as a percentage.}$$

Moisture content (m)

The amount of water present in a soil is usually expressed as a ratio to the amount of dry soil.

$$m = \frac{\text{Weight of water}}{\text{Weight of solids}} = \frac{W_w}{W_s}! \quad \text{or } m = \frac{\text{Mass of water}}{\text{Mass of solids}} = \frac{M_w}{M_s}$$

$$= \frac{V_w \, \rho_w}{V_s \cdot G_s \, \rho_w} = \frac{V_w}{V_s \, G_s} = \frac{c}{G_s}$$

Soils are either air dried or oven dried. Air drying is sufficient for samples to be used in compaction tests, but when all moisture must be removed oven drying is neeessary. It has become standard practice to dry soils at a temperature of 105°C.

Relationship between m, γ_d *and* γ_b

$$\gamma_b = \frac{W_w + W_s}{V} \tag{1}$$

$$\gamma_d = \frac{W_s}{V} \tag{2}$$

$$m = \frac{W_w}{W_s} \tag{3}$$

From (3) $W_w = m W_s$ and, substituting in (1)

$$\gamma_b = \frac{W_s}{V}(1 + m)$$

i.e. $$\gamma_d = \frac{\gamma_b}{1 + m}$$

Thus to find the dry unit weight from the bulk unit weight, divide the latter by $(1 + m)$ where m is the moisture content expressed as a decimal.

Relationship between e, m and G for a saturated soil

$$m = \frac{W_w}{W_s} = \frac{V_w\,\gamma_w}{V_s\,\gamma_w G} = \frac{V_v}{V_s G} = \frac{e}{G} \qquad (V_w = V_v \text{ if the soil is saturated})$$

i.e. $e = mG$

Relationship between e, m and G for a partially saturated soil

$$m = \frac{W_w}{W_s} = \frac{V_w\,\gamma_w}{V_s\,\gamma_w G} = \frac{V_v\,S}{V_s\,G} = \frac{e\,S}{G}$$

i.e. $$e = \frac{mG}{S}$$

SUMMARY OF CHAPTER 1

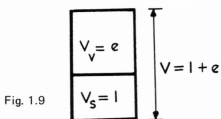

Fig. 1.9

In Fig. 1.9
V_v = Volume of voids, V_s = Volume of solids, V = Total volume.

Void ratio $$e = \frac{V_v}{V_s}$$

Porosity $$n = \frac{V_v}{V} = \frac{e}{1 + e}$$

V_w = Volume of water in voids

Degree of saturation $\quad S = \dfrac{V_w}{V_v}$

Particle specific gravity $\quad G = \dfrac{W_s}{V_s \gamma_w} = \dfrac{M_s}{V_s \rho_w}$

Dry unit weight $\gamma_d \qquad\qquad = \dfrac{\gamma_w\, G}{1 + e}$

Dry density $\rho_d \qquad\qquad\quad = \dfrac{\rho_w\, G}{1 + e}$

Bulk unit weight $\gamma_b \qquad\quad = \gamma_w \dfrac{(G + e\, S)}{1 + e}$

Bulk density $\rho_b \qquad\qquad = \rho_w \dfrac{(G + e\, S)}{1 + e}$

Saturated unit weight $\gamma_{sat.} \quad = \gamma_w \dfrac{(G + e)}{1 + e}$

Saturated density $\rho_{sat.} \qquad = \rho_w \dfrac{(G + e)}{1 + e}$

Submerged unit weight $\gamma_{sub.} = \gamma_w \dfrac{(G - 1)}{1 + e}$

Submerged density $\rho_{sub.} \qquad = \rho_w \dfrac{(G - 1)}{1 + e}$

Relative density R.D. $\quad = \dfrac{e_{max.} - e}{e_{max.} - e_{min.}}$

Moisture content $\qquad m = \dfrac{W_w}{W_s} = \dfrac{M_w}{M_s}$

Note that $\qquad\qquad \gamma_d = \dfrac{\gamma_b}{1 + m} \; ; \; \rho_d = \dfrac{\rho_b}{1 + m}$

$$e = m\, G \text{ (saturated)}$$

$$e = \frac{m\, G}{S} \text{ (partially saturated)}$$

EXAMPLES ON CHAPTER 1

Example 1

1. The results of a sieve analysis on a soil sample were:

Sieve size (mm)	Mass retained (g)
10	0.0
6	5.5
2	25.7
1	23.1
0.6	22.0
0.3	17.3
0.15	12.7
0.075	6.9

2.3 g passed the 0.075 mm sieve.
Plot the particle size distribution curve and describe the soil.

Calculations may be set out as follows:

Sieve size (mm)	Mass retained (g)	Mass passing (g)	Summation percentage
10	0.0	115.5	100
6	5.5	110.0	95
2	25.7	84.3	73
1	23.1	61.2	53
0.6	22.0	39.2	34
0.3	17.3	21.9	19
0.15	12.7	9.2	8
0.075	6.9	2.3	2
Pass 0.075	2.3		
Total weight	115.5		

The particle size distribution curve is shown in Fig. 1.10. The soil has some 30 per cent gravel and 70 per cent sand and would therefore be described as a gravelly sand, whilst the range of particle sizes is fairly wide and the soil could be described as well graded (Casagrande symbol GW–SW).

A soil whose particles are more or less the same size is termed a uniform soil and has a correspondingly steep distribution curve.

Arising out of this example are two well known definitions:

Effective size (D_{10}) The largest size of the smallest 10 per cent; in the example $D_{10} = 0.17$ mm

Uniformity coefficient (U.C.) The ratio $\dfrac{D_{60}}{D_{10}}$;

in the example U.C. $= \dfrac{1.5}{0.17} = 8.8$

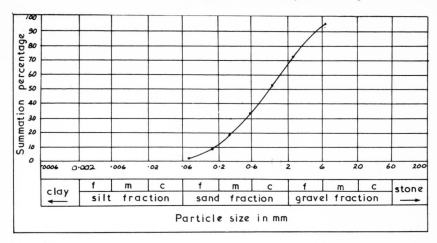

Fig. 1.10 Example 1.1

Example 2

A liquid and a plastic limit determination on a soil gave the following results:

Liquid limit test

Test no.	Tin mass (g)	Tin + wet soil (g)	Tin + dry soil (g)	No. of blows
1	23.68	40.86	34.68	13
2	22.93	42.62	35.78	20
3	26.27	38.02	34.27	47

Plastic limit test

1	25.34	32.17	31.01	
2	24.83	30.48	29.51	

Determine the plasticity index of the soil.

Liquid limit:

1. $m = \dfrac{40.86 - 34.68}{34.68 - 23.68} = \dfrac{6.18}{11.0} = 56.2$ per cent (13 blows)

2. $m = \dfrac{6.84}{12.85} = 53.2$ per cent (20 blows)

3. $m = \dfrac{3.75}{8.0} = 47.0$ per cent (47 blows)

Fig. 1.11 shows the plot of the log, number of blows to moisture content. Moisture content corresponding to 25 blows (the liquid limit) = 51.6 per cent.

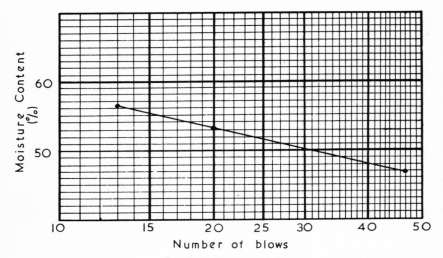

Fig. 1.11 Example 1.2

Plastic limit:

1.
$$m = \frac{1.16}{5.67} = 20.4 \text{ per cent}$$

2.
$$m = \frac{0.97}{4.68} = 20.8 \text{ per cent}$$

Plastic limit = average of results = 20.6 per cent
P.I. = L.L. − P.L. = 51.6 − 20.6 = 31.0 per cent

From Fig. 1.5 soil is a highly compressible inorganic clay.

Example 3 (specific gravity)
The mass of a pycnometer, when empty, was 530 g and when full of water 1567 g. 650 g of oven dried soil was placed in the jar, covered with water and stirred vigorously to remove entrapped air. Eventually the pycnometer was topped up with water and found to have a total mass of 1976 g.

Determine the particle specific gravity of the soil.

Mass of soil + water $\quad\quad\quad\quad$ = 1976 − 530 = 1446 g
Mass of dry soil $\quad\quad\quad\quad\quad$ = 650 g
∴ Mass of water present with soil $\quad$ = 1446 − 650 = 796 g
Mass of water when pycnometer full $\;$ = 1567 − 530 = 1037 g
∴ Mass of water of same volume as soil = 1037 − 796 = 241 g

$$G = \frac{\text{Mass of soil}}{\text{Mass of equal volume of water}} = \frac{650}{241} = 2.7$$

Example 4 (moisture content)
A sample of soil was placed in a moisture content tin of mass 19.52 g. The combined mass of the soil and the tin was 48.27 g. After oven drying the soil and the tin had a mass of 42.31 g.
Determine the moisture content of the soil.

$$m = \frac{M_w}{M_s} = \frac{48.27 - 42.31}{42.31 - 19.52} = \frac{5.96}{22.79} = 26.2 \text{ per cent}$$

Example 5 (bulk density)
In a bulk density determination a sample of clay with a mass of 683 g was coated with paraffin wax. The combined mass of the clay and the wax was 690.6 g. The volume of the clay and the wax was found, by immersion in water, to be 350 ml.
The sample was then broken open and moisture content and particle specific gravity tests gave respectively 16.8 per cent and 2.73.
The specific gravity of the wax was 0.89. Determine the bulk density and unit weight, void ratio and degree of saturation.

Mass of soil $\quad\quad$ = 683 g.
Mass of wax $\quad\quad$ = 690.6 − 683 = 7.6 g.

$$\therefore \text{Volume of wax} = \frac{7.6}{0.89} = 8.55 \text{ ml}$$

$$\therefore \text{Volume of soil} = 350 - 8.6 = 341.4 \text{ ml}$$

$$\rho_b = \frac{683}{341.4} \times 1000 = 2000 \text{ kg/m}^3$$

$$\gamma_b = \frac{2000}{1000} \times 9.81 = 19.6 \text{ kN/m}^3$$

$$\rho_d = \frac{2000}{1.168} = 1713 \text{ kg/m}^3$$

Now $\dfrac{\rho_w G}{1 + e} = 1713$

$$\therefore e = \dfrac{1000 \times 2.73 - 1713}{1713} = 0.594$$

Now $\rho_b = 2000 = \gamma_w \dfrac{(G + eS)}{1 + e}$

$$\therefore 1.594 \times 2000 = 2730 + 594 \times S$$

$$\therefore S = 77.0 \text{ per cent}$$

EXERCISES ON CHAPTER 1

1. The following date refers to a liquid limit (tests 1, 2 and 3) and a plastic limit (tests 4 and 5) determination for a soil.

Test no.	Tin + wet soil (g)	Tin + dry soil (g)	Empty tin (g)	No. of blows
1	42.76	35.75	24.24	7
2	40.80	34.61	23.04	30
3	40.14	34.90	24.77	44
4	16.98	16.78	15.77	
5	15.07	14.88	13.86	

Determine the plasticity index of the soil
Answer 35.4 per cent (MH & OH)

2. Determine the plasticity index of the soil from the following test data:
   (a) Data for determination of liquid limit

Number of blows	49	31	18	11
Mass of moisture (g)	6.52	6.06	6.75	6.60
Mass of dry soil (g)	18.15	16.12	17.23	16.13

   (b) Data for determination of plastic limit

Test number	1	2
Mass of moisture (g)	1.38	1.32
Mass of dry soil (g)	6.37	6.37

Answer 17.2 per cent (CI)

3. The results of a sieve analysis on a soil were:

Sieve size (mm)	Mass retained (g)
50	0
37.5	15.5
20	17
12.5	10
10	11
6	33
3	114.5
1	49
0.6	32.5
0.15	17
0.075	10.5

If the total mass of the sample was 311 g, plot the particle size distribution curve and, from the inspection of this curve, determine the effective size and uniformity coefficient. Describe the soil

Answer   0.6 mm, 7.5, sandy gravel (GW–SW)

4. Plot the particle size distribution curve from the results of the following sieve analysis, given the sieve sizes and the mass retained on each.
   Sample 642 g. Retained on 0.42 mm sieve, 11 g; 0.3 mm, 28 g; 0.2 mm, 77 g; 0.15 mm, 173 g; 0.1 mm, 167 g; 0.075 mm, 77 g.

Answer   uniform medium/fine sand

5. A sand sample has a porosity of 35 per cent and the specific gravity of the particles is 2.73. What is its dry density and void ratio?

Answer $e = 0.54$, $\gamma_d = 1760$ kg/m³

6. A sample of silty clay was found by immersion in mercury to have a volume of 14.88 ml, whilst its mass at natural moisture content was 28.81 g and the particle specific gravity was 2.7. Calculate the void ratio and degree of saturation if, after oven drying, the sample had a mass of 24.83 g.

Answer $e = 0.617$, $S = 70$ per cent

7. A sample of moist sand was cut out of a natural deposit by means of a sampling cylinder. The volume of the cylinder was 478 ml; the weight of the sample alone was 884 g and 830 g after drying. The volume of the dried sample, when rammed tight into a graduated cylinder, was 418 ml and its volume, when poured loosely into the same cylinder, was 616 ml. If the particle specific gravity was 2.67, compute the relative density and the degree of saturation of the deposit.

Answer   R.D. = 69 per cent, S = 32.3 per cent

8. In order to determine the density of a clay soil an undisturbed sample was taken in a sampling tube of volume 0.001 664 m^3
   The following data were obtained:

Mass of tube (empty)   = 1.864 kg
Mass of tube and clay sample   = 5.018 kg
Mass of tube and clay sample after drying = 4.323 kg

Calculate the moisture content, the bulk, and the dry densities. If the particle specific gravity was 2.69, determine the void ratio and the percentage saturation of the clay.

Answer   m = 28.2 per cent, ρ_d = 1490 kg/m^3 ρ_b = 1925 kg/m^3

S = 95.6 per cent, e = 0.795

REFERENCES

Blackwell Scientific Publications
    Clay minerals, published twice yearly.
British Standards Institution
    BS 1377 : 1967 *Methods of testing soils for civil engineering purposes.*
Casagrande, A.
    Classification and identification of soils. *Proc. Am. Soc. civ. Engrs,*
    73 (1947).
Grim, R. E.
    Clay mineralogy (McGraw-Hill, 1953).
Her Majesty's Stationery Office
    Soil mechanics for road engineers (1952).

2. Soil Water, Permeability and Flow

SUBSURFACE WATER

This is the term used to define all water found beneath the Earth's surface. The main source of subsurface water is rainfall, which percolates downwards to fill up the voids and interstices. Water can penetrate to a considerable depth, estimated to be as much as 12 000 metres, but at depths greater than this, due to the large pressures involved, the interstices have been closed by plastic flow of the rocks. Below this level water cannot exist in a free state, although it is often found in chemical combination with the rock minerals, so that the upper limit of plastic flow within the rock determines the lower limit of subsurface water.

Subsurface water can be split into two distinct zones.

Saturation zone

This is the depth throughout which all the fissures, etc., are filled with water under hydrostatic pressure. The upper level of this water is known as the water table, phreatic surface or ground water level, and water within this zone is called phreatic water or ground water.

The water table tends to follow in a more gentle manner the topographical features of the surface above (Fig. 2.1). At ground water level the hydro-

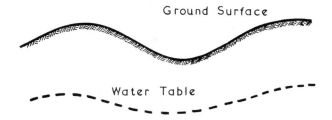

Ground Surface

Water Table

Fig. 2.1 Tendency of the water table to follow the Earth's surface

static pressure is zero, so another definition of water table is the level to which water will eventually rise in an unlined borehole.

The water table is not constant but rises and falls with variations of

rainfall, atmospheric pressure, temperature, etc., whilst coastal regions
are affected by tides.

When the water table reaches the surface, springs, lakes, swamps, and
similar features can be formed.

Aeration zone

This zone occurs between the water table and the surface, and can be
split into three sections.

Capillary fringe

Due to capillarity, water is drawn up above the water table into the interstices of the soil or rock. Water held in this manner is in a state of suction
or negative pressure; its height depends upon the material, and in general
the finer the voids the greater the capillary rise. Clays are largely unaffected
by capillarity but in silts the rise can be as much as two and a half metres.

Intermediate belt

As rainwater percolates downward to the water table a certain amount is
held in the soil by the action of surface tension, capillarity, adsorbtion,
chemical action, etc. The water retained in this manner is termed held
water and is deep enough not to be affected by the atmosphere or plants.

Soil belt

This zone is constantly affected by evaporation and plant transpiration.
Moist soil in contact with the atmosphere either evaporates water or
condenses water into itself until its vapour pressure is equal to atmospheric
pressure. Soil water in atmospheric equilibrium is called hygroscopic

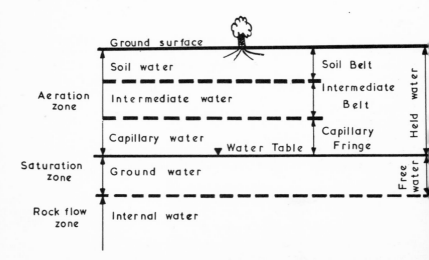

Fig. 2.2 Diagram illustrating types of subsurface water

water, whilst the moisture content (which depends upon relative humidity) is known as the hygroscopic m.c.

Surface tension

Surface tension is a property of water that permits the surface molecules to carry a tensile force. The property causes the surface of a body of water to attempt to contract into a minimum area, hence a drop of water is spherical. Surface tension is easily understood if we imagine the surface of water to be covered with a thin molecular skin capable of carrying tension. Such a skin, of course, cannot exist on the surface of a liquid, but the analogy can explain surface tension effects without going into the relevant molecular theories.

Surface tension is given the symbol T and can be defined as the force in newtons per millimetre length that the water surface can carry. T varies slightly with temperature, but this variation is small and an average value usually taken for the surface tension of water is 0.000 075 N/mm (0.075 N/m).

Capillarity

The fact that surface tension exists can be shown by the familiar laboratory experiment in which an open-ended capillary tube is placed in a basin of water and subjected to atmospheric pressure; the rise of water within the tube is then observed. It is seen that the column of water within the tube reaches a definite height above the liquid in the basin.

The surface of the column forms a meniscus such that the curved surface of the liquid is at an angle α to the walls of the tube (Fig. 2.3A). The arrangement of the apparatus is shown in Fig 2.3B.

The base of the column is at the same level as the water in the basin and, as the system is open, the pressure must be atmospheric. The pressure on the top surface of the column is also atmospheric. There are no externally applied forces that keep the column in position, which shows that there must be a tensile force acting within the surface film of the water.

Let height of water column = h_c

radius of tube = r

unit weight of water = γ_w

If we take atmospheric pressure as datum, i.e. the air pressure = 0, we can equate the vertical forces acting at the top of the column:

$$T2\pi r \cos \alpha + u\pi r^2 = 0$$

$$\therefore u = \frac{-2T \cos \alpha}{r}$$

Hence, as expected, we see that u is negative; the water within the column is in a state of tension, or suction. The maximum value of this negative pressure is $\gamma_w h_c$ and occurs at the top of the column. The pressure distribution along the length of the tube is shown in Fig. 2.3C. It is seen that the water pressure gradually increases with loss of elevation to a value 0 at the base of the column.

An expression for the height h_c can be obtained by substituting $u = -\gamma_w h_c$ in the above expression to yield:

$$h_c = \frac{2T \cos \alpha}{\gamma_w \, r}$$

From the two expressions we see that both u and h_c increase as r decreases.

A further interesting point is that, if we assume that the weight of the capillary tube is negligible, then the only vertical forces acting are the downward weight of the water column supported by the surface tension at the top and the reaction at the base support of the tube. The tube must therefore be in compression. The compressive force acting on the walls of the tube will be constant along the length of the water column and of magnitude $2\pi r T \cos \alpha$ (or $\pi r^2 h_c \gamma_w$).

It may be noted that for pure water in contact with clean glass the value of angle α is zero. In this case the radius of the meniscus is equal to the radius of the tube and the derived formulae can be simplified by removing the term $\cos \alpha$.

Capillary effects in soil

Due to capillarity, water is drawn up above the water table into the interstices of the soil or rock. The region within which this water is encountered is known as the capillary fringe. A soil mass, of course, is not a capillary tube system, but a study of theoretical capillarity enables one to determine a qualitative view of the behaviour of water in the capillary fringe of a soil deposit. Water in this fringe can be regarded as being in a state of negative pressure, i.e. at pressure values below atmospheric. A diagram of a capillary fringe appears in Fig. 2.3D).

The minimum height of the fringe, $h_{c \, min}$, is governed by the maximum size of the voids within the soil. Up to this height above the water table the soil will be sufficiently close to full saturation to be considered as such.

The maximum height of the fringe $h_{c \, max}$ is governed by the minimum size of the voids. Within the range $h_{c \, min}$ to $h_{c \, max}$ the soil can be only partially saturated.

Terzaghi and Peck (1948) give an approximate relationship between $h_{c \, max}$ and grain size:

$$h_{c \, max} = \frac{C}{eD_{10}} mm$$

where C is a constant depending upon the shape of the grains and the surface impurities (varying from 10.0 to 50.0 mm^2) and D_{10} is the effective size expressed in millimetres.

Due to the irregular nature of the conduits in a soil mass it is not possible,

even approximately, to calculate moisture content distributions above the
water table from the theory of capillarity. This is a problem of importance
in highway engineering and is best approached by the concept of soil
suction.

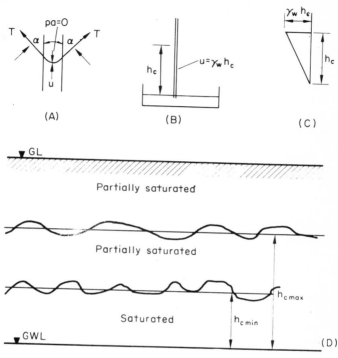

Fig. 2.3

Contact moisture

Water in a moist sand occurs in the form of droplets between the points
of contact of the individual grains and is therefore referred to as contact
moisture. This water, retain by surface tension, holds the particles
together and produces a resistance to applied stress resembling cohesion.
The effect is temporary and will be destroyed if the sand is dried or flooded.

Contact moisture has two main effects, the first being to augment the
strength of the sand and enable slopes to be at steeper angles than if dry
or completely submerged. The second effect is the phenomenon known as
bulking: a damp sand will not settle to the same volume as an equal weight
of dry sand since the temporary cohesion prevents the grains from moving
downwards, with the result that the volume of a damp sand may be 20
to 30 per cent more than for a dry sand similarly placed.

Adsorbed water

Clay minerals, due to their shape and crystalline structure, have surface forces that exceed gravity. These forces attract water molecules to the soil particles and hence, in cohesive soils, each particle is coated with a molecular film of water. This water, known as adsorbed water, has properties that differ considerably from ordinary water: its viscosity, density and boiling point are all higher than normal water and it does not freeze under frost action. It is generally believed that adsorbed water gives fine-grained soils their plastic properties.

FLOW OF WATER THROUGH SOILS

The voids of a soil (and of most rocks) are connected together and form continuous passageways for the movement of water brought about by transpiration of plants, unbalance of chemical energy, variation of intensity of dissolved salts, etc.

The main problem that confronts the foundation engineer is the prediction of the flow of water through soil when this flow is caused by a variation in hydrostatic pressure. In soil mechanics, as in hydraulics, the term generally used is pressure head (h), i.e. the head of water instead of the pressure. The hydraulic pressure (p), is related to the hydraulic head by the expression:

$$p = h\gamma_w$$

The conduits of a soil are irregular and of small diameter — an average value of the diameter is $D_{10}/5$. Any flow quantities calculated by the theory of pipe flow must be in error and it is necessary to think in terms of an average velocity through a given area of soil rather than specific velocities through particular conduits.

If Q is the quantity of flow passing through an area A in time t, then the average velocity (v) is:

$$v = \frac{Q}{At}$$

This average velocity is sometimes referred to as the seepage velocity. In further work the term velocity will infer average velocity.

Darcy's law of saturated flow

In 1856 Darcy showed experimentally that a fluid's velocity of flow through a porous medium was directly related to the hydraulic gradient causing the flow,

i.e. $v \propto i$

where i = hydraulic gradient (the head loss per unit length),

$$\text{or} \quad v = C i$$

where C = a constant involving the properties of both the fluid and the porous material.

Coefficient of permeability (k)

In soils we are generally concerned with water flow: the constant C is determined from tests in which the permeant is water. The particular value of the constant C obtained from these tests is known as the coefficient of permeability and is given the symbol k.

It is important to realize that when a soil is said to have a certain coefficient of permeability this value only applies to water (at 20°C). If heavy oil is used as the permeant the value of C would be considerably less than k.

Temperature causes variation in k, but in most soils work this is insignificant, although in the case of a burning tip the flow of water through its warm regions may increase as the temperature rises.

Determination of k

Provided that the hydraulic gradient is less than 1.0, as is the case in most seepage problems, the flow of water through a soil is linear and Darcy's law applies,

$$\text{i.e.} \quad v = ki$$

$$\text{or} \quad Q = Atki$$

$$\text{or} \quad q = Aki \text{ (where } q = \text{quantity of unit flow} = \frac{Q}{t}\text{)}$$

From this latter expression a definition of k is apparent: the coefficient of permeability is the rate of flow of water per unit area of soil when under a unit hydraulic gradient.

Dimensions for k are usually mm/s, m/day, etc.

Whilst suitable for coarse grained soils, Swartzendruber (1961) showed that Darcy's law is not truly applicable to cohesive soils due to the departure from Newtonian flow (perfect fluid flow) and he therefore proposed a modified flow equation for such soils. Many workers maintain that these variations from Darcy's law are related to the adsorbed water in the soil system, with its much higher viscosity than free water, and also to the soil structure, which can cause small flows along the sides of the voids in the opposite direction to the main flow. Although these effects are not always negligible, the unmodified form of Darcy's law is invariably used in seepage problems as it has the great advantage of simplicity. It may be that, as work in this field proceeds, some form of modification may be adopted.

In the laboratory
Constant head permeameter. A sketch of the constant head permeameter

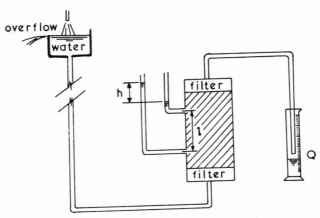

Fig. 2.4 The constant head permeameter

is given in Fig. 2.4. Water flows through the soil under a head which is kept constant by means of the over-flow arrangement. The head loss, h, between two points along the length of the sample, distance 1 apart, is measured by means of a manometer (in practice there are more than just two manometer tappings).

From Darcy's law: $\qquad$ $q = Aki$

The unit quantity of flow, $\quad q, = \dfrac{Q}{t}$

The hydraulic gradient, $\quad i, = \dfrac{h}{l}$

and $\qquad\qquad\qquad$ A = area of sample.
Hence k can be found from the expression

$$k = \frac{q}{Ai} \quad \text{or} \quad k = \frac{Ql}{tAh}$$

A series of readings can be obtained from each test and an average value of k determined. The test is suitabel for gravels and sand and could be used for most coal spoil materials

The falling head permeameter. A sketch of the falling head permeameter is shown in Fig. 2.5. In this test, which is suitable for silts and some clays, the flow of water through the sample is measured at the inlet. The height (h_1) in the stand-pipe is measured and the valve is then opened as a stop clock is started. After a measured time (t), the height to which the water level has fallen (h_2), is determined.

k is given by the formula:

$$k = 2.3 \frac{al}{At} \log_{10} \frac{h_1}{h_2}$$

where A = cross-sectional area of sample
    a = cross-sectional area of stand-pipe
    l = length of sample.

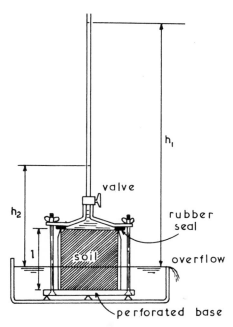

Fig. 2.5 The falling head permeameter

During the test, the water in the stand-pipe falls from a height h_1 to a final height h_2.

Let h be the height at some time, t.

Consider a small time interval, dt, and let the change in the level of h during this time be −dh (negative as it is a drop in elevation).

The quantity of flow through the sample in time dt is −adh and is given the symbol dQ.

Now $dQ = Aki\ dt$

$$= Ak\frac{h}{l}\ dt$$

or $\quad dt = -\dfrac{al}{Ak}\dfrac{dh}{h}$

Integrating between the test limits:

$$\int_0^t dt = -\frac{al}{Ak}\int_{h_1}^{h_2}\frac{1}{h}\ dh$$

i.e. $\qquad\qquad t = -\dfrac{al}{Ak}\log_e\dfrac{h_2}{h_1} = \dfrac{al}{Ak}\log_e\dfrac{h_1}{h_2}$

or $\qquad\qquad k = \dfrac{al}{At}\log_e\dfrac{h_1}{h_2}$

$$2.3\ \frac{al}{At}\log_{10}\frac{h_1}{h_2}$$

In the field

The pumping out test. The pumping out test can be used to measure the average k value of a stratum of soil below the water table and is effective up to depths of about 45 m.

A casing of about 400 mm diameter is driven to bedrock or to impervious stratum. Observation wells of smaller diameter (75 mm) are put down on radial lines from the casing, and both the casing and the observation wells are perforated to allow easy entrance of water. The test consists of pumping' water out from the central casing at a measured rate (q), and observing the resulting drawdown in ground water level by means of the observation wells.

Fig. 2.6 illustrates conditions during pumping.

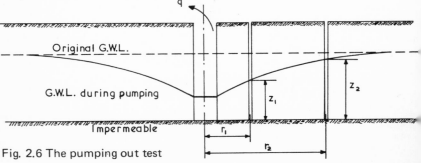

Fig. 2.6 The pumping out test

The formula for k is given by

$$k = \frac{q \, \log_e \dfrac{r_2}{r_1}}{\pi(z_2{}^2 - z_1{}^2)}$$

Consider an intermediate distance r and a depth z. The hydraulic gradient, i, is equal to the slope of the z–r curve $= \dfrac{\partial z}{\partial r}$

$2\pi r z$ = area of walls of an imaginary cylinder of radius r and height z

Now $q = Aki = 2\pi r z \, k \dfrac{\partial z}{\partial r}$

i.e. $q \dfrac{\partial r}{r} = k \, 2\pi z \, \partial z$

and, integrating between test limits:

$$q \int_{r_1}^{r_2} \frac{1}{r} \, \partial r = k 2\pi \int_{z_1}^{z_2} z \, \partial z$$

$$= k 2\pi \left(\frac{z_2{}^2 - z_1{}^2}{2} \right)$$

∴

$$q \, \log_e \frac{r_2}{r_1} = k \, (z_2{}^2 - z_1{}^2)$$

or k

$$= \frac{q \, \log_e \dfrac{r_2}{r_1}}{\pi \, (z_2{}^2 - z_1{}^2)}$$

The pumping in test. Where bedrock level is very deep or where the permeabilities of different strata are required the pumping in test can be used. A casing, perforated for a metre or so at its end, is driven into the ground. At intervals during the driving the rate of flow required to maintain a constant head in the casing is determined and a measure of the soil's permeability obtained.

Relationship between permeability and soil properties

It is obvious that a soil's coefficient of permeability depends upon its porosity, which is itself related to the particle size distribution curve of the soil (a gravel is much more permeable than a clay). It would therefore seem possible to evaluate the permeability of a soil given its particle size distribution, and various formulae have indeed been produced, an excellent summary appearing in the publication of Loudon (1952).

The formula most often used is the one produced by Hazen (1892) who stated that, for cleans sands:

$$k = 10 D_{10}{}^2 \text{ mm/s}$$

where D_{10} = effective size in mm.

At this stage in research, however, no formula is as good as an actual permeability test.

Typical values of permeability

Gravel	Greater than 10 mm/s
Sands	1 to 1 $\times$ 10^{-2} mm/s
Fine sands, coarse silts	1 $\times$ 10^{-2} to 1 $\times$ 10^{-4} mm/s
Silts	1 $\times$ 10^{-4} to 1 $\times$ 10^{-6} mm/s
Clays	$<$1 $\times$ 10^{-6} mm/s

Hydraulic or hydrostatic head

The head of water acting at a point in a submerged soil mass is known as the hydrostatic head and is expressed by Bernoulli's equation:

Hydrostatic head = velocity head + pressure head + elevation head

$$h = \frac{v^2}{2g} + \frac{p}{\gamma_w} + z$$

In seepage problems atmospheric pressure is taken as zero and the velocity is so small that the velocity head becomes negligible; the hydrostatic head is therefore taken as:

$$h = \frac{p}{\gamma_w} + z$$

Excess hydrostatic head

Water flows from points of high to points of low head. Hence flow will occur between two points if the hydrostatic head at one is less than the hydrostatic head at the other, and in flowing between the points the water experiences a head loss equal to the difference in head between them. This difference is known as the excess hydrostatic head.

GRAPHICAL SOLUTION OF SEEPAGE PROBLEMS

Flow nets

The flow of water through a soil can be represented graphically by means of a flow net, which consists of flow lines and equipotential lines.

Flow lines

The paths which water particles follow in the course of seepage are known as flow lines. Water flows from points of high to points of low head, and makes smooth curves when changing direction. Hence we can draw a series of smooth curves representing the paths followed by moving water particles.

Equipotential lines

As the water moves along the flow line it experiences a continuous loss of head. If we can obtain the head causing flow at points along a flow line, then by joining up points of equal potential we obtain a second set of lines known as equipotential lines.

Hydraulic gradient

The potential drop between two adjacent equipotentials divided by the distance between them is known as the hydraulic gradient. It attains a maximum along a path normal to the equipotentials and in isotropic soil the flow follows the paths of the steepest gradients, so that flow lines cross equipotential lines at right angles.

Fig. 2.7 shows a typical flow net representing seepage through a soil

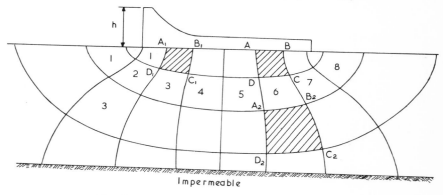

Fig. 2.7 Flow net for seepage beneath a dam

beneath a dam. The flow is assumed to be two dimensional, a condition that covers a large number of seepage problems encountered in practice.

From Darcy's law $q = Aki$, so if we consider unit width of soil and if Δq = the unit flow through a flow channel (the space between adjacent flow lines), then:

$$\Delta q = b \times 1 \times k \times i = bki$$

where b = distance between the two flow lines.

In Fig. 2.7 the figure $ABCD$ is bounded by the same flow lines as figure $A_1 B_1 C_1 D_1$ and by the same equipotentials as figure $A_2 B_2 C_2 D_2$. For any figure in the net $\Delta q = kib = k\Delta h \, b/l$
where Δh = head loss between the two equipotentials
l = distance between the equipotentials (see Fig. 2.8).

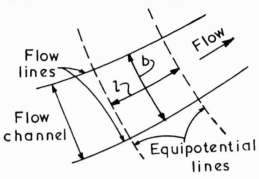

Fig. 2.8 Section of a flow net

Referring to Fig. 2.7:

Flow through $A_1 B_1 C_1 D_1 = \Delta q_1 = k \, \Delta h_1 \dfrac{b_1}{l_1}$

Flow through $A_2 B_2 C_2 D_2 = \Delta q_2 = k \, \Delta h_2 \dfrac{b_2}{l_2}$

Flow through $ABCD \qquad = \Delta q \; = k \, \Delta h \dfrac{b}{l}$

If we assume that the soil is homogeneous and isotropic then k is the same for all figures and it is possible to draw the flow net so that $b_1 = l_1$, $b_2 = l_2$, $b = l$. When we have this arrangement the figures are termed 'squares' and the flow net is a square flow net. With this condition:

$$\frac{b_1}{l_1} = \frac{b_2}{l_2} = \frac{b}{l} = 1$$

Since square $ABCD$ has the same flow lines as $A_1 B_1 C_1 D_1$,

$$\Delta q = \Delta q_1$$

Since square $ABCD$ has the same equipotentials as $A_2 B_2 C_2 D_2$,

$$\Delta h = \Delta h_2$$

$$\therefore \Delta q_2 = k\Delta h_2 = k\Delta h_1 = \Delta q_1$$

i.e. $\quad \Delta q = \Delta q_1 = \Delta q_2$ and $\Delta h = \Delta h_1 = \Delta h_2$

Hence, in a flow net, when all the figure are squares, there is the same quantity of unit flow through each figure and there is the same head drop across each figure.

'Square' figures in a flow net

No figure in a flow net can be truly square, but the vast majority of the figures do approximate to squares in that the four corners of the figure are at right angles and the distance between the flow lines (b) equals the distance between the equipotentials (1). As will be seen, a little imagination is sometimes needed when asserting that a certain figure is a square and some figures are definitely triangular in shape, but provided the flow net is drawn with a sensible number of flow channels (generally five or six) the results obtained will be within the range of accuracy possible. The more flow channels that are drawn the more the figures will approximate to true squares, but the apparent increase in accuracy is misleading and the extra work involved in drawing perhaps twelve channels is not worthwhile.

Calculation of seepage quantities from a flow net

Let N_d = number of potential drops
N_f = number of flow channels
h = total head loss
q = total quantity of unit flow.

Then $\Delta h = \dfrac{h}{N_d}$; $\Delta q = \dfrac{q}{N_f}$

$$\Delta q = k \, \Delta h \dfrac{b}{l} = k \, \Delta h \; (\text{as } \dfrac{b}{l} = 1)$$

$$\therefore k \dfrac{h}{N_d} = \dfrac{q}{N_f}$$

$\therefore$ Total unit flow per unit length (q) = $kh\dfrac{N_f}{N_d}$

Drawing a flow net

A soft pencil, a rubber and a pair of dividers or compasses are necessary.

The first step is to draw in one flow line, upon the accuracy of which the final correctness of the flow net depends. There are various boundary conditions that help to position this first flow line, including:

(i) Buried surfaces (e.g. the base of the dam, sheet piling), which are flow lines as water cannot penetrate into such surfaces.

(ii) The junction between a permeable and an impermeable material, which is also a flow line; for flow net purposes a soil that has a permeability of one-tenth or less the permeability of the other may be regarded as impermeable.

(iii) The horizontal ground surfaces on each side of the dam, which are equipotential lines.

The procedure is as follows:

(a) Draw the first flow line and hence establish the first flow channel.

(b) Divide the first flow channel into squares. At first the use of compasses is necessary to check that in each figure b = 1, but after some practice this sketching procedure can be done by eye.

(c) Project the equipotentials beyond the first flow channel, which gives an indication of the size of the squares in the next flow channel.

(d) With compasses determine the position of the next flow line; draw this line as a smooth curve and complete the squares in the flow channel formed.

(e) Project the equipotentials and repeat the procedure until the flow net is completed

As an example, suppose that it is necessary to draw the flow net for the conditions shown in Fig. 2.9A. The boundary conditions for this problem

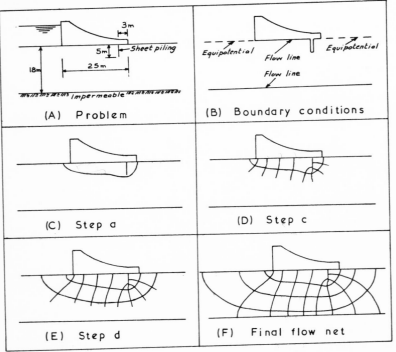

Fig. 2.9 Example of flow net construction

are shown in Fig. 2.9B, and the sketching procedure for the flow net is illustrated in Figs. C, D, E and F of Fig. 2.9.

If the flow net is correct the following conditions will apply:

(i) Equipotentials will be at right angles to buried surfaces and the surface of the impermeable layer.

(ii) Beneath the dam the outermost flow line will be parallel to the surface of the impermeable layer.

After completing part of a flow net it is usually possible to tell whether or not the final diagram will be correct. The curvature of the flow lines and the direction of the equipotentials indicate if there is any distortion, which tends to be magnified as more of the flow net is drawn and gives a good indication of what was wrong with the first flow line. This line must now be redrawn in its corrected position and the procedure repeated again, amending the first flow line if necessary, until a satisfactory net is obtained.

Generally the number of flow channels, N_f, will not be a whole number, and in these cases an estimate is made as to where the next flow line would be if the impermeable layer was lower. The width of the lowest channel can then be found (in Fig 2.9F, $N_f = 3.3$).

NOTE – In flow net problems we assume that the permeability of the soil is uniform throughout the soil's thickness. This is a considerable assumption and we see therefore that refinement in the construction of a flow net is unnecessary, since the difference between a roughly sketched net and an accurate one is small compared with the actual flow pattern in the soil and the theoretical pattern assumed.

Critical hydraulic gradient

Figure 2.10 shows a sample of soil encased in a vessel of cross sectional

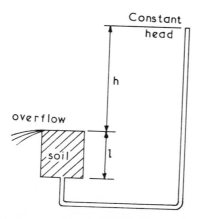

Fig. 2.10 Upward flow through a soil

area A, with upward flow of water through the soil taking place under a constant head. The total head of water above the sample base = h + 1, and the head of water in the sample above the base = 1, therefore the excess hydrostatic pressure acting on the base of the sample = $\gamma_w h$.

If any friction between the soil and the side of the container is ignored, then the soil is on the point of being washed out when the downward forces equal the upward forces:

Downward forces = submerged unit weight × volume

$$= \gamma_w \frac{G-1}{1+e} A\, 1$$

Upward forces $= h\, \gamma_w\, A$

i.e. $h\, \gamma_w\, A \qquad = \gamma_w \dfrac{G-1}{1+e} A\, 1$

or when $\dfrac{h}{1} \qquad = \dfrac{G-1}{1+e}$

This particular value of hydraulic gradient is known as the critical hydraulic gradient and has an average value of about unity for most soils. It makes a material a quicksand, which is not a type of soil but a flow condition within the soil. Generally quicksand conditions occur in fine sands when the upward flow conditions achieve this state, but there is no theoretical reason why they should not occur in gravels (or any granular material) provided that the quantity of flow and the head are large enough. Other terms used to describe this condition are 'piping' or 'boiling', but piping will not occur in fine silts and clays due to cohesive forces holding the particles together; instead there can be a heave of a large mass of soil if the upward forces are large enough.

Seepage forces

Whenever water flows through a soil a seepage force is exerted (as in quicksands). In Fig. 2.10 the excess head h is used up in forcing water through the soil voids over a length 1; this head dissipation is caused by friction and, because of the energy loss, a drag or force is exerted in the direction of flow.

The upward force $h\, \gamma_w\, A$ represents the seepage force, and in the case of uniform flow conditions it can be assumed to spread uniformly throughout the volume of the soil:

$$\frac{\text{Seepage force}}{\text{Unit volume of soil}} = \frac{h\, \gamma_w\, A}{A\, 1} = i\, \gamma_w$$

This means that in an isotropic soil the seepage force acts in the direction of flow and has a magnitude $= i \, \gamma_w$ per unit volume

Alleviation of piping

The risk of piping can occur in several circumstances, such as a cofferdam (Fig. 2.11A) or the downstream end of a dam (Fig. 2.11B).

In order to increase the factor of safety against piping in these cases two methods can be adopted: The first procedure involves increasing the depth of pile penetration in Fig 2.11A and inserting a sheet pile at the toe of the dam in Fig. 2.11B; in either case there is an increase in the length of the

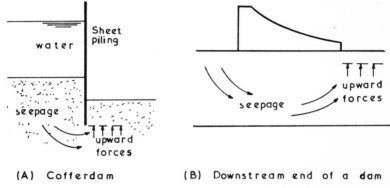

(A) Cofferdam   (B) Downstream end of a dam

Fig. 2.11 Examples where piping can occur

flow path for the water with a resulting drop in the excess pressure at the critical section. A similar effect is achieved by laying down a blanket of impermeable material for some length along the downstream ground surface.

The second procedure is to place a surcharge or filter apron on top of the downstream side, the weight of which increases the downward forces.

Design of filters

The design for a filter is largely empirical, but it must be fine enough to prevent soil particles being washed through it and yet coarse enough to allow the passage of water.

Terzaghi's rule

Terzaghi developed the following formula:

$$D_{15} \text{ filter} > 4 \times D_{15} \text{ of base material}$$

$$D_{15} \text{ filter} < 4 \times D_{85} \text{ of base material}$$

In addition to meeting these requirements filter material should be well graded, with a grading curve more or less parallel to the base material. All material should pass the 75 mm size sieve and not more than 5 per cent should pass the 0.075 mm size sieve.

Reversed filters

Protective filters are usually constructed in layers, each of which is coarser than the one below it, and for this reason they are often referred to as reversed filters. Even when there is no risk of piping, filters are often used to prevent erosion of foundation materials and they are extremely important in earth dams.

EARTH DAMS AND LAGOONS

The disposal of the liquid effluents from washing processes is a major problem in the coal mining industry, as it is not possible to discharge them directly into rivers due to pollution effects and costly clarifying treatments must therefore be used.

At some collieries a convenient method of removing this liquid has been to pump it into a depression in an existing spoil heap, thus forming a lagoon which may often exceed 12 m in depth. The liquid gradually percolates through the tip and is filtered clean in the process.

The problem created by a lagoon is often similar to that posed by an earth dam holding back water.

Seepage patterns through an earth dam

As the upper flow line is subjected to atmospheric pressure, the boundary conditions are not completely defined and it is consequently difficult to sketch a flow net until this line has been located.

Part of such a flow net is shown in Fig. 2.12. It has already been shown

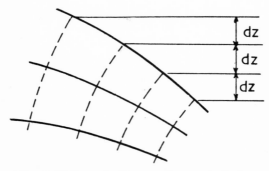

Fig. 2.12 Part of a flow net for an earth dam

that the hydrostatic head at a point is the summation of velocity, pressure and elevation heads. As the top flow line is at atmospheric pressure the only type of head that can exist along it is elevational, so that between each successive point where an equipotential cuts an upper flow line there must be equal drops in elevation. This is the first of three conditions that must be satisfied by the upper flow line.

The second condition is that, as the upstream face of the dam is an equipotential, the flow line must start at right angles to it (see Fig. 2.13A), but an exception to this rule is illustrated in Fig. 2.13B where the coarse material is so permeable that the resistance to flow is negligible and the upstream equipotential is, in effect, the downstream face of the coarse material. The top flow line cannot be normal to this surface as water with

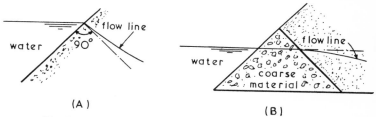

Fig. 2.13 Conditions at the start of an upper flow line

elevation head only cannot flow upwards, so that in this case the flow line starts horizontally.

The third condition concerns the downstream end of the flow line where the water tends to follow the direction of gravity and the flow line either exits at a tangent to the downstream face of the dam (Fig. 2.14A) or, if a filter of coarse material is inserted, takes up a vertical direction in its exit into the filter.

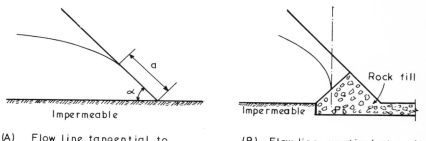

(A) Flow line tangential to downstream slope

(B) Flow line vertical at exit

Fig. 2.14 Conditions at the downstream end of an upper flow line

Types of flow occurring in an earth dam

From Fig. 2.14 it is seen that an earth dam may be subjected to two types of seepage: when the dam rests on an impermeable base the discharge must occur on the surface of the downstream slope (the upper flow line for this case is shown in Fig. 2.15A), whereas when the dam sits on a base that is permeable at its downstream end the discharge will occur within the dam (Fig. 2.15B). This is known as the underdrainage case. From a stability point of view underdrainage is more satisfactory since there is less chance of erosion at the downstream face and the slope can therefore be steeper, but on the other hand seepage loss is smaller in dams resting on impermeable bases.

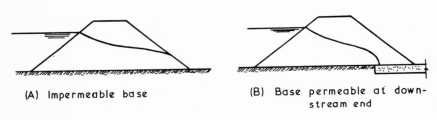

(A) Impermeable base   (B) Base permeable at down-
                               stream end

Fig. 2.15 Types of seepage through an earth dam

Parabolic solution for seepage through an earth dam

In Fig. 2.16 is shown the cross-section of a theoretical earth dam the flow net of which consists of two sets of parabolas. The flow lines all have the same focus, F, as do the equipotential lines. Apart from the upstream end, actual dams do not differ substantially from this imaginary example, so that the flow net for the middle and downstream portions of the dam are similar to the theoretical parabolas. (A parabola is a curve such that any point along it is equidistant from both a fixed point, called the focus, and a fixed straight line, called the directrix. In Fig. 2.17 FC = CB.)

The graphical method for determining the phreatic surface in an earth dam was evolved by Casagrande (1937) and involves the drawing of an actual parabola and then the correction of the upstream end. Casagrande showed that this parabola should start at the point C of Fig. 2.18 (which depicts a cross-section of a typical earth dam) where AC $\doteqdot$ 0.3 AB (the focus, F, is the upstream edge of the filter). To determine the directrix, draw with compasses the arc of the circle as shown, using centre C and radius CF; the vertical tangent to this arc is the directrix, DE. The parabola passing through C, with focus F and directrix DE, can now be constructed. Two points that are easy to establish are G and H, as FG = GD and FH = FD; other points can quickly be obtained by compasses. Having

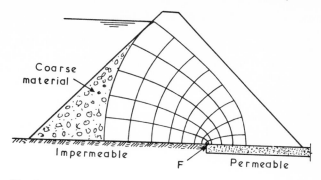

Fig. 2.16 Flow net for a theoretical earth dam

completed the parabola a correction is made as shown to its upstream
end so that the flow line actually starts from A.

This graphical solution is only applicable to a dam resting on a permeable
material. When the dam is sitting on impermeable soil the phreatic surface
cuts the downstream slope at a distance (a) up the slope from the toe
(Fig. 2.14A). The focus, F, is the toe of the dam, and the procedure is now
to establish point C as before and draw the theoretical parabola (Fig. 2.19A).
This theoretical parabola will actually cut the downstream face at a
distance Δa above the actual phreatic surface; Casagrande established a
relationship between a and Δa in terms of a, the angle of the downstream

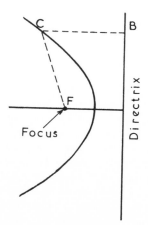

Fig. 2.17 The parabola

48

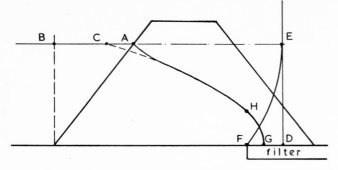

Fig. 2.18 Determination of upper flow line

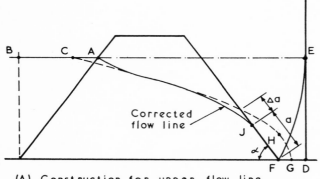

(A) Construction for upper flow line

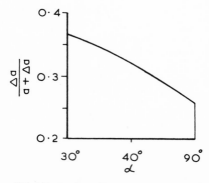

(B) Relationship between a & Δa

(After Casagrande)

Fig. 2.19 Dam resting on an impermeable soil

slope (Fig. 2.19B). In Fig. 2.19 the point J can thus be established and the corrected flow line sketched in as shown.

Lagoons

The discharge into a lagoon can consist of slurry (untreated coal below the 2 mm size and soil, pumped with water), tailings (the water, soil and coal residue from the froth flotation cleaning process), and mine water (dirty water from the mine itself). The sediment that eventually fills a slurry pond often has commercial value as a low grade fuel, so slurry ponds are usually kept separate from tailings.

Whether or not a lagoon will set up seepage forces in the spoil heap that is supporting it will depend upon many factors. If the volume of water pumped into a lagoon is extremely large then it is possible for the whole base of the lagoon to become covered with water and, in theory, a flow net condition similar to that shown in Fig. 2.20A could be established. If no

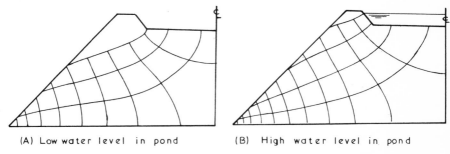

(A) Low water level in pond   (B) High water level in pond

Fig. 2.20 Form of flow nets that may occur in a spoil heap if the quantity of effluent supplied is vast

overflow arrangement is provided and if the quantity of water is vast enough, then the level in the pond could rise until flow takes place through the embankment on the pond (Fig 2.20B). A deposit of silt will very quickly form on the bottom of the pond and penetrate slightly into the spoil material (probably to about a foot) resulting in the creation of a layer of low permeability material above the relatively high permeability of the tip.

The seepage rate through this silt layer will be slow, and will decrease further as the thickness of the deposit is augmented. It may be that the quantity of water flowing through the silt will be insufficient to supply the spoil material with enough water to maintain a continuous flow condition and hydrostatic water pressures within the tip will consequently disappear. How long this effect will take to occur depends upon such factors as the particle sizes in the effluent, the permeability of the tip and the input quantity; any conclusions drawn from one lagoon will not necessarily apply to another.

If the input quantity is low then the bottom of the pond, in the initial stages, will not become covered over with water and silt will be deposited first at the inlet pipe and then gradually across the pond. Water will tend to run over this layer so that there may be a pool at the edge of the silt deposit, but there is little chance that this amount of water will set up seepage forces in the spoil heap. Eventually, when the bottom of the pond has silted over, water may cover a large area of the lagoon, but with the layer of low permeability material overlying the tip and the small quantity of water involved there is no chance of seepage forces developing provided an overflow arrangement is installed.

Some lagoons are constructed on natural ground. If the input quantity is large enough and if the level of water is not controlled by an overflow, then seepage through the embankment can occur. The flow conditions in this case will be much the same as for an earth dam sitting on an impermeable base.

It would appear that lagoons can only become hazardous from a seepage point of view when the quantity of effluent supplied in the initial stages is sufficient to set up continuous flow conditions through the tip before the silt deposit has been formed. The pumping of large quantities of mine water, with little solid material, into a newly excavated lagoon could give rise to this condition.

Another problem arising from lagoons is the risk of deterioration in the spoil heap material. Even though there are not continuous flow conditions a large quantity of water will percolate through a spoil heap supporting a lagoon and some gravel-like materials rapidly achieve the consistency of mud when immersed in water. In such cases a gradual change in the strength properties of the tip material may lead to a stability failure even after the lagoon has ceased to be used, so before a lagoon is installed it is advisable to check on the suitability of the material in the tip from the deterioration point of view.

The problem of stratification

Most loosely tipped deposits are probably isotropic, i.e. the value of permeability in the horizontal direction is the same as in the vertical direction. In future most coal spoil heaps will be created by spreading in direction, but, generally, earth embankments and dams are created by spreading the soil in loose layers which are then compacted. This construction technique results in a greater value of permeability in the horizontal direction, k_x, than that in the vertical direction (the anisotropic condition). The value of k_z is usually $1/5$ to $1/10$ the value of k_x.

In the next chapter the general differential equation for flow through an orthotropic soil is derived:

$$k_x \frac{\partial^2 h}{\partial x^2} + k_y \frac{\partial^2 h}{\partial y^2} + k_z \frac{\partial^2 h}{\partial z^2} = 0$$

For the anisotropic case the equation becomes:

$$k_x \frac{\partial^2 h}{\partial x^2} + kz \frac{\partial^2 h}{\partial z^2} = 0$$

Unless k_x is equal to k_z the equation is not a true Laplacian and cannot therefore be solved by a flow net.

To obtain a graphical solution the equation must be written in the form:

$$\frac{k_x}{k_z} \frac{\partial^2 h}{\partial x^2} + \frac{\partial^2 h}{\partial z^2} = 0$$

or

$$\frac{\partial^2 h}{\partial x_t^2} + \frac{\partial^2 h}{\partial z^2} = 0$$

where

$$x_t = x\sqrt{\frac{k_z}{k_x}}$$

This equation is Laplacian and involves the two co-ordinate variables x_t and z. It can be solved by a flow net provided that the net is drawn to a

vertical scale of z and a horizontal scale of $x_t = z\sqrt{\frac{k_z}{k_x}}$

Calculation of seepage quantities in an anisotropic soil
This is exactly as before:

$$q = kh \frac{N_f}{N_d}$$

and the only problem is what value to use for k.

Using the transformed scale a square flow net is drawn and N_f and N_d obtained. If we consider a 'square' in the transformed flow net it will appear as shown in Fig. 2.21A. The same figure, drawn to natural scales (i.e. scale x = scale z), will appear as shown in Fig. 2.21B.

Let k' be the effective permeability for the anisotropic condition. Then k' is the operative permeability in Fig. 2.21A.

Hence, in Fig. 2.21A: flow $= ak' \frac{\Delta h}{a} = k'\Delta h$

and, in Fig. 2.21B: flow $= a k_x \frac{\Delta h}{a\sqrt{\frac{k_x}{k_z}}} = \sqrt{k_x k_z}\, \Delta h$

i.e. the effective permeability, $k' = \sqrt{k_x k_z}$

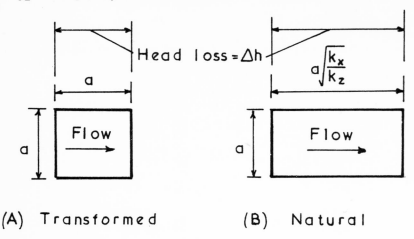

(A) Transformed   (B)   Natural

Fig. 2.21

EXAMPLES ON CHAPTER 2

Example 2.1
Compute an approximate value for the coefficient of permeability for the soil in example 1.1.

Solution $k = 10\,D_{10}^2 = 10 \times 0.17^2 = 2.9 \times 10^{-1}$ mm/s

Example 2.2
In a constant head permeameter test the following results were obtained:

Duration of test	$= 4.0$ min
Quantity of water collected	$= 300$ ml
Head difference in manometer	$= 50$ mm
Distance between manometer tappings	$= 100$ mm
Diameter of test sample	$= 100$ mm

Determine the coefficient of permeability in mm/s

Solution $A = \dfrac{\pi \times 100^2}{4} = 7850 \text{ mm}^2 \quad q = \dfrac{300}{4 \times 60} = 1.25 \text{ ml/s}$

$$k = \frac{ql}{Ah} = \frac{1250 \times 100}{7850 \times 50} = 3.18 \times 10^{-1} \text{ mm/s}$$

Example 2.3
An undisturbed soil sample was tested in a falling head permeameter.
Results were:

> Initial head of water in stand-pipe   = 1500 mm
> Final head of water in stand-pipe   = 605 mm
> Duration of test   = 281 s
> Sample length   = 150 mm
> Sample diameter   = 100 mm
> Stand-pipe diameter   = 5 mm

Determine the permeability of the soil in mm/s

Solution $a = \dfrac{\pi \times 5^2}{4} = 19.67 \text{ mm}^2$ $A = \dfrac{\pi \times 100^2}{4} = 7854 \text{ mm}^2$

$$\log_{10}\frac{H_1}{H_2} = \log_{10} 2.48 = 0.3945$$

$$k = \frac{2.3 \times 19.67 \times 150 \times 0.3945}{7854 \times 281} = 1.21 \times 10^{-3} \text{ mm/s}$$

Example 2.4
A 9.15 m thick layer of sandy soil overlies an impermeable rock. Ground
water level is at a depth of 1.22 m below the top of the soil. Water was
pumped out of the soil from a central well at the rate of 5680 kg/min and
the drawdown of the water table was noted in two observation wells. These
two wells were on a radial line from the centre of the main well at distances
of 3.05 and 30.5 m

During pumping the water level in the well nearest to the pump was 4.57 m
below ground level and in the furthest well was 2.13 m below ground level.
Determine an average value for the permeability of the soil in m/min.

Solution $q = 5680$ kg/min $= 5.68$ m^3/min

$z_1 = 9.15 - 4.57 = 4.58$m $z_2 = 9.15 - 2.13 = 7.02$ m

$$k = \frac{q \log_e \dfrac{r_2}{r_1}}{(z_2{}^2 - z_1{}^2)\pi} = \frac{5.68 \times 2.3026}{28.3 \times \pi} = 0.147 \text{ m/min}$$

Example 2.5
Using Fig. 2.9F, determine the loss through seepage under the dam in cubic metres per year if k = 0.003 mm/s and the level of water above the base of the dam is 10 m upstream and 2 m downstream. The length of the dam perpendicular to the plane of seepage is 300 m.

Solution From the flow net $N_f = 3.3$, $N_d = 9$

Total head loss (h) = 10 − 2 = 8 m

$$q/\text{metre length of dam} = kh\frac{N_f}{N_d} = \frac{0.003}{1000} \times 8 \times \frac{3.3}{9}$$

$$= 8.8 \times 10^{-6} \text{ m}^3/\text{s}$$

Total seepage loss per year = $300 \times 8.8 \times 60 \times 60 \times 24 \times 365 \times 10^{-6}$ m^3

$$= 83\ 000 \text{ m}^3$$

Example 2.6
An 8 m thick layer of silty clay is overlaying a gravel stratum containing water under artesian pressure. A stand-pipe was inserted into the gravel and water rose up the pipe to reach a level of 2 m above the top of the clay (Fig. 2.22).

The clay has a particle specific gravity of 2.7 and a natural moisture content of 33.3 per cent. The permeability of the silty clay is 3.0×10^{-5} mm/s.

It is proposed to excavate 2m into the soil in order to insert a wide foundation which, when constructed, will exert a uniform pressure of 100 kN/m^2 on to its supporting soil.

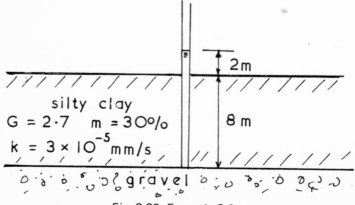

Fig. 2.22 Example 2.6

Determine (a) the unit rate of flow of water through the silty clay in m³ per year before the work commences. (b) The factor of safety against heaving: (i) at end of excavation (ii) after construction of the foundation.

Solution

(a)   Assume that G.W.L. occurs at top of clay.
      Head of water in clay = 8 m
      Head of water in gravel = 10 m
      ∴ Head of water lost in clay = 2 m
      $q = Aki$
      Consider a unit area of one square metre

$$\text{Then } q = 1 \times \frac{3}{1000} \times \frac{2}{8} \times 60 \times 60 \times 24 \times 365 \times 10^{-5}$$

$$= 0.237 \text{ m}^3/\text{year per m}^2 \text{ of surface area}$$

(b)   (i) $e = mG = 0.333 \times 2.7 = 0.9$

$$\gamma_{sat} = \gamma_w \frac{G+e}{1+e} = 9.81 \times \frac{3.6}{1.9}$$

$$= 18.6 \text{ kN/m}^3$$

Height of clay left above gravel after excavation = $8 - 2 = 6$ m
Upward pressure from water on base of clay = $10 \times 10 = 100$ kN/m²
Downward pressure of clay = $6 \times 18.6 = 111.6$ kN/m²

$$\text{Factor of safety} = \frac{\text{downward forces}}{\text{upward forces}} = \frac{111.6}{100} = 1.12$$

(b)   (ii) Downward pressure after construction = $111.6 + 100 = 211.6$ kN/m²
          Factor of safety = 2.12

Example 2.7
Determine the approximate limits for a filter material suitable for the material shown in Fig. 2.23.

Solution From the particle size distribution curve:

$$D_{15} = 0.01 \text{ mm}; D_{85} = 0.2 \text{ mm}$$

Using Terzaghi's method:
      Maximum size of D_{15} for filter = $4 \times D_{85}$ of base = $4 \times 0.2 =$
                                        0.8 mm
      Minimum size of D_{15} for filter = $4 \times D_{15}$ of base = $4 \times 0.01 =$
                                         0.04 mm

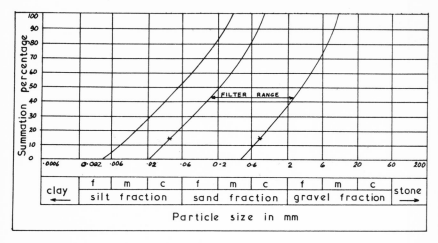

Fig. 2.23 Example 2.7

This method gives two points on the 15 per cent summation line. Two lines can be drawn through these points roughly parallel to the grading curve of the soil, and the space between them is the range of material suitable as a filter (Fig. 2.23).

Example 2.8
The cross-section of an earth dam is shown in Fig. 2.24A. Assuming that the water level remains constant at 35 m, determine the seepage loss through the dam. The width of the dam is 300 m, and the soil is isotropic with $k = 5.8 \times 10^{-4}$ mm/s.

Solution The flow net is shown in Fig. 2.24B; from it $N_f = 4.0$ and $N_d = 14$

$$q/\text{metre width of dam} = \frac{5.8}{1000} \times 35 \times \frac{4.0}{14} \times 60 \times 60 \times 24 \times 10^{-4}$$
$$= 5.0 \times 10^{-1} \text{ m}^3/\text{day}$$
$$\text{Total seepage loss per day} = 300 \times 5.0 \times 10^{-1}$$
$$= 150 \text{ m}^3/\text{day}$$

Example 2.9
A dam has the same details as in example 2.8 except that the soil is anisotropic with $k_x = 5.8 \times 10^{-4}$ mm/s and $k_z = 2.3 \times 10^{-4}$ mm/s. Determine the seepage loss through the dam.

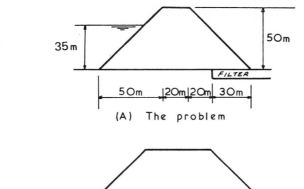

(A)   The   problem

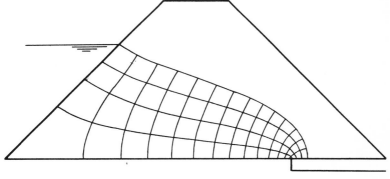

(B)   Flow net

Fig. 2.24 Example 2.8

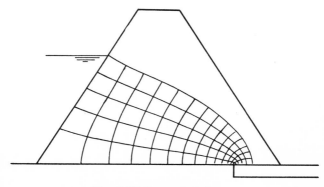

Fig. 2.25 Example 2.9

Solution Transformed scale for x direction $x_t = x.\sqrt{\dfrac{k_z}{k_x}}$

$$= x.\sqrt{\dfrac{2.3}{5.8}}$$

$$= 0.63x$$

This means that, if the vertical scale is 1:500, then the horizontal scale is 0.63:500 or 1:794

The flow net is shown in Fig. 2.25.

From the flow net, $N_f = 5.0$ and $N_d = 14$

$$k' = \sqrt{k_x k_z} = \sqrt{5.8 \times 2.3} \times 10^{-4} = 3.65 \times 10^{-4} \text{ mm/s}$$

Total seepages loss $= 300 \times \dfrac{3.65}{1000} \times 35 \times \dfrac{5.0}{14} \times 60 \times 60 \times 24 \times 10^{-4}$

$$= 118 \text{ m}^3/\text{day}$$

Example 2.10

A dam has the same details as in Example 2.8, except that there is no filter drain at the toe.

Solution The flow net is shown in Fig. 2.26; from it $N_f = 4.0$ and $N_d = 18$
(average)

From the flow net it is also seen that $a + \Delta a = 22.4$ m.

Now $a = 45°$, and hence (according to Casagrande) $\dfrac{\Delta a}{a + \Delta a} = 0.34$ (taken from Fig. 2.19B).

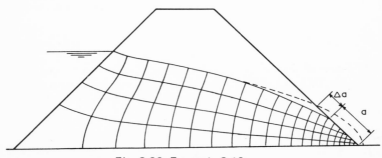

Fig. 2.26 Example 2.10

Hence $\Delta a = 7.6$ m

$$\text{Total seepage loss} = 300 \times \frac{5.8}{1000} \times \frac{4}{18} \times 35 \times 60 \times 60 \times 24 \times 10^{-4}$$
$$= 117 \text{ m}^3 \text{ /day}$$

EXERCISES ON CHAPTER 2

2.1 In a falling head permeameter test on a fine sand the sample had a diameter of 76 mm and a length of 152 mm with a stand-pipe of 12.7 mm diameter. A stop watch was started when h was 508 mm and read 19.6 s when h was 254 mm; the test was repeated for a drop from 254 mm to 127 mm and the time was 19.4 s.
　Determine an average value for k in mm/s.

Answer　　　0.15 mm/s

2.2 A sample of coarse sand 150 mm high and 55 mm in diameter was tested in a constant head permeameter. Water percolated through the soil under a head of 400 mm for 6.0 s and the discharge water had a mass of 400 g. Determine k in mm/s.

Answer　　　10.5 mm/s

2.3 In order to determine the average permeability of a bed of sand 12.5 m thick overlying an impermeable stratum, a well was sunk through the sand and a pumping test carried out. After some time the discharge was 850 kg/ min and the drawdown in observation wells 15.2 m and 30.4 m from the pump were 1.625 m and 1.360 m respectively. If the original water table was at a depth of 1.95 m below ground level, find the permeability of the sand (in mm/s) and an approximate value for the effective grain size.

Answer　　　$k = 6.7 \times 10^{-1}$ mm/s; $D_{10} \doteqdot 0.26$ mm

2.4 A cylinder of cross-sectional area 2500 mm^2 is filled with sand of permeability 5.0 mm/s. Water is caused to flow through the sand under a constant head using the arrangement shown in Fig. 2.27. Determine the quantity of water discharged in 10 min.

Answer　　　9×10^6 mm^3

2.5 The specific gravity of particles of a sand is 2.54 and their porosity is

45 per cent in the loose state and 37 per cent in the dense state. What are the critical hydraulic gradients for these two states?

Answer   0.85, 0.98

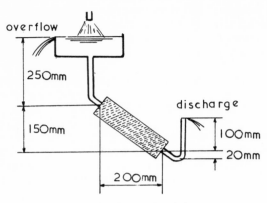

Fig. 2.27 Exercise 2.4

2.6 A large open excavation was made into a stratum of clay with a saturated unit weight of 17.6 kN/m³. When the depth of the excavation reached 7.63 m the bottom rose, gradually cracked, and was flooded from below with a mixture of sand and water; subsequent borings showed that the clay was underlain by a bed of sand with its surface at a depth of 11.3 m. Compute the elevation to which water would have risen from the sand into a drill hole before excavation was started.

Answer   6.45 m above top of sand

2.7 A concrete dam, with a base length of 24.4 m, holds back water to a height of 12.2 m above its base.
    The dam, which is 457 m wide, sits on a stratum of soil 18.3 m thick which overlies impermeable rock. The base of the dam is horizontal and, at the downstream end, a sheet pile cut-off has been driven to a depth of 6.1 m.
    The coefficient of permeability of the soil is 4×10^{-3} mm/s. Determine the seepage loss through the soil, in m³/day, if there is a head of 1.52 m of water above the base on the downstream side.

Answer   Approximately 536 m³/day

2.8 A sand (G = 2.65, n = 0.42) forms the bottom of a sheet-piled coffer dam. The piling is driven 10 m into the sand, and the height of water retained will eventually reach 20 m above the top of the sand. Investigate the danger of piping.

NOTE It has been found from model tests that the rise of the sand as piping occurs is over a horizontal distance of D/2 where D = pile penetration. The downward forces resisting piping are therefore derived from a prism of depth D and width D/2 adjacent to the pile on its downstream edge. By means of a flow net various excess head values along the base of this prism can be obtained and hence the total upthrust force can be evaluated.

Factors of safety evolved by this method should not be less than 3.0.

Answer   F = 1.28 and is too low

Practice in flow net drawing

The reader is advised to make up his own flow net exercises. At first the results may be discouraging but, if a pair of dividers are at hand to check on the 'squareness' of the figures, a reasonable result can be attained with perseverance.

REFERENCES

Casagrande, A.
Seepage through earth dams. *New England Water Works Association*, **51**, no. 2 (1937).

Darcy, H.
Les fontaines publiques de la ville de Dijon (Paris, 1856).

Hazen, A.
Some physical properties of sand and gravels with special reference to their use in filtration. *Massachusetts State Board of Health, 24th Annual Report* (1892).

Loudon, A. G.
The computation of permeability from simple soil tests. *Géotechnique*, (1952).

Swartzendruber, D.
Modification of Darcy's law for the flow of water in soils. *Soil Sci.*, **93** (1961).

Terzaghi, K. & Peck, R. B.
Soil mechanics in engineering practice (John Wiley, 1948).

3. Other Solutions to Seepage Problems

Besides the graphical procedure there are three other common methods by which a flow net may be determined.

ELECTRICAL ANALOGUE

As is shown later in this chapter, the differential equation for two dimensional flow in an isotropic medium is the Laplacian equation:

$$\frac{\partial^2 h}{\partial x^2} + \frac{\partial^2 h}{\partial z^2} = 0$$

A similar equation holds for the two-dimensional flow of electricity through a conducting medium, so that the solution of a two dimensional seepage problem can be obtained from studying the form of electrical flow through a conducting medium that is geometrically similar to the cross-section of the soil through which flow is taking place.

Various methods are available, the most common being the use of a special type of electrically conducting paper in which the area to be analysed is cut out to some convenient scale and an electrical potential is applied at the boundaries corresponding to the upstream and downstream equipotentials. With a Wheatstore bridge it is possible to determine the position of any required equipotential by simply setting a dial on the field plotter to the required potential (usually 90 per cent, 80 per cent, etc.) and determining the position of the equipotential by noting the points on the paper at which the galvanometer needle does not deflect. After a complete set of equipotentials have been obtained it is a relatively simple matter to complete the flow net.

In the case of a flow line at atmospheric pressure, the boundary conditions are unknown and the analogue will not give correct values in this region. The procedure to get over this difficulty is to cut the paper along the approximate position of the flow line (erring on the safe side) and if the boundary thus obtained happens to be correct then the equipotentials along it will be at equal vertical distances apart. This is not generally found to occur, and a portion of the boundary has to be trimmed off so that the equipotentials may be re-established; the procedure is repeated until the equipotentials do have equal increments of elevation between them, at which stage the correct position of the flow line has been found.

The electrical analogue can be very helpful for cases where the boundaries are irregular.

SEEPAGE TANK

With this method a model of the percolation medium is made up from

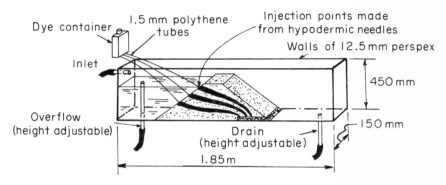

Fig. 3.1 Seepage tank

sand in a perspex tank (Fig. 3.1). At certain points along the upstream equipotential coloured dye is injected into the model and very soon traces out a flow line that enables the whole flow pattern to be seen (fluorescein powder, dissolved in water, makes a green coloured dye that is suitable). The sand used must be clean and fairly coarse, as too many fines in the model will induce capillarity effects that tend to make the flow lines run into each other. A sand with a grading of Leighton Buzzard gives good results.

The seepage tank can give an excellent demonstration of a flow pattern and is therefore useful for teaching purposes, but the solution of actual seepages problems by this method is not altogether satisfactory due to the scale effects involved.

NUMERICAL METHODS

Most seepage problems can be tackled if one can draw a flow net and the remaining part of this chapter may be omitted by the practising engineer with little time to study. The approach is largely academic, although the relaxation technique itself is very practical and produces a method that enables the determination of flow net to be computerized.

General differential equation of flow

Consider an element in an orthotropic soil of dimensions dx, dy and dz;

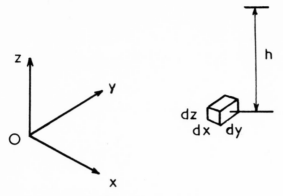

Fig. 3.2 Element in an orthotropic soil

let the excess hydrostatic head at the centre of the element be h (Fig. 3.2). Let the coefficients of permeability in the co-ordinate directions x, y and z be k_x, k_y and k_z respectively. Consider the component of flow in the x direction.

The component of the hydraulic gradient, i_x, at the centre of the element will be

$$i_x = -\frac{\partial h}{\partial x}$$

(Note that it is of negative sign as there is a head loss in the direction of flow.)

The rate of change of the hydraulic gradient i_x along the length of the element in the x direction will be:

$$\frac{\partial i_x}{\partial x}$$

Hence the gradient at the face of the element nearest the origin

$$= -\frac{\partial h}{\partial x} + \left(\frac{\partial i_x}{\partial x}\right)\left(\frac{-dx}{2}\right)$$

$$= -\frac{\partial h}{\partial x} + \frac{\partial^2 h}{\partial x^2}\frac{dx}{2}$$

From Darcy's law: Flow = Aki = $k_x \left(-\dfrac{\partial h}{\partial x} + \dfrac{\partial^2 h}{\partial x^2} \dfrac{dx}{2} \right)$ dy.dz ... (1)

The gradient at the face furthest from the origin is

$$-\frac{\partial h}{\partial x} + \left(\frac{\partial i_x}{\partial x} \right) \frac{dx}{2}$$

$$= -\frac{\partial h}{\partial x} - \frac{\partial^2 h}{\partial x^2} \frac{dx}{2}$$

Therefore flow $= k_x \left(-\dfrac{\partial h}{\partial x} - \dfrac{\partial^2 h}{\partial x^2} \dfrac{dx}{2} \right)$ dy.dz ... (2)

Expressions (1) and (2) represent respectively the flow into and out of the element in the x direction, so that the net rate of increase of water within the element, i.e. the rate of change of the volume of the element, is (1)-(2).

Similar expressions may be obtained for flow in the y and z directions. The sum of the rates of change of volume in the three directions gives the rate of change of the total volume:

$$\left(\frac{k_x \partial^2 h}{\partial x^2} + \frac{k_y \partial^2 h}{\partial y^2} + \frac{k_z \partial^2 h}{\partial z^2} \right) dx.dy.dz$$

Under the laminar flow conditions that apply in seepage problems there is no change in volume and the above expression must equal zero.

$$\frac{k_x \partial^2 h}{\partial x^2} + \frac{k_y \partial^2 h}{\partial y^2} + \frac{k_z \partial^2 h}{\partial z^2} = 0$$

This is the general expression for three-dimensional flow.

In many seepage problems the analysis can be carried out in two dimensions, the y term usually being taken as zero so that the expression becomes:

$$\frac{k_x \partial^2 h}{\partial x^2} + \frac{k_z \partial^2 h}{\partial z^2} = 0$$

If the soil is isotropic, $k_x = k_z = k$ and the expression is:

$$\frac{\partial^2 h}{\partial x^2} + \frac{\partial^2 h}{\partial z^2} = 0$$

It should be noted that these expressions only apply when the fluid flowing through the soil is incompressible. This is more or less the case in seepage problems when submerged soils are under consideration, but in partially saturated soils considerable volume changes may occur and the expressions are no longer valid.

Potential and stream functions

The Laplacian equation just derived can be expressed in terms of the two conjugate functions ϕ and ψ.

If we put

$$\frac{\partial \phi}{\partial x} = v_x = ki_x = -\frac{k\partial h}{\partial x} \quad \text{and} \quad \frac{\partial \phi}{\partial z} = v_z = -\frac{k\partial h}{\partial z}$$

Then

$$\frac{\partial^2 \phi}{\partial x^2} = -\frac{k\partial^2 h}{\partial x^2} \quad \text{and} \quad \frac{\partial^2 \phi}{\partial z^2} = -\frac{k\partial^2 h}{\partial z^2}$$

Hence

$$\frac{\partial^2 \phi}{\partial x^2} + \frac{\partial^2 \phi}{\partial z^2} = 0 \qquad \qquad \dots (3)$$

Also, if we put $\dfrac{\partial^2 \psi}{\partial x^2} = v_x = \dfrac{\partial \phi}{\partial x}$ and $-\dfrac{\partial \psi}{\partial x} = v_z = \dfrac{\partial \phi}{\partial z}$

Then

$$\frac{\partial^2 \psi}{\partial z^2} = \frac{\partial^2 \phi}{\partial x \, \partial z} \quad \text{and} \quad \frac{\partial^2 \psi}{\partial z^2} = -\frac{\partial^2 \phi}{\partial x \, \partial z}$$

Hence

$$\frac{\partial^2 \psi}{\partial x^2} + \frac{\partial^2 \psi}{\partial z^2} = 0$$

ϕ and ψ are known respectively as potential and stream functions. If ϕ is given a particular constant value then an equation of the form h = a constant can be derived (the equation of an equipotential line); if ψ is given a particular constant value then the equation derived is that of a stream or flow line.

Direct integration of these expressions in order to obtain a solution is possible for straightforward cases and readers interested in this subject are referred to Harr (1962). Generally such integration cannot be carried out and the solution is obtained by drawing a flow net or by relaxation.

Flow nets by relaxation

A brief revision of the relevant mathematics is set out below.
Maclaurin's series
Assuming that $f(x)$ can be expanded as a power series:

$$y = f(x) = a_0 + a_1 x + a_2 x^2 + a_3 x^3 + \ldots + a_n x^n$$

$$\frac{dy}{dx} = f'(x) = a_1 + 2a_2 x + 3a_3 x^2 + 4a_4 x^3 + \ldots + n a_n x^{n-1}$$

$$\frac{d^2 y}{d_x{}^2} = f''(x) = 2a_2 + 2.3a_3 x + 3.4a_4 x^2 + \ldots n(n-1)a_n x^{n-2}$$

$$\frac{d^3 y}{d_x{}^3} = f'''(x) = 2.3a_3 + 2.3.4a_4 x + \ldots + n(n-1)(n-2)a_n x^{n-3}$$

etc.

If we put $x = 0$ in each of the above,

$$a_0 = f(0); a_1 = f'(0); a_2 = \frac{f''(0)}{2!}; a_3 = \frac{f'''(0)}{3!}; \text{etc.}$$

Generally $a_n = \dfrac{f^n(0)}{n!}$

Substituting these values:

$$f(x) = f(0) + x f'(0) + \frac{x^2 f''(0)}{2!} + \frac{x^3 f'''(0)}{3!} + \ldots + \frac{x^n f^n(0)}{n!}$$

This is the Maclaurin's series for the expansion of $f(x)$.
Taylor's series
If a curve $y = f(x)$ cuts the y-axis above the origin 0 at a point A (Fig. 3.3) we can interpret Maclaurin's expression as follows:

Let P be a point on the curve with abcissa x.
Let the values of $f(x)$, $f'(x)$, $f''(x)$, etc., at A be:

$$y_0, y'_0, y''_0, \text{etc.}$$

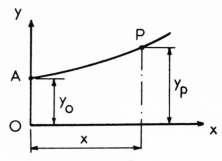

Fig 3.3 Taylor's series

Let the value of f(x) at P be y_p

Then f(x) at $P = y_p = y_0 + xy'_0 + \dfrac{x^2 y''_0}{2!} + \dfrac{x^3 y'''_0}{3!} + \ldots$

This is a Taylor's series and gives us the value of the co-ordinate of P in terms of the ordinate gradient, etc., at A and the distance x between A and P.

Finite difference form of flow equation

The equation for two dimensional flow through a medium has already been established:

$$\frac{\partial^2 h}{\partial x^2} + \frac{\partial^2 h}{\partial z^2} = 0$$

If we cover such a medium with a square mesh of grid points and consider one of these points and its four adjacent ones the resulting diagram is that shown in Fig. 3.4A.

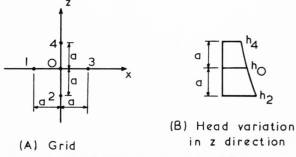

(A) Grid

(B) Head variation in z direction

Fig. 3.4 Grid for two dimensional flow

Consider flow in the z direction.
If point 0 is taken as the origin then, by applying Taylor's theorem:

$$h_2 = h_0 + ah'_0 + \frac{a^2 h''_0}{2!} + \frac{a^3 h'''_0}{3!} + \ldots$$

$$h_4 = h_0 - ah'_0 + \frac{a^2 h''_0}{2!} - \frac{a^3 h'''_0}{3!} + \ldots$$

(a is taken as negative in the direction of flow)
Adding and ignoring terms greater than the second order:

$$h_2 + h_4 = 2h_0 + a^2 h''_0$$

i.e.
$$h''_0 = \frac{\partial^2 h}{\partial z^2} = \frac{h_2 + h_4 - 2h_0}{a^2}$$

Similarily for flow in the x direction:

$$\frac{\partial^2 h}{\partial x^2} = \frac{h_1 + h_3 - 2h_0}{a^2}$$

i.e.
$$\frac{\partial^2 h}{\partial x^2} + \frac{\partial^2 h}{\partial z^2} = \frac{h_1 + h_2 + h_3 + h_4 - 4h_0}{a^2} = 0$$

The finite difference equation for the point 0 is therefore:

$$h_1 + h_2 + h_3 + h_4 - 4h_0 = 0$$

The value of potential at a particular grid point is the average of the four values at the adjacent points.

Residuals

If, at a point 0, $h_1 + h_2 + h_3 + h_4 - 4h_0$ does not equal zero but equals some value R_0, then the system is unbalanced and R_0 is termed the residual at point 0. In a balanced flow net all residuals are zero.

Starting with a set of assumed h values it is possible to calculate the residuals and then gradually adjust them to zero by altering the h values until the system is balanced and the h values are correct. Such a process can be carried out by relaxation.

Let h_1, h_2, h_3, h_4 and h_0 be the values of potential at points 1, 2, 3, 4 and 0.

Let R_1, R_2, R_3, R_4 and R_0 be the residuals or potential at points 1, 2, 3, 4 and 0.

Then $h_1 + h_2 + h_3 + h_4 - 4h_0 = R_0$ (part of a net is shown in Fig. 3.5A).

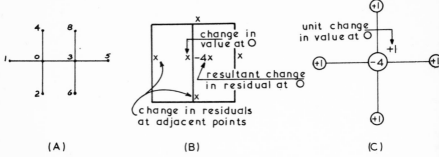

Fig. 3.5 Change in residuals

Let there be a small change in the value of h_0, say Δh_0

Now $R_0 = h_1 + h_2 + h_3 + h_4 - 4h_0$, therefore $\Delta R_0 = -4\Delta h_0$

and $R_3 = h_0 + h_5 + h_6 + h_8 - 4h_3$, therefore $\Delta R_3 = \Delta h_0$

Similarly
$$\Delta R_1 = \Delta h_0$$
$$\Delta R_2 = \Delta h_0$$
$$\Delta R_4 = \Delta h_0$$

Fig. 3.5B illustrates this effect more clearly. If x is the change in value of potential at 0 then the resulting change in residuals is shown in the diagram. Conventionally the value is written on the left of the vertical line through the point, and the residual is written on the right. The schematic form of the operation is shown in Fig. 3.5C.

Boundary conditions

A typical seepage problem is illustrated in Fig. 3.6.

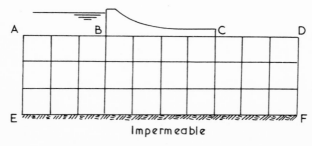

Fig. 3.6 Typical seepage problem

The heads at all points on the lines AB and CD are known exactly, no relaxation procedure is necessary, and there will be no carry over of residuals to these points; EF is an impermeable boundary; AE and DF are lateral boundaries that have been taken far enough out to minimize inaccuracy and may be looked upon as impermeable.

NOTE The centre line of this symmetrical arrangement can be considered as a permeable boundary, similar to boundaries AB and CD, and only half the potentials of the flow net evaluated.

The finite difference equations for boundary conditions

At an impermeable boundary $\dfrac{\partial h}{\partial z}$ or $\dfrac{\partial h}{\partial x} = 0$. Consider flow in the z direction (Fig. 3.7).

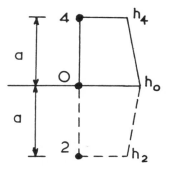

Fig. 3.7

An imaginary point (2) is assumed to lie within the boundary with a potential h_2.

$$\frac{\partial h}{\partial z} \doteqdot \frac{h_4 - h_2}{2a} = 0$$

i.e. $$h_4 \doteqdot h_2$$

Hence the finite difference equation becomes

$$h_1 + h_3 + 2h_4 - 4h_0 = R_0$$

The schematic form for the relaxation of this point is shown in Fig. 3.8A. The schematic form for the relaxation of the point next to an impermeable boundary is given in Fig. 3.8B; in this case Δh_0 causes a change in R_2 of $2\Delta h_0$ (see above equation). Similar equations exist for flow in the x direction, and the schematic form for the relaxation of a point next to

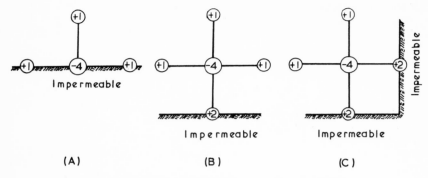

Fig. 3.8 Relaxation forms for two dimensional flow

two impermeable boundaries is given in Fig. 3.8C. Each diagram shows the residual changes caused by a unit change in value at the point relaxed.

This treatment of an impermeable boundary is that suggested by Scott (1963) and is less complicated than the method used by Harr (1962) although giving much the same result.

Permeability of sedimentary deposits

A sedimentary deposit may consist of several different soils and it is often necessary to determine the average values of permeability in two directions, one parallel to the bedding planes and the other at right angles to them.

Let there be n layers of thicknesses $H_1, H_2, H_3, \ldots H_n$.

Let the total thickness of the layers be H.

Let $k_1, k_2, k_3, \ldots k_n$ be the respective coefficients of permeability for each individual layer.

Let the average permeability for the whole deposit be k_x for flow parallel to the bedding planes and k_z for flow perpendicular to this direction.

Consider flow parallel to the bedding planes:

Total flow = $q = Ak_x i$, where A = total area and i = hydraulic gradient.

This total flow must equal the sum of the flow through each layer.

Therefore $Ak_x i = A_1 k_1 i + A_2 k_2 i + A_3 k_3 i + \ldots + A_n k_n i$

Considering unit width of soil:

$H k_x i = i(H_1 k_1 + H_2 k_2 + H_3 k_3 + \ldots + H_n k_n)$

Hence $k_x = \dfrac{H_1 k_1 + H_2 k_2 + H_3 k_3 + \ldots + H_n k_n}{H}$

Consider flow perpendicular to the bedding planes:

Total flow = $q = Ak_z i = Ak_1 i_1 = Ak_2 i_2 = Ak_3 i_3 = Ak_n i_n$

Considering unit area:

$$q = k_z i = k_1 i_1 = k_2 i_2 = k_3 i_3 = k_n i_n$$

Now $k_z i = k_z \dfrac{(h_1 + h_2 + h_3 + \ldots + h_n)}{H}$

where h_1, h_2, h_3, etc., are the respective head losses across each layer.

Now $\dfrac{k_1 h_1}{H_1} = q; \dfrac{k_2 h_2}{H_2} = q; \dfrac{k_3 h_3}{H_3} = q; \dfrac{k_n h_n}{H_n} = q$

$\therefore h_1 = \dfrac{qH_1}{k_1}; h_2 = \dfrac{qH_2}{k_2}; h_3 = \dfrac{qH_3}{k_3}; h_n = \dfrac{qH_n}{k_n}$

$\therefore k_z \dfrac{\left(\dfrac{qH_1}{k_1} + \dfrac{qH_2}{k_2} + \dfrac{qH_3}{k_3} + \ldots + \dfrac{qH_n}{k_n} \right)}{H} = q$

Hence $k_z = \dfrac{H}{\dfrac{H_1}{k_1} + \dfrac{H_2}{k_2} + \dfrac{H_3}{k_3} + \ldots + \dfrac{H_n}{k_n}}$

Seepage through soils of different permeability

When water seeps from a soil of permeability k_1 into a soil of permeability k_2 the principle of the square flow net is no longer valid. If we consider a flow net in which the head drop across each figure, Δh, is a constant then, as has been shown, the flow through each figure is given by the expression:

$$\Delta q = k\Delta h \frac{b}{1}$$

If Δq is to remain the same when k is varied, then $b/1$ must also vary. As an illustration of this effect consider the case of two soils with $k_1 = k_2/3$

Then $\Delta q = k_1 \, \Delta h \dfrac{b_1}{l_1}$

and $\Delta q = k_2 \, \Delta h \dfrac{b_2}{l_2} = 3 \, k_1 \, \Delta h \dfrac{b_2}{l_2}$

i.e. $\dfrac{b_1}{l_1} = 3 \dfrac{b_2}{l_2}$

If the portion of the flow net in the soil of permeability k_1 is square, then:

$$\frac{b_2}{l_2} = \frac{1}{3} \quad \text{or} \quad \frac{b_2}{l_2} = \frac{k_1}{k_2}$$

The effect on a flow net is illustrated in Fig. 3.9.

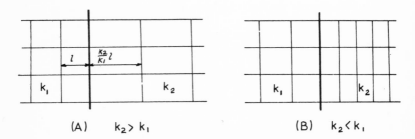

(A) $k_2 > k_1$ (B) $k_2 < k_1$

Fig. 3.9 Effect of variation of permeability on a flow net

Refraction of flow lines at interfaces

An interface is the surface or boundary between two soils. If the flow lines across an interface are normal to it, then there will be no refraction and the flow net appears as shown in Fig. 3.9. When the flow lines meet the interface at some acute angle to the normal, then the lines are bent as they pass into the second soil.

In Fig. 3.10 let RR be the interface of two soils of permeabilities k_1 and k_2. Consider two flow lines, f_1 and f_2, making angles to the normal of α_1 and α_2 in soils 1 and 2 respectively.

Let f_1 cut RR in B and f_2 cut RR in A.

Let h_1 and h_2 be the equipotentials passing through A and B respectively and let the head drop between them be Δh.

With uniform flow conditions the flow into the interface will equal the

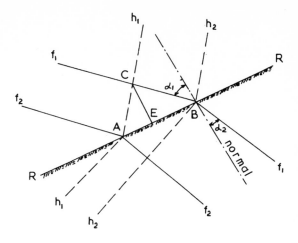

Fig. 3.10 Flow across an interface when the flow lines are at an angle to it

flow out. Consider flow normal to the interface.
In soil (1):

$$\text{Normal component of hydraulic gradient} = \frac{\text{head drop along CE}}{\text{CE}}$$

$$\text{Head drop from A to E} = \Delta h \frac{AE}{AB} = \text{head drop from C to E}$$

$$\therefore \quad q_1 = AB \, k_1 \frac{\Delta h}{CE} \frac{AE}{AB} = k_1 \, \Delta h \frac{AE}{CE} = \frac{k_1 \, \Delta h}{\tan \alpha_1}$$

Similarity it can be shown that, in soil (2)

$$q_2 = \frac{k_2 \, \Delta h}{\tan \alpha_2}$$

$$\text{Now } q_1 = q_2$$

$$\therefore \quad \frac{k_1}{k_2} = \frac{\tan \alpha_1}{\tan \alpha_2}$$

A flow net which illustrates the effect is illustrated in Fig. 3.11.

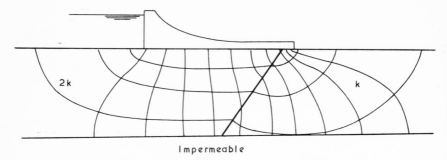

Impermeable

Fig. 3.11 Flow net for seepage through two soils of different permeabilities

EXAMPLES ON CHAPTER 3

Example 3.1

During the process of relaxation the various values shown in Fig. 3.12A have been obtained. Determine a more accurate value of the potential at the central point

Solution $R_0 = 40 + 62 + 34 + 20 - 4 \times 38 = +4$

To eliminate $R_0 = +4$ we must add $R_0 = -4$. This is achieved by adding 1 to the value of potential at 0. The operation also adds 1 to the residuals at points 1, 2, 3 and 4 (Fig. 3.12B).

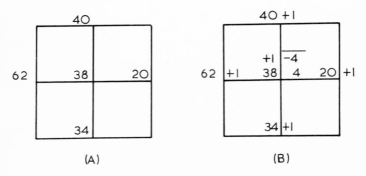

(A)   (B)

Fig. 3.12 Example 3.1

Example 3.2

Determine the values of potential at the four central points in Fig. 3.13A, assuming that the outer potentials are correct.

Solution. The first step is to assume a set of values for the unknown equipotentials so that the relaxation procedure can be carried out. At this

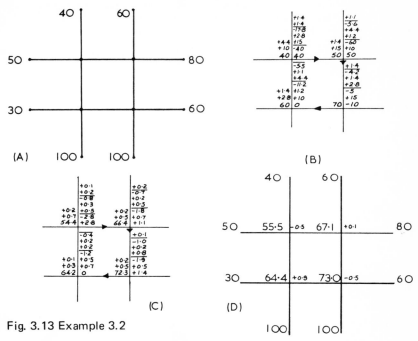

Fig. 3.13 Example 3.2

stage an intelligent guess can save time, although even if the assumed values
are wildly out the relaxation process will eventually lead to the correct
solution.

The figures assumed for this example are shown in Fig. 3.13B, and the
following steps are now carried out:

(i)   Obtain the value of the residual at each of the four points.

(ii) Taking each point in turn, reduce its residual to zero by adding the
same amount but of opposite sign. This will have the effect of changing the
value of the point by an amount equal to one-quarter of the residual that
has been removed and of corresponding sign. The residuals at all adjacent
points are changed by the same amount as the value of the original point.
When the value at a point is fixed, as in the outer points in this example,
there will be no carry-over of residuals to that point.

(iii) Repeat until the residuals become negligible.

The reader familiar with the Hardy Cross method of moment distribution
will find that this procedure is similar.

Figs. 3.13B and 3.13C show the complete relaxation necessary to reduce
all residuals to less than 1.0. With a lengthy relaxation it is sometimes
necessary to redraw the grid as shown; Fig 3.13C is merely a continuation
of Fig. 3.13B.

When the residuals have been reduced, a check on the working can be carried out by summing up the value of each point and recalculating the residuals (Fig. 3.13D). If there is a point with a large residual there has obviously been a mistake in the previous working, but there is no need to go back over these former calculations as the relaxation can be continued using the new set of residuals obtained.

Example 3.3

The values of potential shown in Fig. 3.14A have been obtained from a

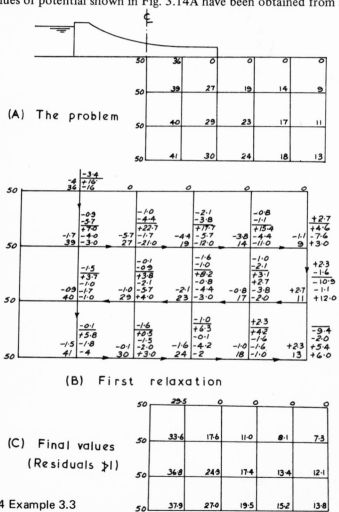

(A) The problem

(B) First relaxation

(C) Final values
(Residuals ≯1)

Fig. 3.14 Example 3.3

rough flow net. Flow is symmetrical about the centre line of the dam; determine a more accurate set of values.

Solution. The first relaxation is shown in Fig 3.14B and the final values obtained in Fig. 3.14C. The figures have been rounded off to the nearest 0.1, but greater accuracy is obtained if, at some stage during the working, the figures are taken to two decimal places. It will be noted that no relaxation is carried out at points of fixed potential, nor is there any carry over of residuals to these points.

In order to facilitate checking it is useful if the direction in which the relaxation was carried out is marked on the sheet, and after each relaxation it is best to draw a line immediately above the figures to show that that particular node has been balanced.

Example 3.4

A three-layered soil system consisting of fine sand, coarse silt, and fine silt in horizontal layers is shown in Fig. 3.15.

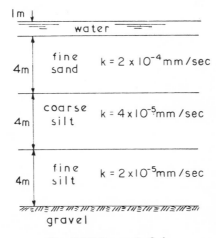

Fig. 3.15 Example 3.4

Beneath the fine silt layer there is a stratum of water-bearing gravel with a water pressure of 155 kN/m^2. The surface of the sand is flooded with water to a depth of 1 m.

Determine the quantity of flow per unit area in mm^3/s, and the excess hydrostatic heads at the sand/coarse silt and the coarse silt/fine silt interfaces.

Solution $k_z = \dfrac{12}{\dfrac{4}{2.0 \times 10^{-4}} + \dfrac{4}{4.0 \times 10^{-5}} + \dfrac{4}{2.0 \times 10^{-5}}} = 3.75 \times 10^{-5} \text{ mm/s}$

Taking the top of the gravel as datum:
Head of water due to artesian pressure = 15.5 m
Head of water due to ground water = 3 × 4 + 1 = 13 m
Therefore excess head causing flow = 15.5 − 13 = 2.5 m.

$$\text{Flow} = q = Aki = 3.75 \times \frac{2.5}{12} \times 10^{-5} = 7.8 \times 10^{-6} \text{ mm}^3/\text{s}$$

This quantity of flow is the same through each layer.
Excess head loss through fine silt

$$\text{Flow} = 7.8 \times 10^{-6} = 2.0 \times 10^{-5} \times \frac{h}{4}$$

$$\text{Therefore, } h = \frac{31.2 \times 10^{-6}}{2 \times 10^{-5}} = 1.56 \text{ m}$$

Excess head loss through coarse silt

$$h = \frac{7.8 \times 10^{-6} \times 4}{4 \times 10^{-5}} = 0.78 \text{ m}$$

Excess head loss through fine sand

$$h = \frac{7.8 \times 10^{-6} \times 4}{2 \times 10^{-4}} = 0.16 \text{ m}$$

Excess head at interface between fine and coarse silt
= 2.5 − 1.56 = 0.94 m

Excess head at interface between fine sand coarse silt
= 0.94 − 0.78 = 0.16 m

EXERCISES ON CHAPTER 3

3.1 Part of a relaxation grid is shown in Fig. 3.16.
   Assuming that the outer values are correct, calculate the values of potential at points A and B.
Answer   At A, h = 56.3; at B, h = 35.3

3.2 Recalculate example 3.2, taking the initial trial values as equal to zero.

3.3 A sheet pile cofferdam is to hold back a 20 m head of water. The

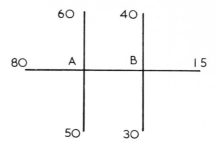

Fig. 3.16 Exercise 1

pattern of water flow through the soil is symmetrical. Rough values of potential, shown in Fig. 3.17A, have been determined from a flow net. Determine the residuals at all relevant points, reduce these residuals by relaxation to not greater than 1.0, and hence determine a more accurate set of potentials

Corrected heads are shown in Fig. 3.17B.

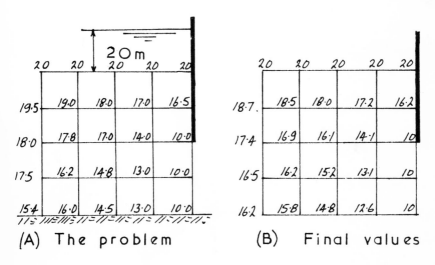

(A) The problem   (B) Final values

Fig. 3.17 Exercise 3

NOTE — The treatment of unsymmetrical flow around a sheet pile is different to the symmetrical case of the preceding exercise.

Fig. 3.18(A) illustrates the relevant part of such a problem.

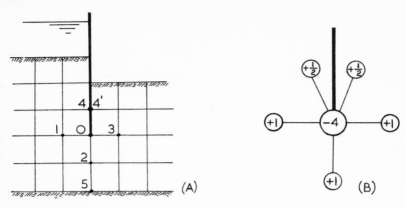

Fig. 3.18 Treatment of unsymmetrical flow around a sheet pile

The line 05 no longer represents a permeable boundary and the assumed initial values of head at grid points 0, 2 and 5 cannot be assumed constant and relaxation of these points is necessary.

The flow channel from 0 to 4 is divided into two parts by the sheet pile leading to two values of head for point 4, h_4 on the upstream side and h_4' on the downstream side.

To determine the residual at 0 the finite difference equation becomes:

$$R_0 = h_1 + h_2 + h_3 + \tfrac{1}{2}(h_4 + h_4') - 4h_0$$

and the relaxation for point 0 is as shown in Fig. 3.18(B).

3.4 A soil deposit consists of three horizontal layers of soil: an upper stratum A (1 m thick), a middle stratum B (2 m thick) and a lower stratum C (3 m thick). Permeability tests gave the following values:

Soil A 3×10^{-1} mm/s   Soil B 2×10^{-1} mm/s
Soil C 1×10^{-1} mm/s

Determine the ratio of the average permeabilities in the horizontal and vertical directions.

Answer   1.22

Beneath the deposit there is a gravel layer subjected to artesian pressure, the surface of the deposit coinciding with the ground water level. Stand-pipes show that the fall in head across soil A is 150 mm. Determine the value of the water pressure in the gravel.

Answer   80 kN/m²

REFERENCES
Harr, M. E.
       Groundwater and seepage (McGraw-Hill, 1962)
Scott, R. F.
       Principles of soil mechanics (Addison-Wesley, 1963)

4. Shear Strength of Soils

The property that enables a material to remain in equilibrium when its surface is not level is defined as its shear strength. Soils, when not in liquid form, generally have a shear strength of small magnitude when compared with such materials as steel or concrete.

FRICTION

Consider a block of weight W resting on a horizontal plane (Fig. 4.1A).

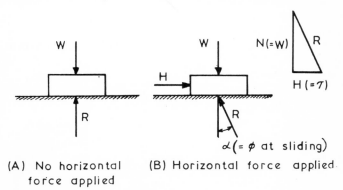

(A) No horizontal   (B) Horizontal force applied
    force applied

Fig. 4.1 Friction

The vertical reaction (R) equals W, and there is consequently no tendency for the block to move. If a small horizontal force (H) is now applied to the block and the magnitude of H is such that the block still does not move, then the reaction R will no longer act vertically but becomes inclined at some angle (α) to the vertical.

By considering the equilibrium of forces, first in the horizontal direction and then in the vertical direction, it is seen that:

Horizontal component of R   = H = R $\sin \alpha$
Vertical component of R   = W = R $\cos \alpha$ (Fig. 4.1B)

The angle α is called the angle of obliquity and is the angle that the reaction on the plane of sliding makes with the normal to that plane. If H is slowly increased in magnitude a stage will be reached at which sliding is imminent as H is increased the value of $\propto$ will also increase until, when sliding is imminent, α has reached a limiting value, ϕ. If H is now increased still further the angle of obliquity (ϕ) will not become greater and the block, having achieved its maximum resistance to horizontal movement, will move (ϕ is known as the angle of friction). The frictional resistance to sliding is the horizontal component of R and, as can be seen from the triangle of forces in Fig. 4.1B, equals N tan ϕ where N equals the normal force on the surface of sliding (in this case N = W).

As α only achieves the value ϕ when sliding occurs, it is seen that the frictional resistance is not constant and varies with the applied load until movement occurs. The term tan ϕ is known as the coefficient of friction.

Sliding in a soil mass

In a soil mass sliding can occur on any plane and the relationships between applied stresses at a point in such a mass must now be considered. Generally planes through a point are acted upon by a stress that is inclined to the normal to the plane; such a stress has both a normal and a tangential component and is known as a compound, or a complex stress. (Fig. 4.2).

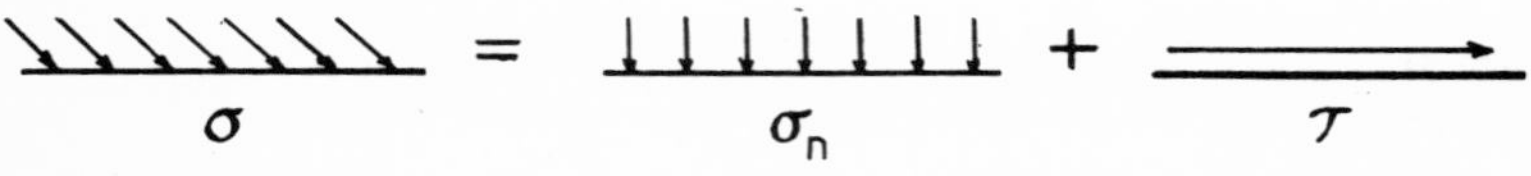

$$\sigma = \sigma_n + \mathcal{T}$$

Fig 4.2 Complex stress

Principal plane
A plane that is acted upon by a normal stress only is known as a principal plane. There is no tangential, or shear, stress present.
Principal stress
The normal stress acting on a principal plane is referred to as a principle stress. At every point in a soil mass, the applied stress system that exists can be resolved into three principal stresses that are mutually orthogonal.
The principal planes corresponding to these principal stresses are called the major, intermediate and minor principal planes and are so named from a consideration of the relative magnitudes of the stresses. Critical stress values and obliquities generally occur on planes normal to the intermediate plane, so that a two dimensional solution is possible.

The Mohr circle diagram

Fig. 4.3A shows a major principal plane, acted upon by a major principal stress, σ_1, and a minor principal plane, acted upon by a minor principal stress, σ_3.

By considering the equilibrium of an element within the stressed mass

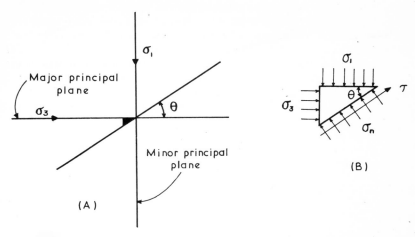

Fig. 4.3 Stresses induced by two principal stresses, σ_1 and σ_3, on a plane inclined at θ to σ_3

(Fig. 4.3B) it can be shown that on any plane, inclined at angle θ to the direction of the major principal plane, there is a shear stress, τ, and a normal stress, σ_n. The magnitudes of these stresses are:

$$\tau = \frac{\sigma_1 - \sigma_3}{2} \sin 2\theta$$

$$\sigma_n = \sigma_3 + (\sigma_1 - \sigma_3) \cos^2 \theta$$

These formulae lend themselves to graphical representation, and it can be shown that the locus of stress conditions for all planes through a point is a circle (generally called a Mohr circle). In order to draw a Mohr circle diagram a specific convention must be followed, all normal stresses (including principal stresses) being plotted along the axis OX whilst shear stresses are plotted along the axis OY; for most cases the axis OX is horizontal and OY is vertical, but the diagram is sometimes rotated to give correct orientation. The convention also assumes that the direction of the major principal stress is parallel to axis OY, i.e. the direction of the major principal plane is parallel to axis OX.

To draw the diagram, first lay down the axes OX and OY, then set off OA and OB along the OX axis to represent the magnitudes of the minor and principal stresses respectively, and finally construct the circle with diameter AB. This circle is the locus of stress conditions for all planes passing through the point A, i.e. a plane passing through A and inclined to the major principal plane at angle θ cuts the circle at D. The co-ordinates of the point D are the normal and shear stresses on the plane (Fig. 4.4).

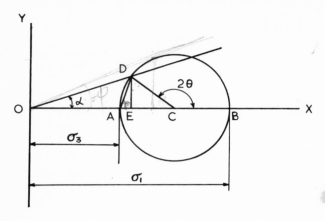

Fig. 4.4 Mohr circle diagram

Proof

$$\text{Normal stress} = \sigma_n = OE \quad = OA + AE = \sigma_3 + AD \cos \theta$$

$$= \sigma_3 + AB \cos^2 \theta$$

$$= \sigma_3 + (\sigma_1 - \sigma_3) \cos^2 \theta$$

$$\text{Shear stress} = \tau = DE \quad = DC \sin (180° - 2\theta)$$

$$= DC \sin 2\theta$$

$$= \frac{\sigma_1 - \sigma_3}{2} \sin 2\theta$$

In Fig. 4.4, OE and DE represent the normal and shear stress components of the complex stress acting on plane AD. From the triangle of forces ODE it can be seen that this complex stress is represented in the diagram by the line OD, whilst the angle DOB represents the angle of obliquity (α) of the resultant stress on plane AD.

Limit conditions
It has been stated that the maximum shearing resistance is developed when the angle of obliquity equals its limiting value, ϕ. For this condition the line

OD becomes a tangent to the stress circle, inclined at angle ϕ to axis OX (Fig. 4.5).

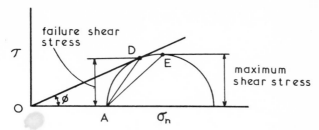

Fig. 4.5 Mohr circle diagram for limit shear resistance

An interesting point that arises from Fig. 4.5 is that the failure plane is not the plane subjected to the maximum value of shear stress. The criterion of failure is maximum obliquity, not maximum shear stress. Hence, although the plane AE in Fig. 4.5 is subjected to a greater shear stress than the plane AD, the latter is nevertheless the plane of failure.

Strength envelopes

If ϕ is assumed constant for a certain material, then the shear strength of the material can be represented by a pair of lines passing through the origin (O) at angles $+\phi$ and $-\phi$ to the axis OX (Fig. 4.6). These lines comprise the

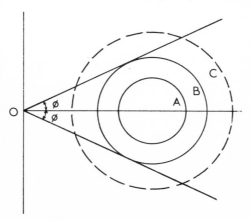

Fig. 4.6 Mohr strength envelope

Mohr strength envelope for the material.

In Fig. 4.6 a state of stress represented by circle A is quite stable as the

The beginning of

circle lies completely within the strength envelope. Circle B is tangential to the strength envelope and represents the condition of incipient failure, since a slight increase in stress values will push the circle over the strength envelope and failure will occur. Circle C cannot exist as it is beyond the strength envelope.

Relationship between ϕ and θ
　In Fig. 4.7 $<$ DCO $= 180° - 2\theta$

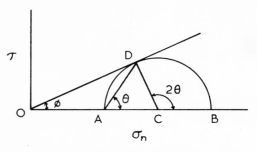

Fig. 4.7 Relationship between ϕ and θ

In triangle ODC: $<$ DOC $= \phi$, $<$ ODC $= 90°$, $<$ OCD $= 180° - 2\theta$

These angles summate to $180°$,

i.e. $\quad \phi + 90° + 180° - 2\theta = 180°$

Hence $\quad \theta = \dfrac{\phi}{2} + 45°$

Cohesion
　It is possible to make a vertical cut in silts and clays and for this cut to remain standing, unsupported, for some time. This cannot be done with a dry sand which, on removal of the cutting implement, will slump until a slope with an angle approximately equal to the angle of internal friction (the friction between the grains) is formed. In silts and clays, therefore, some other factor must contribute to shear strength. This factor is called cohesion, and results from the mutual attraction that exists between fine particles and tends to hold them together in a solid mass without the application of external forces.
　Cohesive soils exhibit shear strength even when the normal stress on the plane considered is zero. In terms of the Mohr diagram this means that the strength envelope will no longer go through the origin but instead intercepts the shear axis. The intercept formed gives a measure of cohesive strength and is called the cohesion of the soil, c.

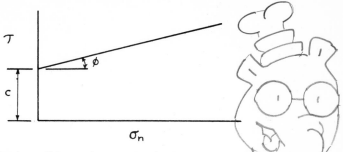

Fig. 4.8 A cohesive soil has a shear strength even when the normal stress is zero

TOTAL STRESSES

It can now be seen that the resistance to shear exhibited by a soil is made up of two parts: *internal friction* (resistance due to the interlocking of the soil particles), and *cohesion* (resistance due to forces tending to hold the soil particles together in a solid mass).

Coulomb's law of soil shear strength

Frictional resistance is not a constant value but varies with the value of applied normal stress on the shear plane, whereas cohesive resistance is a assumed to be a constant value independent of applied stress. The strength envelope of a soil may be expressed by the straight line equation:

$$\tau = c + \sigma_n \tan \phi$$

where
τ = shear stress at failure, i.e. the shear strength
c = cohesion
σ_n = normal stress on shear plane
ϕ = angle of internal friction.

From the point of view of shear stress three types of soil can exist (Fig. 4.9).

Laboratory testing for shear strength

The shear box test

The apparatus consists of a brass box, split horizontally at the centre of the soil specimen. The soil is gripped by metal grilles, behind which porous discs can be placed if required to allow the sample to drain.

The usual plan size of the sample is 60×60 mm^2, but for testing granular materials such as gravel or stoney clay it is necessary to use a larger box, generally 300×300 mm^2 although even greater dimensions are sometimes used.

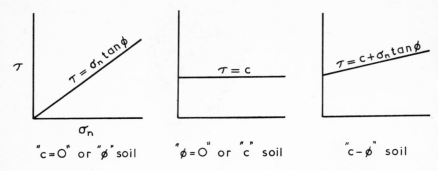

Fig. 4.9 Soil classification by shear strength

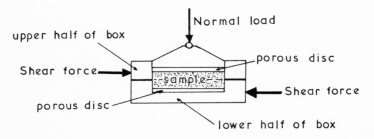

Fig. 4.10 Diagrammatic sketch of the shear box apparatus

A vertical load is applied to the top of the sample by means of weights. As the shear plane is predetermined in the horizontal direction the vertical load is also the normal load on the plane of failure. Having applied the required vertical load a shearing force is gradually exerted on the box, usually from an electrically driven screwjack. The shear force is measured by means of a proving ring — quite a common item of equipment in soils laboratories which consists of an annular steel ring that has been carefully machined and balanced. When a load is applied to such a ring a deflection will take place that can be measured on a dial gauge, enabling the causative force to be obtained from the ring calibration supplied by the manufacturer (usually in the form of a graph giving deflection against force).

By means of another dial gauge (fixed to the shear box) it is possible to determine the strain of the test sample at any point during shear:

$$\text{strain} = \frac{\text{movement of box}}{\text{height of sample}} \quad \text{(approximately)}$$

The proving ring reading is taken at fixed displacements, and failure of the soil specimen is indicated by a sudden drop in the magnitude of the proving ring reading or a levelling off in successive readings. In most cases the electric motor produces a constant rate of strain so that there is no need for the second dial gauge and proving ring readings can be taken at fixed intervals of time.

The triaxial test

As its name implies, this test (Fig. 4.11) subjects the soil specimen to three

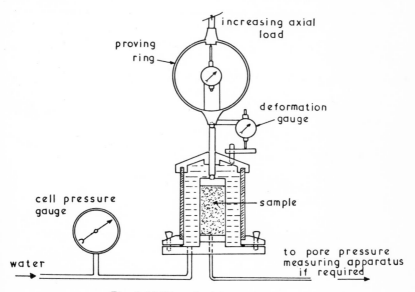

Fig. 4.11 The triaxial apparatus

compressive stresses at right angles to each other, one of the three stresses being increased until the sample fails in shear. Its great advantage is that the plane of shear failure is not predetermined as in the shear box test.

The soil sample is cylindrical with a height equal to twice its diameter. In the United Kingdom the usual sizes are 70 mm high by 35 mm diameter and 200 mm high by 100 mm diameter.

The specimen is subjected to an all-round stress by water pressure and fails under an increasing axial stress. The test sample is first inserted in a thin rubber membrane to prevent it being affected by the water, which is contained in a cell (generally of perspex).

The water pressure, usually called cell pressure, can be measured directly from a manometer or a gauge, and an adaptation also enables the pore water pressure inside the sample to be recorded. The additional axial stress is obtained by an axial load applied through a proving ring in a similar manner to the horizontal shear force used in the shear box.

Determination of the additional axial stress in the triaxial test. From the proving ring it is possible at any time during the test to determine the additional axial load that is being applied to the sample.

During the application of this load the sample experiences shortening in the vertical direction with a corresponding expansion in the horizontal direction. This means that the cross sectional area of the sample varies, and it has been found that very little error is introduced if the cross sectional area is evaluated on the assumption that the volume of the sample remains unchanged during the test. In other words the cross sectional area is found from:

$$\text{Cross sectional area} = \frac{\text{volume of sample}}{\text{original length} - \text{vertical deformation}}$$

Principal stresses in the triaxial test. The intermediate principal stress, σ_2, and the minor principal stress, σ_3, are equal and are the radial stresses caused by the cell pressure, p_c. The major principal stress, σ_1, consists of two parts: the cell water pressure acting on the ends of the sample and the additional axial stress from the proving ring, q.

From this we see that the triaxial test can be considered as happening in two stages (Fig. 4.12), the first being the application of the cell water

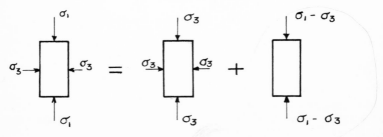

Fig. 4.12 Stresses in the triaxial test

pressure (p_c, i.e. σ_3), whilst the second is the application of a deviator stress (q, i.e. $[\sigma_1 - \sigma_3]$).

A set of at least three samples are tested. The deviator stress is plotted against vertical strain and the point of failure of each sample is obtained. The Mohr circles for each sample are then drawn and the best common tangent to the circles is taken as the strength envelope (Fig. 4.13). A small curvature occurs in the strength envelope of most soils, but this effect is slight and for all practical work the envelope can be taken as a straight line.

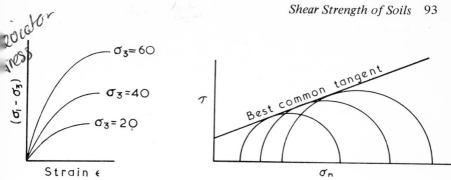

Fig. 4.13 Typical triaxial test results

Types of failure in the triaxial test. Not all soil samples will fail in pure shear: there are generally some barrelling effects as well. In a sample that fails completely by barrelling there is no definite failure point, the deviator stress simply increasing slightly with strain. In this case an arbitrary value of the failure stress is taken as the stress value at 20 per cent strain (see Fig. 4.14)

Shear   Barrelling   Barrelling
                         and   shear

Fig. 4.14 Types of failure in the triaxial test

The unconfined compression test
This is a special case of the triaxial test in which the all-round pressure on the sample is zero and no rubber membrane is necessary to encase the specimen (Fig. 4.15). It is often used as a simple field test, but can only be employed for cohesive soils.

The test specimen is loaded through a calibrated spring by a simple manually-operated screwjack at the top of the machine. In order to test soils of varying strengths a range of springs are supplied, generally with stiffnesses in the order of 2, 4, 10 and 20 N/mm extension. By means of an autographic recording arm the graph of load against deformation is drawn directly onto a sheet of paper. Knowing the vertical deformation, the area of the sample at failure can be obtained and hence the stress; in common practice the cohesion of the soil is taken to be one half of the stress at failure (i.e. ϕ is assumed = 0).

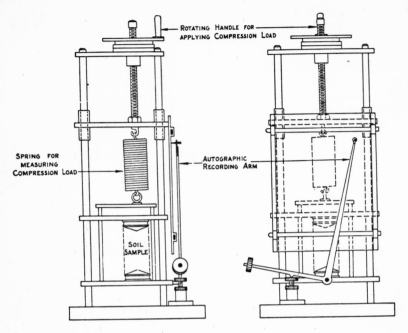

Fig. 4.15 The unconfined compression apparatus

The undrained shear test

In this test the sample is prevented from draining during shear. The test sample is therefore usually sheared either immediately after the application of the normal load (in the shear box) or immediately after the cell pressure has been applied (in the triaxial method). A sample can be tested in 15 minutes or less, so that there is no time for any pore pressures developed to dissipate or to distribute themselves evenly throughout the sample. Measurements of pore water pressure are therefore not possible and the results of the test can only be expressed in terms of total stress.

The unconfined compression apparatus is only capable of carrying out an undrained test, with no radial pressure.

EFFECTIVE STRESS σ'

The stress that controls changes in the volume and the strength of a soil is known as effective stress. When a load is applied to a saturated soil it will be carried by the water in the soil voids (causing an increase in the pore water pressure) or by the soil skeleton (in the form of grain to grain contact stresses), or else it will be shared between the water and the soil skeleton.

The effect that a load has on a soil depends upon the drainage conditions, but Terzaghi showed that for most practical cases the effective stress is equal to the intergranular stress and can be determined from the equation:

$$\sigma' = \sigma - u$$

where σ = total applied normal stress and u = pore water pressure.

This equation has stood the test of time for almost 50 years and is now regarded as satisfactory for all types of soil, although it can lead to errors in rocks (Skempton, 1960).

In 1955 Bishop suggested a similar formula for a partially saturated soil:

$$\sigma' = \sigma - [u_a - \chi(u_a - u_w)]$$

when $\chi = 1$ is $S = 100\%$.
$u_a = 0$.

where u_a and u_w are the pore pressures in the air and water phases respectively and χ is a parameter related to the degree of saturation. The formula agrees with Terzaghi when $S = 100$ per cent, $\chi = 1$ and the expression is $\sigma' = \sigma - u$, or when $S = 0$ per cent, $\chi = 0$ and the expression is $\sigma' = \sigma$. *how from the expression? logically it is ok*

✕Modified Coulomb's law or Hvorslev's theory

Shear strength depends upon effective stress and not total stress. Coulomb's equation must therefore be modified in terms of effective stress and becomes:

$$\tau = c' + \sigma_n' \tan \phi'$$

where c' = cohesion with respect to effective stresses
and ϕ' = angle of internal friction, with respect to effective stresses.

Determination of the effective stress parameters

Either the drained shear test or the consolidated undrained test can be used to obtain c' and ϕ'. The tests are usually carried out in the triaxial apparatus, although the shear box can also be used.

The drained test

The sample is fitted with a porous disc at its base (and sometimes also at the top) which will allow water to escape during the test. It is then placed in a triaxial cell and a water pressure is applied that induces a pressure in the water contained in the voids of the soil. The sample is then left until this pore water pressure has been dissipated by water seeping out through the porous discs, which usually takes about a day and leads to what is known as consolidation. During this stage a burette is attached to the base of the sample to indicate when the point of full consolidation has been attained (i.e. when the water level in the burette stops rising).

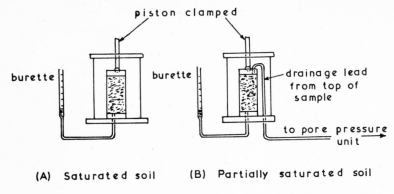

(A) Saturated soil   (B) Partially saturated soil

Fig. 4.16 Alternative arrangements for consolidation of test sample

An alternative method (sometimes preferable with a partially saturated soil) is to allow drainage into a burette from one end of the sample and to connect a pore pressure measuring device to the other. When the pore water pressure reaches zero the sample is consolidated.

When consolidation has been completed the sample is sheared by applying a deviator stress applied at such a low rate of strain that any pore water pressures induced in the sample have time to dissipate through the porous discs. In this test the pore water pressure is therefore always zero and the effective stresses are consequently equal to the applied stresses.

The main drawback of the drained test is the length of time it takes, with the attendant risk of testing errors: an average test time for a clay sample is about three days but with some soils a test may last as long as two weeks.

The consolidated undrained test

This is the most common form of triaxial test used in soils laboratories to determine c' and ϕ'. It has the advantage that the shear part of the test can be carried out in only two to three hours.

The sample is consolidated exactly as for the drained test, but at this stage the drainage connection is shut off and the sample is sheared under undrained conditions. The application of the deviator stress induces pore water pressures (which are measured), and the effective deviator stress is then simply the total deviator stress less the pore water pressure.

Although the sample is sheared undrained, the rate of shear must be slow enough to allow the induced pore water pressures to distribute themselves evenly throughout the sample. For most soils a strain rate of 0.05 mm/min is satisfactory, which means that the majority of samples can be sheared in under three hours.

NOTE With respect to total stress (i.e. the undrained parameters) c and ϕ are often written as c_u and ϕ_u, whilst with respect to effective stresses (i.e. the drained parameters) c' and ϕ' are often written as c_d and ϕ_d.

The pore pressure coefficients A and B

These coefficients were proposed by Skempton in 1954 and are now almost universally accepted. The relevant theory is set out below.

$$\text{Volumetric strain} = \frac{\text{change in volume}}{\text{original volume}} = \frac{-\Delta V}{V}$$

(ΔV is negative when dealing with compressive stresses as is the general case in soil mechanics.)

Consider an elemental cube of unit dimensions and acted upon by compressive stress increases p_1, p_2 and p_3 (Fig. 4.17).

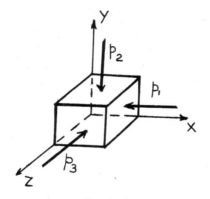

Fig. 4.17

On vertical plane (y, z): compressive strain $= \dfrac{p_1}{E}$

lateral strain from stresses p_2 and p_3 $= -\left(\dfrac{\nu p_2}{E} + \dfrac{\nu p_3}{E}\right)$

where ν = Poisson's ratio

i.e. total strain on this plane $= \dfrac{p_1}{E} - \nu(p_2 + p_3)$

Similarily, strains on other two planes are:

$$\frac{p_2}{E} - \frac{v}{E}(p_3 + p_1)$$

$$\frac{p_3}{E} - \frac{v}{E}(p_1 + p_2)$$

Now it can be shown that, no matter what the stresses on the faces of the cube, the volumetric strain is equal to the sum of the strains on each face.

$$-\frac{\Delta V}{V} = \frac{(p_1 + p_2 + p_3)}{E} - \frac{2v}{E}(p_1 + p_2 + p_3)$$

i.e.
$$\frac{-\Delta V}{V} = \frac{1 - 2v}{E}(p_1 + p_2 + p_3)$$

Compressibility of a material is the volumetric strain per unit pressure, i.e., for a soil skeleton, $C_c = \frac{-\Delta V}{V}$ per unit pressure increase. Average pressure increase $= \frac{1}{3}(p_1 + p_2 + p_3)$. Therefore, for a perfectly elastic soil:

$$C_c = \frac{3(1 - 2v)}{E} \cdot \frac{p_1 + p_2 + p_3}{p_1 + p_2 + p_3}$$

$$= \frac{3(1 - 2v)}{E} = \text{Coeff. of volume compre}$$
$$\text{lili}$$

Consider a sample of saturated soil subjected to an undrained triaxial test. The applied stress system for this test has already been discussed (Fig. 4.12). The pore water pressure, u, produced during the test will be made up of two parts corresponding to the application of the cell pressure and the deviator stress.

Let u_a = pore pressure due to σ_3

u_d = pore pressure due to $(\sigma_1 - \sigma_3)$

If we consider the effects of small total pressure increments $\Delta\sigma_3$ and $\Delta\sigma_1$

then $\Delta\sigma_3$ will cause a pore pressure change Δu_a
and $\Delta\sigma_1 - \Delta\sigma_3$ will cause a pore pressure change Δu_d.

Effect of $\Delta\sigma_3$
When an all-round pressure is applied to a saturated soil and drainage is prevented the proportions of the applied stress carried by the pore water and by the soil skeleton depend upon their relative compressibilities.

Compressibility of the soil $C_c = \frac{-1}{V}\frac{\Delta V}{\Delta\sigma_3'}$

Compressibility of the pore water $= C_v = \frac{-1}{V}\frac{V}{\Delta u}$

Consider a saturated soil of initial volume V.
Then volume of pore water $= nV$ where $n = $ porosity.
Assume a change in total ambient stress $= \Delta\sigma_3$
Assume that the change in effective stress caused by this total stress increment is $\Delta\sigma_3'$ and that the corresponding change in pore water pressure is Δu_a.
Then, decrease in volume of soil skeleton $= C_c V \Delta\sigma_3'$
and decrease in volume of pore water $= C_v nV \Delta u_a$
With no drainage these changes must be equal:

i.e.
$$C_c V \Delta\sigma_3' = C_v n V \Delta u_a$$

$$\therefore \Delta\sigma_3' = \frac{nC_v}{C_c} \Delta u_a$$

Now
$$\Delta\sigma_3' = \Delta\sigma_3 - \Delta u_a$$

$$\therefore \frac{nC_v}{C_c} \Delta u_a = \Delta\sigma_3 - \Delta u_a$$

or
$$\Delta u_a \left(1 + \frac{nC_v}{C_c}\right) = \Delta\sigma_3$$

$$\therefore \Delta u_a = \frac{\Delta\sigma_3}{1 + \frac{nC_v}{C_c}}$$

i.e.
$$\Delta u_a = B\Delta\sigma_3 \text{ where } B = \frac{1}{1 + \frac{nC_v}{C_c}}$$

The compressibility of water is in the order of 1.63×10^{-7} kN/m^2.
Typical results from soil tests are given in Table 4.1 and show that, for all saturated soils, B can be taken as equal to 1.0 for practical purposes.

Table 4.1. Compression of saturated soils

Soil type	Soft clay	Stiff clay	Compact silt	Loose sand	Dense sand
n (%)	60	37	35	46	43
C_c (kN/m^2)	4.79×10^{-4}	3.35×10^{-5}	9.58×10^{-5}	2.87×10^{-5}	1.44×10^{-5}
B	0.9998	0.9982	0.9994	0.9973	0.9951

Effect of $\Delta\sigma_1 - \Delta\sigma_3$
Increase in effective stresses:
$$\Delta\sigma_1' = (\Delta\sigma_1 - \Delta\sigma_3) - \Delta u_d$$
$$\Delta\sigma_2' = \Delta\sigma_3' = -\Delta u_d$$

Change in volume of soil skeleton, $\Delta V_c = - V\dfrac{(1 - 2\nu)}{E}(\Delta\sigma_1' + 2\,\Delta\sigma_3')$

i.e. $\qquad\qquad \Delta V_c = - V\dfrac{C_c}{3}[(\Delta\sigma_1 - \Delta\sigma_3) - 3\,\Delta u_d]$

Now $\Delta V_v = - C_v n \Delta u_d V$ and ΔV_c must equal ΔV_v

$\therefore \qquad\qquad \dfrac{1}{3}C_c(\Delta\sigma_1 - \Delta\sigma_3) - C_c\Delta u_d = C_v n \Delta u_d$

or $\qquad\qquad \Delta u_d(C_c + nC_v) = \dfrac{1}{3}C_c(\Delta\sigma_1 - \Delta\sigma_3)$

$\therefore \qquad\qquad \Delta u_d = \dfrac{1}{1 + \dfrac{nC_v}{C_c}}\dfrac{1}{3}(\Delta\sigma_1 - \Delta\sigma_3)$

$$= B \times \dfrac{1}{3}(\Delta\sigma_1 - \Delta\sigma_3)$$

Now $\Delta u = \Delta u_a + \Delta u_d$

$\therefore \qquad\qquad \boxed{\Delta u = B[\Delta\sigma_3 + \dfrac{1}{3}(\Delta\sigma_1 - \Delta\sigma_3)]}$

Generally a soil is not perfectly elastic and the above expression must be written in the form:

$$\Delta u = B\,\Delta\sigma_3 + A(\Delta\sigma_1 - \Delta\sigma_3)$$

where A is a coefficient determined experimentally.

The expression is often written in the form:

$$\boxed{\Delta u = B\Delta\sigma_3 + \bar{A}(\Delta\sigma_1 - \Delta\sigma_3)}\ \text{where } \bar{A} = AB.$$

$\bar{A}$ and B can be obtained directly from the undrained triaxial test. As has been shown, for a saturated soil B = 1.0 and the above expression must be

$$\boxed{\Delta u = \Delta\sigma_3 + A(\Delta\sigma_1 - \Delta\sigma_3)}$$

For a partially saturated soil B varies from 0 (when dry) to 1 (when saturated). This phenomenon is discussed in Chapter 11.

Values of A
For a given soil, A varies with both the stress value and the rate of strain, due mainly to the variation of Δu_d with the deviator stress. The value of Δu_d under a particular stress system depends upon such factors as the degree of saturation and whether the soil is normally consolidated or over consolidated. The value of A must be quoted for some specific point, e.g. at maximum deviator stress or at maximum effective stress ratio (σ_1'/σ_3'); at maximum deviator stress it can vary from 1.5 (for a highly sensitive clay) to -0.5 (for a heavily over-consolidated clay).

A comprehensive survey of present day techniques used in the triaxial test has been prepared by Bishop & Henkel (1962).

THE BEHAVIOUR OF SOILS UNDER SHEAR

Before discussing this important subject the following definitions must be established.

Overburden. The overburden pressure at a point in a soil mass is simply the weight of the material above it. The effective overburden is the pressure from this material less the pore water pressure due to the height of water extending from the point up to the water table.

Normally consolidated clay. Clay which, at no time in its history, has been subjected to pressures greater than its existing overburden pressure.

Overconsolidated clay. Clay which, during its history, has been subjected to pressures greater than its existing overburden pressure. One cause of overconsolidation is the erosion of material that once existed above the clay layer. Boulder clays are overconsolidated, as the many tons of pressure exerted by the mass of ice above them has been removed.

Preconsolidation pressure. The maximum value of pressure exerted on an overconsolidated clay before the pressure was relieved.

Sands and other granular materials

Unless drainage is deliberately prevented, a shear test on a sand will be a drained one as the high value of permeability makes consolidation and drainage virtually instantaneous.

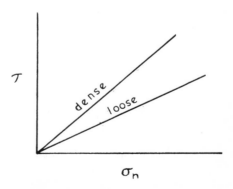

Fig. 4.18 Strength envelope of a granular material, showing the greater shear resistance of a dense sand

A sand can be tested either dry or saturated. If dry there will be no pore water pressures and the intergranular pressure will equal the applied stress; if the sand is saturated, the pore water pressure will be zero due to the quick drainage, and the intergranular pressure will again equal the applied stress.

A dense sand tends to dilate (increase in volume) during shear whereas a loose sand tends to decrease in volume, and if the movement of pore water is restricted the shear strength of the sand will be affected: a dense sand will have negative pore pressures induced in it, causing an increase in shear strength, whilst a loose sand will have positive pore pressures induced with a corresponding reduction in strength. The density at which there is no increase or decrease in shear strength when the sand is maintained at constant volume is called the critical density of the sand. A practical application of this effect occurs when a pile is driven into sand, the load on the sand being applied so suddenly that, for a moment, the water it contains has no time to drain away.

Normally consolidated clays

When this material is subjected to a drained test (which is carried out with zero pore pressures) the applied stress equals the effective stress. A strength envelope obtained with this test gives a zero cohesive intercept and an angle of friction, the clay behaving as if it were a granular material (Fig. 4.19).

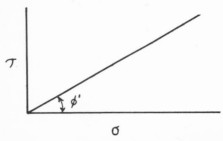

Fig. 4.19 Strength envelope for a normally consolidated clay subjected to a drained shear test

The same strength envelope is obtained from a consolidated undrained test conducted with pore pressure measurements during shear.

In an undrained test the clay sample is placed in the triaxial cell, the drainage connection is removed, and the cell pressure is applied to effect shearing of the soil. The pore water pressure (u) generated during the test is not allowed to dissipate.

The effective stresses are:

$$\sigma_3' = \sigma_3 - u; \; \sigma_1' = \sigma_1 - u$$

so that the shear strength obtained is considerably less than in the drained test.

If the procedure is repeated using a cell pressure of $p_c + \Delta p_c$ the value of undrained strength will be exactly the same as that obtained from the first test because the increase in applied pressure (Δp_c) induces an increase in pore pressure (Δu) which is numerically equal to Δp_c. The effective stress circle is therefore the same as for the first test (Fig. 4.20), the soil acting as if it were purely cohesive.

From Figs. 4.19 and 4.20 it will be seen that the strength of a clay varies

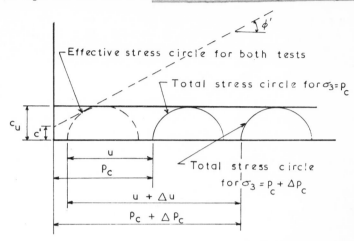

Fig. 4.20 Strength envelope for a normally consolidated clay subjected to an undrained shear test

enormously with the test conditions, and laboratory tests must be carried out under drainage conditions as near as possible to those that will apply in-situ.

Overconsolidated clays

An overconsolidated clay is considerably stronger at a given pressure than it would be if normally consolidated, and also tends to dilate during shear whereas a normally consolidated clay will consolidate. Hence when an overconsolidated clay is sheared under undrained conditions negative pore water pressures are induced, the effective stress is increased, and the undrained strength is much higher than the drained strength—the exact opposite to a normally consolidated clay.

If an excavation is made through overconsolidated clay the negative pressures set up give an extremely high undrained strength, but these pore pressures gradually dissipate and the strength falls by as much as 60 or 80 per cent to the drained strength. A well-known example of overconsolidated clay is London Clay, which when first cut will stand virtually unsupported to a height of 7.5 m. It does not remain stable for long, and so great is the loss in strength that there have been cases of retaining walls built to support it being pushed over.

NOTE Most clays are saturated, but in the case of a partially saturated soil (such as obtained by compaction) the pore pressures generated are not equal to the applied stresses. The resultant strength envelopes indicate a $c' - \phi'$ soil.

Sensitivity of clays

If the strength of an undisturbed sample of clay is measured and it is then re-tested at an identical water content, but after it has been remoulded to the same dry density, a reduction in strength is often observed.

$$\text{Sensitivity} = S_t = \frac{\text{undisturbed, undrained strength}}{\text{remoulded, undrained strength}}$$

Normally consolidated clays tend to have sensitivity values varying from 5 to 10 but certain clays in Canada and Scandanavia have sensitivities as high as 100 and are referred to as quick clays. Sensitivity can vary, slightly, depending upon the moisture content of the clay. Generally, overconsolidated clays have negligible sensitivity, but some quick clays have been found to be overconsolidated. A classification of sensitivity appears in Table 4.2.

Table 4.2 Sensitivy classification

S_t	Classification
1	insensitive
1 − 2	low
2 − 4	medium
4 − 8	sensitive
8 − 16	extra sensitive
> 16	quick (can be up to 150)

Thixotropy

Some clays, if kept at a constant moisture content, regain a portion of their original strength after remoulding, with time (Skempton & Northley (1952)). This property is known as thixotropy.

Liquidity index I_L

The definition of this index has already been given in Chapter 1:

$$I_L = \frac{m - \text{P.L.}}{\text{P.I.}}$$

where m is the in-situ moisture content.

This index probably more usefully reflects the properties of plastic soil than the generally-used consistency limits (L.L. and P.L.). Liquid and plastic limit tests are carried out on remoulded soil in the laboratory, but the same soil, in its in-situ state (i.e. undisturbed), may exhibit a different consistency at the same moisture content as the laboratory specimen, due to sensitivity effects. It does not necessarily mean, therefore, that a soil found to have a liquid limit of 50 per cent will be in the liquid state if its in-situ moisture content (m) is also 50 per cent.

If m is greater than the test value of L.L. than I_L is > 1.0 and it is obvious that if the soil were remoulded it would be transformed into a slurry. In such a case the soil is probably an unconsolidated sediment with an undrained shear strength, c_u, in the order of $15-50$ kN/m^2.

Most cohesive soil deposits have I_L values within the range 1.0−0.0. The lower the value of m, the greater the amount of compression that must have taken place and the nearer I_L will be to zero.

If m is less than the test value of the plastic limit then $I_L < 0.0$ and the soil cannot be remoulded (as it is outside the plastic range). In this case the soil is most likely a compressed sediment.

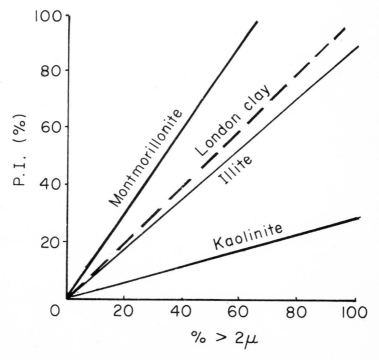

Fig. 4.21 (After Skempton, 1965)

Soil in this state will have a c_u value varying from 50–250 kN/m^2.

Activity of a clay

Apart from their value in soil classification, the L.L. and P.L. values of a plastic soil give an indication of the types and amount of the clay minerals present in the soil. The three major clay mineral groups have been briefly described in Chapter 1, although there are, of course, many variations.

It has been found that, for a given soil, the plasticity index increases in proportion to the percentage of clay particles in the soil. Indeed, if a group of soils is examined and their P.I. values are plotted against their clay percentages, a straight line, passing through the origin, is obtained.

If a soil sample is taken and its clay percentage artificially varied, a relationship between P.I. and clay percentage can be obtained. Each soil will have its own straight line because, although in two differing soils the percentages of clay may be the same, they will contain different minerals.

The relationship between Montmorillonite, Illite, Kaolinite and the plasticity index is shown in Fig. 4.21. Note that $1\mu = 1$ micron = 0.001 mm.

The plot of London Clay is also shown on the figure and, from its position, it is seen that the mineral content of this soil is predominantly Illite. London clay has a clay fraction of about 46 per cent and consists of Illite (70%), Kaolinite (20%) and Montmorillonite (10%). The remaining fraction of 54 per cent consists of silt (quartz, feldspar and mica: 44%) and sand (quartz and feldspar: 10%).

In Fig. 4.21 the slope of the line is the ratio $\dfrac{\text{P.I.}}{\%\ \text{clay}}$

This ratio is termed the *activity* of the clay. Clays with large activities are called active clays and exhibit plastic properties over a wide range of m values.

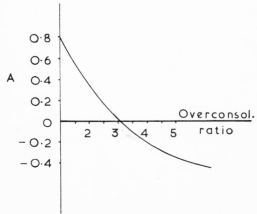

Fig. 4.22 Effect of overconsolidation on the pore pressure coefficient A

Variation of the pore pressure coefficient A

An important effect of overconsolidation is its effect on the pore pressure parameter A. With a normally consolidated clay the value of A at maximum deviator stress, A_f, is virtually the same in a consolidated undrained test no matter what cell pressure is used, but with an overconsolidated clay the value of A_f falls off rapidly with increasing overconsolidation ratio (Fig. 4.22)

Overconsolidation ratio is the ratio of preconsolidation pressure divided by the cell pressure used in the test. When the overconsolidation ratio is 1.0 the soil is normally consolidated.

The strength envelope for an overconsolidated clay

The effective stress strength envelope obtained from a drained test on a normally consolidated clay has been shown in Fig. 4.19. The strength envelope obtained from the same test on an overconsolidated clay is shown in Fig. 4.24.

The clay is sheared with a cell pressure, σ_3, that is less than its preconsolidation pressure. The failure envelope is slightly curved and

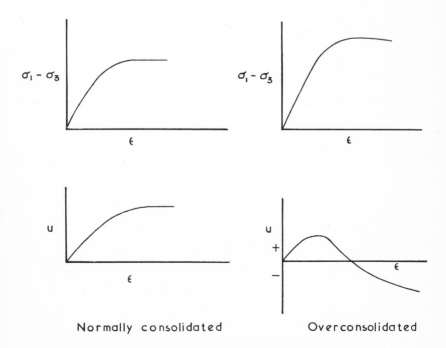

Normally consolidated   Overconsolidated

Fig. 4.23 Typical results from consolidated undrained shear tests on clays

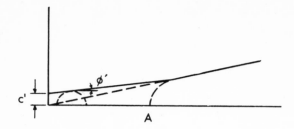

Fig. 4.24 Strength envelope for an overconsolidated soil subjected to a drained shear test

has a cohesive intercept c', but as the curvature is very slight the envelope is approximated to a straight line inclined at ϕ' to the normal stress axis.

In Fig. 4.24 the point A represents the cell pressure that is equal to the preconsolidation pressure. At cell pressures higher than this the strength envelope is the same as for a normally consolidated clay, the value of ϕ' being increased slightly. If this line is projected backwards it will pass through the origin.

Due to the removal of stresses during sampling, even normally consolidated clays will have a slight degree of overconsolidation and may give a small c' value, but this is usually so small that it is difficult to measure and has little importance.

RESIDUAL STRENGTH OF SOIL

In an investigation concerning the stability of a clay slope, the normal procedure is to take representative samples, conduct shear tests, establish the strength parameters c' and ϕ' from the peak values of the tests, and conduct an effective stress analysis. For this analysis the shear strength of the soil can be expressed by the equation:

$$s_f = c' + \sigma_n' \tan \phi'$$

There have been many cases of slips in clay slopes which have afforded a means of checking this procedure. Obviously when a slope slipped its factor of safety was 1.0 and, knowing the mass of material involved and the location of the slip plane, it is possible to deduce the value of the average shear stress on the slip plane, $\bar{s}$, at the time failure occurred. It has often been found that s is considerably less than s_f, especially with slopes that have been in existence for some years, and Professor Skempton, in his Rankine lecture of 1964, presented a comprehensive study of the subject supported by case records.

Fig. 4.25A shows a typical stress-to-strain relationship obtained in a

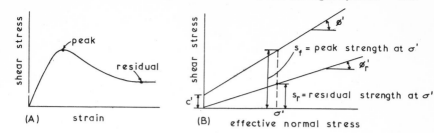

Fig. 4.25 The residual strength of clays (after Skempton)

drained shear test on a clay. Normal practice is to stop the test as soon as the peak strength has been reached, but if the test is continued it is found that as the strain increases the shear strength decreases and finally levels out. This constant stress value is termed the residual strength, s_r, of the clay. The strength envelopes from the two sets of strength values are shown in Fig. 4.25B: it will be seen that the cohesive intercept, based on residual strength, is so negligible that it may be taken as zero.

Residual strength tests are best carried out in a shear box with a large travel of about 150 mm so that the sample can be continually strained in one direction (the normal shear box may be used provided it is capable of reversing its direction at the end of the travel). The reduction down to zero and back to its original value of the applied stress at the point of reversal can be assumed as occurring over zero strain, and the total displacement of the sample is taken as the length of travel of the box times the number of reversals.

Residual strength of clays

The reduction from peak to residual strength in clays is considered to result primarily from the formation of extremely thin layers of fine particles orientated in the direction of shear: these particles would originally have been in a random state of orientation and must therefore have had a greater resistance to shear than when they became parallel to each other in the shear direction.

The development of residual strength in a soil is a continuous process. If at a particular point the soil is stressed beyond its peak strength, its strength will decrease and additional stress will be transmitted to other points in the soil; these likewise becoming overstressed and decreasing in strength, the failure process continues once it has started (unless the slope slips) until the strength at every point along the potential slip surface has been reduced to residual strength.

Clays, especially overconsolidated deposits, contain fissures, such as those in London Clay which occur some 150–200 mm apart; these fissures are already established points of weakness, the strength between their contact surfaces probably being about residual. An important feature of fissures is that they can tend to act as stress concentrators at their edges, leading to overstressing beyond the peak strength and hence to a progressive strength decrease.

Tests carried out by Skempton indicate that the residual strength of a clay under a particular effective stress is the same, whether the clay was normally or overconsolidated. Hence in any clay layer, provided the particles are the same, the value of ϕ_r' will be constant.

Residual strength of silts and silty clays

From a study of case records Skempton showed that the value of ϕ_r' decreases with increasing clay percentage. Sand-sized particles, being roughly spherical in shape, cannot orientate themselves in the same way as flakey clay particles and when they are present in silts or clays the residual strength becomes greater as the percentage of sand increases.

Residual strength of sands

Shear tests on sand indicate that the stress-displacement curve for the loose and dense states are as shown in Fig. 4.2.6. The residual strength is seen to

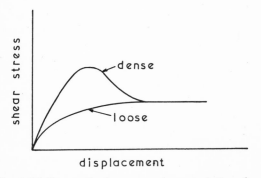

Fig. 4.26 Stress–displacement characteristics of sands

correspond to the peak strength of the loose density and is usually reached fairly quickly in one travel of the shear box, succeeding reversals having little effect.

Residual factor, R

In the slips investigated by Skempton, some were found to have an $\bar{s}$ value corresponding to s_r and some an $\bar{s}$ value lying between s_f and s_r. The use of the term residual factor, R, was therefore suggested, where R is the proportion of the total slip surface in the clay along which its strength has fallen to the residual value.

$$R = \frac{s_f - \bar{s}}{s_f - s_r}$$

If there is no reduction in strength, $\bar{s} = s_f$ and $R = 0.0$, but if there is a complete reduction in strength then $\bar{s} = s_r$ and $R = 1.0$. The work so far carried out on residual strength has involved existing slopes and cuttings, for which Skempton's findings may be summarized as follows:

Unfissured clays:	$R \doteq 0.0$
Pre-existing slip:	$R \doteq 1.0$
Fissured clays	R varies from 0.0 to 1.0

Indications are that R increases with time, but there is at present no way of predicting its value from soil tests and it is not known if residual strengths can become evident in compact material; standard practice is to base stability analyses on peak soil strengths. If an earth embankment settles unevenly fissures can develop within it, but bearing pressures are generally kept within reasonable limits. With coal spoil heaps higher bearing capacities are often used which could lead to larger settlements. Such tips may also be subjected to mining subsidence (sometimes of several metres) and it does not seem impossible for fissuring to occur under these conditions. If there is fissuring then a potential slip surface will tend to travel through this weakened zone (which may have a strength closer to the loose than the compacted density), leading to a reduction in stability.

EXAMPLES ON CHAPTER 4

Total stresses
Example 4.1
  On a failure plane in a cohesionless soil mass the stresses at failure were: shear = 3.5 kN/m^2; normal = 10.0 kN/m^2. Determine **(A)** by calculation and **(B)** graphically the resultant stress on the plane of failure, the angle of

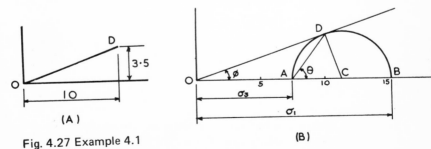

Fig. 4.27 Example 4.1

internal friction of the soil, and the angle of inclination of the failure plane
to the major principal plane.

Solution. (A) By calculation

The soil is cohesionless, therefore the strength envelope must go through
the origin. The failure point is represented by point D in **Fig. 4.27A**
with co-ordinates (10, 3.5).

Resultant stress = OD = $\sqrt{3.5^2 + 10^2}$ = 10.6 kN/m²

$$\text{Tan } \phi = \frac{3.5}{10} = 0.35$$

$$\therefore \quad \phi = 19°17'$$

$$\theta = \frac{\phi}{2} + 45° = 54° \, 38'$$

(B) Graphically

The procedure (**Fig. 4.27B**) is first to draw the axes OX and OY and then,
to a suitable scale, set off point D with co-ordinates (10, 3.5); join OD
(this is the strength envelope). The stress circle is tangential to OD at the
point D; draw line DC perpendicular to OD to cut OX in C, C being the
centre of the circle.

With centre C and radius CD draw the circle establishing the points A and
B on the x-axis.

By scaling, OD = resultant stress = 10.6 kN/m². With protractor,
$\phi = 19°$; $\theta = 55°$.

NOTE: From the diagram we see that   OA = σ_3 = 7.6 kN/m²
                                       OB = σ_1 = 15 kN/m²

Example 4.2

A series of shear tests were performed on a soil. Each test was carried out
until the sample sheared, and the principal stresses for each test were:

Test no.	σ_3 (kN/m²)	σ_1 (kN/m²)
1	200	570
2	300	875
3	400	1162

Plot the Mohr stress circles and hence determine the strength envelope
and the angle of internal friction of the soil.

Solution

The Mohr circle diagram is shown in Fig. 4.28. The circles are drawn first and then, by constructing the best common tangent to these circles, the strength envelope is obtained.

In this case it is seen that the soil is cohesionless as there is no cohesive intercept.

By measurement, $\phi = 29°$

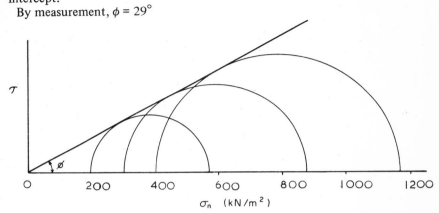

Fig. 4.28 Example 4.2

Example 4.3

A particular soil failed under a major principal stress of 288 kN/m² with a corresponding minor principal stress of 100 kN/m². If, for the same soil, the minor principal stress had been 200 kN/m², determine graphically what the major principal stress at failure would have been if (a) $\phi = 0°$ and (b) = 30°:

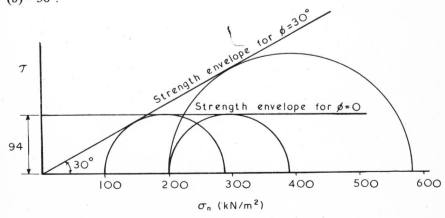

Fig. 4.29 Example 4.3

Solution. Draw the stress circle, to which the strength envelope will be tangential; draw strength envelopes for $\phi = 0°$ and $\phi = 30°$; draw two stress circles, each starting at a minor principal stress value of 200 kN/m^2, one tangential to one strength envelope and one tangential to the other.

It can now be determined that when $\phi = 30°$, $\sigma_1 = 580$ kN/m^2, and when $\phi = 0°$, $\sigma_1 = 388$ kN/m^2.

NOTE: When $\phi = 0°$ the soil has a cohesion of 94 kN/m^2.

Example 4.4

Shear box tests were carried out on a series of soil samples with the following results:

Test no.	Normal stress (kN/m^2)	Shear stress at failure (kN/m^2)
1	100	98
2	200	139
3	300	180
4	400	222

Determine the cohesion and the angle of friction of the soil.

Solution. In this case both the normal and the shear stresses at failure are known, so there is no need to draw stress circles and the four failure points may simply be plotted. These points must lie on the strength envelope and the best straight line through the points will establish it (Fig. 4.30).

From the plot, c = 55 kN/m^2; $\phi = 23°$.

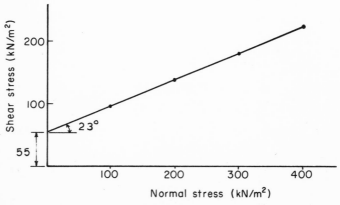

Fig. 4.30 Example 4.4

Example 4.5

The following results were obtained from an undrained shear box test
carried out on a set of undisturbed soil samples:

Normal load (kN)	0.2	0.4	0.6
Strain (%)	Proving ring dial gauge readings (no. of divisions)		
1	8.5	16.5	28.0
2	16.0	27.0	39.0
3	22.5	34.9	46.8
4	27.5	39.9	52.3
5	31.3	45.0	56.6
6	33.4	46.0	59.7
7	33.4	47.6	61.7
8	33.4	47.6	62.7
9		47.6	62.7
10			62.7

The cross sectional area of the box was 3600 mm^2 and one division of the
proving ring dial gauge equalled 0.01 mm. The calibration of the proving
ring was 0.01 mm deflection equalled 8.4 N.

Determine the strength parameters of the soil in terms of total stress.

Solution. The plot of proving ring readings against strain is shown in
Fig. 4.30A. From this plot the maximum readings for normal loads of
0.2, 0.4 and 0.6 were 33.4, 47.6 and 62.7 divisions.

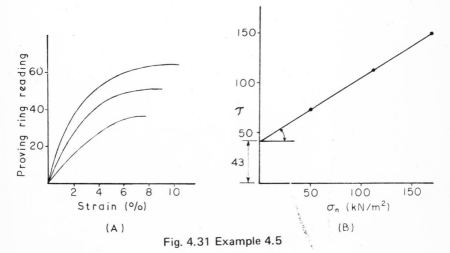

Fig. 4.31 Example 4.5

For this particular case the maximum readings could obviously have been obtained directly from the tabulated results, but drawing a plot is sometimes useful to demonstrate whether one of the sets of readings differs from the other two. Most test operators would plot these graphs directly onto paper without noting down the readings.

Normal load (kN)	Normal stress (kN/m²)	Shear force (N)	Shear stress (kN/m²)
0.2	$\dfrac{0.2 \times 10^6}{3600} = 56$	8.4×33.4 $= 280$	$\dfrac{280}{3600} \times 10^6 = 78$
0.4	111	400	111
0.6	167	528	147

The plot of shear stress to normal stress is given in Fig. 4.31B. The total stress envelope is obtained by drawing a straight line through the three points.

The strength parameters are: $\phi = 32°$; $c = 43$ kN/m²

Example 4.6

The following results were obtained from a series of undrained triaxial tests carried out on undisturbed samples of a soil:

Cell pressure (kN/m²)	Additional axial load at failure (N) *Deviator stress*
200	291
400	331
600	396

Each sample, originally 70 mm long and 35 mm in diameter, experienced a vertical deformation of 5.1 mm.

Draw the strength envelope and determine the Coulomb equation for the shear strength of the soil in terms of total stresses.

Solution

$$\text{Volume of sample} = \frac{\pi}{4} \times 35^2 \times 70 = 67\,348 \text{ mm}^3$$

$$\text{Therefore cross sectional area at failure} = \frac{67\,348}{70-5.1} = \frac{67\,348}{65} = 1036 \text{ mm}^2$$

Cell pressure σ_3 (kN/m^2)	Deviator stress $(\sigma_1 - \sigma_3)$ (kN/m^2)	Major principal stress σ_1 (kN/m^2)
200	$\dfrac{0.291 \times 10^6}{1036} = 281$	481
400	$\dfrac{0.331 \times 10^6}{1036} = 319$	719
600	$\dfrac{0.396 \times 10^6}{1036} = 382$	982

The Mohr circles for total stress and the strength envelope are shown in Fig. 4.32. From the diagram $\phi = 7°$; c = 100 kN/m^2

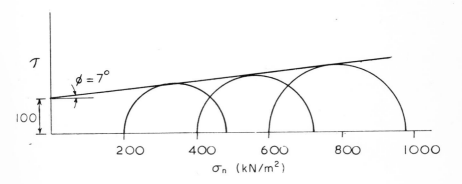

Fig. 4.32 Example 4.6

Coulomb's equation is $= c + \sigma_n \tan \phi$

$$= 100 + \sigma_n \tan 7°$$

$$= 100 + 0.123 \, \sigma_n \text{ kN/m}^2$$

Effective stresses
Example 4.7
A series of undisturbed samples from a normally consolidated clay was subjected to consolidated undrained tests.

$\sigma_1 = \dfrac{\sigma_1 - \sigma_3}{} + \sigma_3 =$

$118 + 200 = 318$

Results were:

σ_3

$\sigma_1 - \sigma_3$

Cell pressure (kN/m^2)	Deviator stress at failure (kN/m^2)	Pore water pressure at failure (kN/m^2)
200	118	110
400	240	220
600	352	320

Plot the strength envelope of the soil (a) with respect to total stresses, and (b) with respect to effective stresses.

Solution. The two Mohr circle diagrams are shown in Fig. 4.33. The total

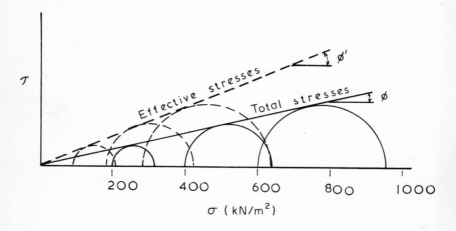

Fig. 4.33 Example 4.7

stress circles are obtained as previously described and are shown with full lines. To determine an effective stress circle it is necessary to subtract the pore water pressure for that circle from each of the principal stresses, e.g. for a cell pressure of 200 kN/m² the major principal total stress was 200 + 118 = 318 kN/m². The pore water pressure was 110 kN/m².

$$\sigma_3' = 200 - 110 = 90 \text{ kN/m}^2 ; \sigma_1' = 318 - 110 = 208 \text{ kN/m}^2$$

Example 4.8
A series of consolidated undrained triaxial tests were carried out on undisturbed samples of an overconsolidated clay.

Results were:

$\Delta \sigma, -\Delta \sigma_3$

Cell pressure (kN/m^2)	Deviator stress at failure (kN/m^2)	Pore water pressure at failure (kN/m^2)
100	410	−65
200	520	−10
400	720	80
600	980	180

(i) Plot the strength envelope for the soil (a) with respect to total stresses, and (b) with respect to effective stresses.

(ii) If the preconsolidation to which the clay had been subjected was 800 kN/m², plot the variation of the pore pressure parameter A_f with the overconsolidation ratio.

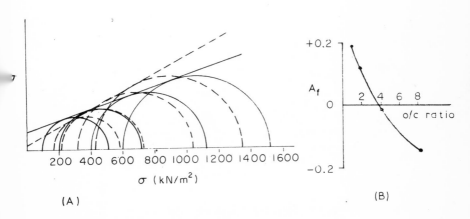

(A)   σ (kN/m²)   (B)

Fig. 4.34 Example 4.8

Solution. The Mohr circle diagrams are shown in Fig. 4.34A. When a pore pressure is negative the principle of effective stress still applies, i.e. $\sigma' = \sigma - u$; for a cell pressure of 100 kN/m², $\sigma_1 = 510$ and $u = -65$, so that

$$\sigma_3' = 100 - (-65) = 165 \text{ kN/m}^2 \text{ and } \sigma_1' = 510 - (-65) = 575 \text{ kN/m}^2$$

After consolidation in a consolidated undrained test (i.e. when shear commences) the soil is saturated, B = 1, and hence the pore pressure coefficient $\bar{A} = A$.

σ_3	o/c ratio	$A = \dfrac{\Delta u_d}{\Delta \sigma_1 - \Delta \sigma_3}$
100	8	$-65/410 = -0.146$
200	4	-0.02
400	2	0.111
600	1.33	0.185

The results are shown plotted in Fig. 4.34B.

Example 4.9

The following results were obtained from an undrained triaxial test on a compacted soil sample using a cell pressure of 300 kN/m². Before the application of the cell pressure the pore water pressure within the sample was zero.

Strain (%)	σ_1 (kN/m²)	u (kN/m²)
0.0	300	120
2.5	500	150
5.0	720	150
7.5	920	120
10.0	1050	80
15.0	1200	10
20.0	1250	−60

(i) Determine the value of the pore pressure coefficient B and state whether or not the soil was saturated.

(ii) Plot the variation of deviator stress with strain.

(iii) Plot the variation of the pore pressure coefficient A with strain.

Solution. (i)

$$B = \frac{\Delta u_a}{\Delta \sigma_3} = \frac{120}{300} = 0.4$$

The soil was partially saturated as B was less than 1.0

Strain (%)	Δu_d	$(\Delta \sigma_1 - \Delta \sigma_3)$	$\overline{A}$	$A \left(= \dfrac{\overline{A}}{B}\right)$
2.5	30	200	$\dfrac{30}{200} = 0.15$	0.375
5.0	30	420	0.071	0.178
7.5	0	620	0	0
10.0	40	750	−0.053	−0.132
15.0	−110	900	−0.122	−0.304
20.0	−180	950	−0.188	−0.470

(ii)

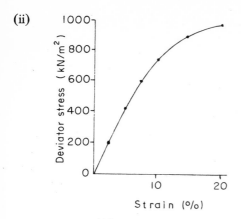

(A)

Fig. 4.35 Example 4.9

(iii)

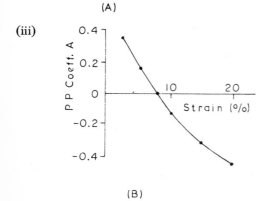

(B)

EXERCISES ON CHAPTER 4

4.1 A granular soil is subjected to a minor principal stress of 200 kN/m². If the angle of internal friction of the soil is 29°, determine the inclination of the planes of failure and of maximum shear stress with respect to the direction of the major principal stress. What are the stresses on the plane of failure and what is the maximum shear stress induced in the soil?

Answer   Failure plane inclined at 30.5° to major principal stress.
Maximum shear plane inclined at 45° to major principal stress.
Normal stress on failure plane = 310 kN/m²
Shear stress on failure plane = 170 kN/m²
Maximum shear stress = 190 kN/m².

4.2 A soil has a cohesion of 20 kN/m^2 and an angle of internal friction of 20°.

The soil is subjected to a vertical principal stress of 250 kN/m^2. What are the greatest and least values of the horizontal principal stress?

In each case determine the magnitude of the stresses on the failure plane and the direction of this plane.

Answer   Minimum value of horizontal principal stress = 100 kN/m^2
Stresses on failure plane: $\sigma_n = 150$; $\tau = 74$ kN/m^2
Inclination of failure plane = 56° to horizontal.
Maximum value of horizontal principal stress = 564 kN/m^2
Stresses on failure plane: $\sigma_n = 350$; $\tau = 148$ kN/m^2
Inclination of failure plane = 34° to horizontal.

4.3 Two samples of a soil were subjected to shear tests. The results were as follows:

Test no.	σ_3 (kN/m^2)	σ_1 (kN/m^2)
1	100	260
2	300	670

If a further sample of the same soil were tested under a minor principal stress of 200 kN/m^2, what would you expect the value of the major principal stress at failure to be?

Answer   467 kN/m^2.

4.4 A shear box test carried out on a soil sample gave:

Test no.	Vertical stress (kN/m^2)	Horizontal shear stress (kN/m^2)
1	100	79
2	200	141
3	300	208

Determine the magnitudes of the major and minor principal stresses acting at failure when the vertical stress on the sample was 200 kN/m^2. Determine also the inclination to the horizontal of these stresses.

Answer $\sigma_1 = 493$ kN/m^2 at 27°30′ to horizontal.
$\sigma_3 = 126$ kN/m^2 at 62°30′ to horizontal.

4.5 A series of undrained shear box tests (area of box = 360 mm^2) were carried out on a soil with the following results:

Normal load on sample (N)	Shearing force at failure (N)
91	68
182	91
273	118

(i) Determine the cohesion and angle of friction of the soil with respect to total stresses.

(ii) If a 38.1 mm diameter, 76.2 mm long sample of the same soil was tested in the triaxial machine with a cell pressure of 276 kN/m², what would you expect the additional axial load at failure to be if the sample shortened by 6.3 mm?

(iii) If a further sample of the soil was tested in an unconfined compression apparatus, at what value of compressive stress would you expect failure to occur?

Answer   (i) $\phi = 16\frac{3}{4}°$; c = 11.1 kN/m²

            (ii) 295 N

           (iii) 30.2 kN/m²

4.6 The following results were obtained from an undrained triaxial test on a soil:

Cell pressure (kN/m²)	Additional axial stress at failure (kN/m²)
200	70
400	85.5
600	104

Determine the cohesion and angle of friction of the soil with respect to total stresses.

Answer $\phi = 18.5°$; c = 180 kN/m²

4.7 An undisturbed soil sample, 100 mm in diameter and 200 mm in height, was tested in a triaxial machine. The sample sheared under an additional axial load of 2.9 kN with a vertical deformation of 19 mm. The failure plane was inclined at 50° to the horizontal and the cell pressure was 300 kN/m².

(i) Draw the Mohr circle diagram representing the above stress conditions and from it determine:

(a) Coulomb's equation for the shear strength of the soil, in terms of total stress.

(b) The magnitude and obliquity of the resultant stress on the failure plane.

(ii) A further undisturbed sample of the soil was tested in a shear box under the same drainage conditions as used for the previous test. If the area of the box was 3600 mm² and the normal load was 500 N what would you expect the failure shear stress to have been?

Answer   (i)   (a) $\tau = 80 + 0.1763\,\sigma_n$ kN/m²
                  (b)   465 kN/m²; 20½°
         (ii)   105 kN/m²

4.8 Undisturbed samples were taken from a compacted fill material and subjected to consolidated undrained triaxial tests. Results were:

Cell pressure (kN/m²)	Additional axial stress at failure (kN/m²)	Pore water pressure at failure (kN/m²)
200	65	5
400	77	20
600	88	35

Determine the values of the cohesion and the angle of internal friction with regard to (a) total stresses and (b) effective stresses.

Answer   c = 220 kN/m², $\phi = 12\frac{3}{4}°$; c' = 140 kN/m², $\phi' = 26\frac{1}{4}°$

4.9 An undrained triaxial test carried out on a compacted soil gave the following results:

Strain (%)	Deviator stress (kN/m²)	Pore water pressure (kN/m²)
0	0	240
1	240	285
2	460	300
3	640	270
4	840	200
5	950	160
7.5	1100	110
10.0	1150	75
12.5	1170	55
15.0	1150	50

The cell pressure was 400 kN/m², and before its application the pore water pressure in the sample was zero.

(i) Determine the value of the pore press coefficient B
(ii) Plot deviator stress (total) against strain.
(iii) Plot pore water pressure against strain.
(iv) Plot the variation of the pore press coefficient A with strain.
Answer   (i) 0.6

(iv) Value of A at maximum deviator stress = -0.275.

REFERENCES

Bishop, A. W., & Henkel, D. J.
   The measurement of soil properties in the triaxial test
   (Edward Arnold, 1962).
Bishop, A. W.,
   The principle of effective stress. *Tek. Ukebl.,* no. 39 (1959).
Skempton, A. W.
   Effective stress in soils, concrete and rocks. Pore Pressure Conference,
   London (1960).
   Long term stability of slopes. (Rankine Memorial Lecture).
   Géotechnique, 1964.
   The colloidal activity of clays. *Proc 3rd. Int. Conf. Soil Mechanics
   and Foundation Engineering,* (1953).
Skempton, A. W., & Northley, A.
   The sensitivity of clays, *Géotechnique* (1952).

5. Stability of Slopes

GRANULAR MATERIALS

Materials with no cohesion, such as sands and gravels, are known as granular materials.

Slope   Triangle of forces

Fig. 5.1 Forces involved in a slope of granular material

Fig. 5.1 illustrates an embankment of granular material with its surface sloping at angle β to the horizontal.

Consider an element of the embankment of weight W.

$$\text{Force parallel to slope} = W \sin \beta$$
$$\text{Force perpendicular to slope} = W \cos \beta$$

For stability, sliding forces $= \dfrac{\text{restraining forces}}{\text{factor of safety (F)}}$

i.e. $W \sin \beta = \dfrac{W \cos \beta \tan \phi}{F}$

Therefore $F = \dfrac{\tan \phi}{\tan \beta}$

For limiting equilibrium (F = 1), $\tan \beta = \tan \phi$, i.e. $\beta = \phi$.

From this it is seen that (a) the weight of a material does not affect the stablility of the slope, (b) the safe angle for the slope is the same whether the soil is dry or submerged, and (c) the embankment can be of any height.

Failure of a submerged sand slope can occur, however, if the water level of the retained water falls rapidly while the water level in the slope lags behind, since seepage forces are set up in this situation.

Purely granular soils are infrequent as most soils possess some cohesion, but a study of them affords a useful introduction to the treatment of cohesive-frictional soils.

Seepage forces in a granular slope subjected to rapid drawdown

In Fig. 5.2A the level of the river has dropped suddenly due to tidal effects.

(A)   (B)

Fig. 5.2 Seepage due to rapid drawdown

The permeability of the soil in the slope is such that the water in it cannot follow the water level changes as rapidly as the river, with the result that seepage occurs from the high water level in the slope to the lower water level of the river. A flow net can be drawn for this condition and the excess hydrostatic head for any point within the slope can be determined.

Consider an element within the slope of weight W. Let the excess pore water pressure induced by seepage be u at the base of the element.

$$\text{Normal reaction } N = W \cos \beta$$

$$\text{Normal stress } \sigma_n = \frac{W \cos \beta}{1} = \frac{W \cos^2 \beta}{b} \quad \left(1 = \frac{b}{\cos \beta}\right)$$

$$\text{Normal effective stress } \sigma_n{}' = \frac{W \cos^2 \beta}{b} - u = \frac{\gamma z b \cos^2 \beta}{b} - u = \gamma z \cos^2 \beta - u$$

(Where γ = the average unit weight of the whole slice, it is usually taken that the whole slice is saturated.)

$$\text{Tangential force} = W \sin \beta$$

$$\therefore \text{ tangential shear stress, } \tau = \frac{W \sin \beta}{1} = \gamma z \sin \beta \cos \beta$$

$$\text{Ultimate shear strength of soil} = \sigma_n' \tan \phi = \tau F$$

$$\therefore \gamma z \sin \beta \cos \beta = (\gamma z \cos^2 \beta - u) \frac{\tan \phi}{F}$$

$$\therefore F = \left(\frac{\cos \beta}{\sin \beta} - \frac{u}{\gamma z \sin \beta \cos \beta} \right) \tan \phi$$

$$= \left(1 - \frac{u}{\gamma z \cos^2 \beta} \right) \frac{\tan \phi}{\tan \beta}$$

This expression may be written

$$F = \left(1 - \frac{r_u}{\cos^2 \beta} \right) \frac{\tan \phi}{\tan \beta}$$

$$\text{where } r_u = \frac{u}{\gamma z}$$

Pore pressure ratio
The ratio, at any given point, of the pore water pressure to the weight of the material acting on unit area above it is known as the pore pressure ratio and is given the symbol r_u.

Flow parallel to the surface and at the surface
The flow net for these special conditions is illustrated in Fig. 5.3,

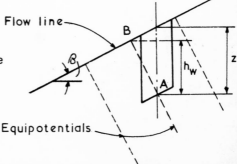

Fig. 5.3 Flow net when
flow is parallel and at the surface

If we consider the same element as before, the excess pore water head, at the centre of the base of the element, is represented by the height h_w in Fig. 5.3. In the figure, $AB = z \cos B$ and $h_w = AB \cos B$. Hence, $h_w = z \cos^2 \beta$, so that excess pore water pressure at the base of the element $= \gamma_w z \cos^2 \beta$

$$\therefore r_u = \frac{u}{\gamma z} = \frac{\gamma_w z \cos^2 \beta}{\gamma z} = \frac{\gamma_w}{\gamma} \cos^2 \beta$$

The equation for F becomes:

$$F = \left(1 - \frac{\gamma_w}{\gamma}\right) \frac{\tan \phi}{\tan \beta} = \left(\frac{\gamma - \gamma_w}{\gamma}\right) \frac{\tan \phi}{\tan \beta} = \frac{\gamma_{sub.} \tan \phi}{\gamma_{sat.} \tan \beta}$$

Numerical example illustrating the effects of seepage
A granular soil has a saturated unit weight of 18.0 kN/m³ and an angle of internal friction of 30°. A slope is to be made of this material. If the factor of safety is to be 1.25, determine the safe angle of the slope (i) when the slope is dry or submerged and (ii) if seepage occurs at and parallel to the surface of the slope.

(i) When dry or submerged

$$F = \frac{\tan \phi}{\tan \beta} \qquad \therefore \tan \beta = \frac{0.5774}{1.25} = 0.462$$

$$\therefore \beta \doteqdot 25°$$

(ii) When flow occurs at and parallel to the surface

$$F = \frac{\gamma_{sub.} \tan \phi}{\gamma_{sat.} \tan \beta} \qquad \therefore \tan \beta = \frac{8 \times 0.5774}{1.25 \times 18} = 0.205$$

$$\therefore \beta \doteqdot 11\tfrac{1}{2}°$$

Seepage more than halves the safe angle of slope in this particular example.

COHESIVE-FRICTIONAL SOILS

Failures in embankments made of cohesive-frictional soils tend to be rotational, the actual slip surface approximating to the arc of a circle (Fig. 5.4).

Fig. 5.4 Typical rotational slip in a cohesive soil

Methods of investigating slope stability

Contemporary methods of investigation are based on (i) assuming a slip surface and a centre about which it rotates, (ii) studying the equilibrium of the forces acting on this surface, and (iii) repeating the process until the worst slip surface is found.

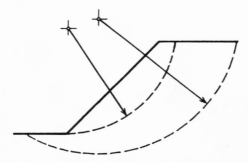

Fig. 5.5 Example of two possible slip surfaces

Total stress analysis

This analysis, often called the $\phi = 0$ analysis, is intended to give the stability of an embankment immediately after its construction. At this stage it is assumed that the soil in the embankment has had no time to drain and the strength parameters used in the analysis are the ones representing the undrained strength of the soil (with respect to total stresses), which is found from either the unconfined compression test or an undrained triaxial test without pore pressure measurements.

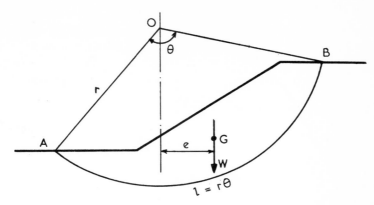

Fig. 5.6 Total stress analysis

Consider in Fig. 5.6 the sector of soil cut off by arc AB of radius r. Let W equal the weight of the sector and G the position of its centre of gravity. As $\phi = 0°$, maximum shear strength $= c$.

Taking moments about 0, the centre of rotation:

$$W.e = c.l.r. = c.r\theta . r. = cr^2 \theta \text{ for equilibrium}$$

$$F = \frac{\text{restraining moment}}{\text{disturbing moment}} = \frac{cr^2 \theta}{We}$$

The position of G is not needed, and it is only necessary to ascertain where the line of action of W is. This can be obtained by dividing the sector into a set of vertical slices and taking moments of area of these slices about a convenient vertical axis.

Effect of tension cracks

With a slip in a cohesive soil there will always be a tension crack at the top of the slope (Fig. 5.7) along which no shear resistance can develop. In a purely cohesive soil the depth of the crack, h_c, is given by the formula:

$$h_c = \frac{2c}{\gamma \sqrt{K_a}}$$

The effect of the tension crack is to shorten the arc AB to AB'. If the crack is to be allowed for the angle θ' must be used instead of θ in the formula for F, and the full weight W of the sector is used to compensate

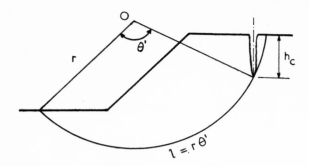

Fig. 5.7 Tension crack in a cohesive soil

for any water pressures that may be exerted if the crack fills with rain water.

The Swedish method of slices analysis

With partially saturated soils the undrained strength envelope is no longer parallel to the normal stress axis and the soil has a value of both ϕ and c.

The total stress analysis can be adapted to cover this case by assuming a slip circle procedure and dividing the sector into a suitable number of vertical slices, the stability of one such slice being considered in Fig. 5.8

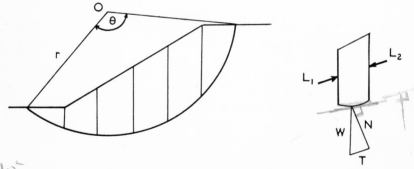

Fig. 5.8 The Swedish method of slices

(the lateral reactions on the two vertical sides of the wedge, L_1 and L_2, are assumed to be equal).

At the base of the slice set off its weight to some scale. Draw the direction of its normal component (N) and by completing the triangle of forces determine its magnitude, together with the magnitude of the tangential component T.

Taking moments about the centre of rotation, 0:

Disturbing moment = $r\Sigma T$
Restraint moment   = $r(cr\theta + \Sigma N \tan \phi)$

Hence $$F = \frac{cr\theta + \Sigma N \tan \phi}{\Sigma T}$$

The effect of a tension crack can again be allowed for, and in this case:

$$h_c = \frac{2c}{\gamma} \tan \left(45° + \frac{\phi}{2}\right).$$

Location of the most critical circle
The centre of the most critical circle can only be found by trial and error, various slip circles being analysed and the minimum factor of safety eventually obtained.

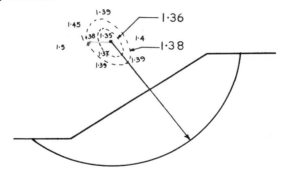

Fig. 5.9 Method for determining centre of critical circle

A suitable procedure is suggested in Fig. 5.9. The centre of each trial circle is plotted and the F value for the circle is written alongside it. After several points have thus been established it is possible to draw 'contours' of F values, which are roughly elliptical so that their centre indicates where the centre of the critical circle will be. Note that the value of F is more sensitive to horizontal movements of the circle's centre than to vertical movements.

To determine a reasonable position for the centre of a first trial slip circle is not easy, but a study of the various types of slips that can occur is helpful (it should be remembered, however, that the following considerations apply to homogeneous soils). In the case of soils with angles of friction that are not less than 3°, the critical slip circle is invariably through the toe—as it is for any soil (no matter what its ϕ value)

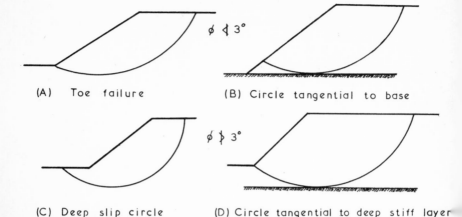

(A)   Toe failure

(B) Circle tangential to base

(C) Deep slip circle

(D) Circle tangential to deep stiff layer

Fig. 5.10 Types of slip failures

if the angle of slope exceeds 53° (Fig. 5.10A). An exception to this rule occurs when there is a layer of relatively stiff material at the base of the slope, which will cause the circle to be tangential to this layer (Fig. 5.10B).

For cohesive soils with little angle of friction the slip circle tends to be deeper and usually extends in front of the toe (Fig. 5.10C); this type of circle can of course be tangential to a layer of stiff material below the embankment which limits the depth to which it would have extended (Fig. 5.10D).

In the case of a slope made out of homogeneous cohesive soil it is possible to determine directly the centre of the critical circle by a method that Fellenius proposed in 1936 (Fig. 5.11); the centre of the circle is the intersection of two lines set off from the bottom and top of the slope at angles α and β respectively (Fellenius's values for α and β are given in the table).

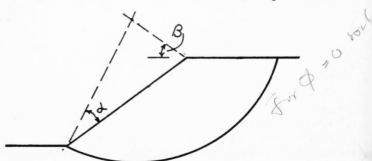

Fig. 5.11 Fellenius's construction for centre of critical circle

Slope	Angle of slope	Angle α	Angle β
1:0.58	60°	29°	40°
1:1	45°	28°	37°
1:1.5	33.79°	26°	35°
1:2	26.57°	25°	35°
1:3	18.43°	25°	35°
1:5	11.32°	25°	37°

This technique is not applicable in its original form to frictional cohesive soils but has been adapted by Jumikis (1962) to suit them provided that they are homogeneous (Fig. 5.12). It is necessary first to obtain the

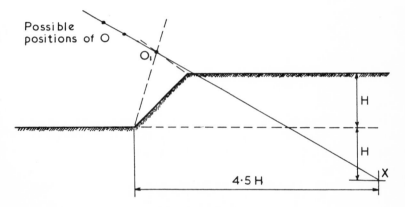

Fig. 5.12 Construction for centre of critical circle for a c-ϕ soil

centre of the Fellenius circle (O_1) as before, after which a point X is established such that X is 2H below the top of the slope and a distance of 4.5H horizontally away from the toe of the slope (H = the vertical height of the slope). The centre of the critical circle, O, lies on the line XO_1 extended beyond O_1, the distance of O beyond O_1 becoming greater as the angle of friction increases.

Such a method can only be used as a means of obtaining a set of sensibly positioned trial slip circles. When the slope is irregular or when there are pore pressures in the soil, conditions are no longer homogeneous and the method becomes less reliable.

Rapid determination of F for a homogeneous, regular slope

It can be shown that for two similar slopes made from two different soils

the ratio

$$\frac{c}{\gamma H}$$

is the same for each slope provided that the two soils have the same angle of friction. The ratio

$$\frac{c}{\gamma H}$$

is known as the stability number and is given the symbol N, where c = cohesion mobilised with regard to total stress; γ = density of soil; H = vertical height of embankment.

Taylor (1948) prepared two curves that relate the stability number to the angle of the slope: the first (Fig. 9.13) is for the general case of a c–ϕ soil

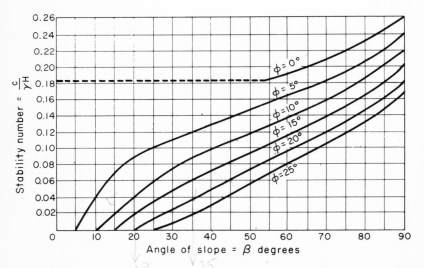

Fig 5.13 Taylor's curves for total stress analysis (for ϕ = 0° and i < 53°, see Fig. 5.14)

with an angle of slope less than 53°, whilst the second (Fig. 5.14) is for a soil with ϕ = O and a layer of stiff material or rock at a depth DH below the top of the embankment. D is known as the depth factor, and depending upon its value the slip circle will either emerge at a distance nH in front of the toe or pass through the toe (the value of n can be obtained from the curves).

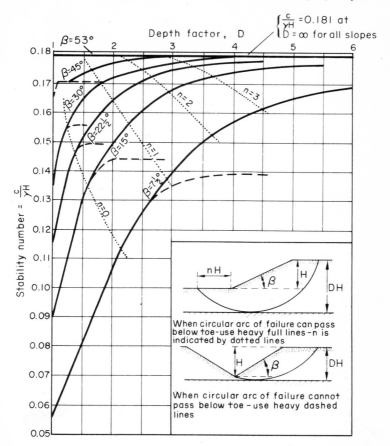

Fig. 5.14 Effect of depth limitation on Taylor's curves (for $\beta > 53°$, use Fig. 5.13)

Effective stress analysis for the determination of F
The methods for analysing a slip circle that have been discussed so far can be used to give an indication of the factor of safety immediately after construction has been completed, but they are not applicable in the case of an existing embankment or coal tip if water pressures are present.
However, if an analysis is carried out in terms of effective stress then it can be used to determine F after drainage has occurred or for any intermediate value of r_u between undrained and drained, such an analysis affording a better estimate for stability immediately after construction than the total stress methods.

Before this system can be examined, the determination of the pore pressure ratio, r_u, must be considered.

The pore pressure ratio, r_u

The prediction of pore pressures in an earth dam or an embankment has been discussed by Bishop (1954). There are two main types of problem: those in which the value of the pore water pressure depends upon the magnitude of the applied stresses (e.g. during the rapid construction of an embankment), and those where the value of the pore water pressure depends upon either the ground water level within the embankment or the seepage pattern of water impounded by it.

Rapid construction of an embankment. The pore pressure at any point in a soil mass is given by the expression:

$$u = u_o + \Delta u$$

where u_o =   initial value of pore pressure before any stress change, and
Δu =   change in pore pressure due to change in stress.

From chapter 4, $\Delta u = B[\Delta\sigma_3 + A(\Delta\sigma_1 - \Delta\sigma_3)]$

Skempton (1954) showed that the ratio of the pore pressure change to the change in the total major principal stress gives another pore pressure coefficient $\bar{B}$:

$$\frac{\Delta u}{\Delta\sigma_1} = \bar{B} = B\left[\frac{\Delta\sigma_3}{\Delta\sigma_1} + A\left(1 - \frac{\Delta\sigma_3}{\Delta\sigma_1}\right)\right]$$

The coefficient $\bar{B}$ can be used to determine the magnitude of pore pressures set up at any point in an embankment if it is assumed that no drainage occurs during construction (a fairly reasonable thesis if the construction rate is rapid).

$$\text{Now} \quad r_u = \frac{u}{\gamma z}$$

$$\text{i.e.} \quad r_u = \frac{u_o}{\gamma z} + \frac{\bar{B}\,\Delta\sigma_1}{\gamma z}$$

A reasonable assumption to make for the value of the major principal stress is that it equals the weight of the material above the point considered.

Hence $\Delta\sigma_1 = \gamma z$, and $r_u = \dfrac{u_o}{\gamma z} + \bar{B}$

For soils placed at or below optimum moisture content, u_o is small and can even be negative, its effect is of little consequence and may be ignored so that the analysis for stability at the end of construction is often determined from the relationship $r_u = \bar{B}$.

The pore pressure coefficient $\bar{B}$ is determined from a special form of triaxial test known as a dissipation test and has been described by Bishop & Henkel (1962). Briefly, a sample of the soil is inserted in a triaxial cell and subjected to increases in the principal stresses $\Delta\sigma_1$ and $\Delta\sigma_3$ of magnitudes approximating to those expected in the field. The resulting pore pressure is measured and $\bar{B}$ obtained.

Steady seepage. It is easy to determine r_u from a study of the flow net (Fig. 5.15). The procedure is to trace the equipotential through the point

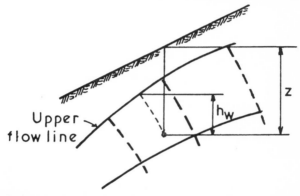

Fig. 5.15 Determination of excess head at a point on a flow net

considered up to the top of the flow net, so that the height to which water would rise in a standpipe inserted at the point is h_w. Since $u = \gamma_w h_w$,

$$r_u = \frac{h_w \gamma_w}{\gamma z}$$

Rapid drawdown. In the case of lagoons a sudden drawdown in the level of the slurry is unlikely, but the problem is important in the case of a normal earth dam. Bishop (1954) considered the case of the upstream face of a dam subjected to this effect, the slope having a rock fill protection as shown in Fig. 5.16. A simplified expression for u under these conditions is obtained by the following calculation:

$$u = u_0 + \Delta u$$

and

$$u_0 = \gamma_w(h_w + h_r + h_c - h')$$

If it is assumed that the major principal stress equals the weight of material, then the initial total major principal stress is given by the expression:

$$\sigma_{1_0} = \gamma_c h_c + \gamma_r h_r + \gamma_w h_w$$

where γ_c and γ_r are the saturated unit weights of the clay and the rock. The final total major principal stress, after drawdown, will be:

$$\sigma_{1F} = \gamma_c h_c + \gamma_{dr} h_r$$

where γ_{dr} equals the drained unit weight of the rock fill.

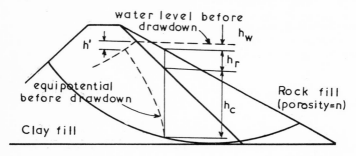

Fig. 5.16 Upstream dam face subjected to sudden drawdown (after Bishop, 1954)

Change in major principal stress = $\sigma_{1F} - \sigma_{1_0}$

i.e. $$\Delta\sigma_1 = -\gamma_w n h_r - \gamma_w h_w$$

[NOTE: Porosity of rock fill, $\dfrac{V_v}{V}$ or, when we consider unit volume, $n = V_v$

Hence $(\gamma_{dr} - \gamma_r = -\gamma_w n]$

∴ $$\Delta u = -\bar{B}[\gamma_w n h_r + \gamma_w h_w]$$

The pore pressure coefficient $\bar{B}$ can be obtained from a laboratory test but standard practice is to assume, conservatively, that $\bar{B} = 1.0$. In this case

$$\Delta u = -\gamma_w (n h_r + h_w)$$

and the expression for u becomes:

$$u = \gamma_w \left[h_c + h_r(1 - n) - h' \right]$$

Measurements of in situ pore water pressures
For any important structures the theoretical evaluations of pore pressures must be checked against actual values measured in the field. These

measurements can be obtained by an instrument known as a piezometer, which consists of a tip containing a porous stone connected by plastic tubing to a pressure gauge or mercury manometer at some convenient part of the site. The tip (which is buried in the soil), tube and gauge are filled with de-aired water so that any pore pressures in the soil are transmitted through the stone and along the tube to the gauge.

The stability of an existing coal spoil heap cannot be properly checked until piezometers have been installed and readings taken, particularly in cases where water is seen seeping out from under the material and the source is not known.

Effective stress analysis by Bishop's method

The effective stress methods of analysis now in general use were evolved by Professor Bishop of Imperial College, London. Figure 5.17 illustrates a

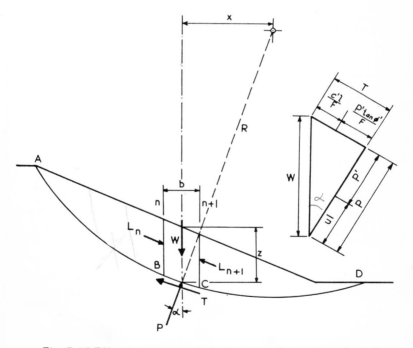

Fig. 5.17 Effective stress analysis: forces acting on a vertical slice

circular failure arc (ABCD) and shows the forces on a vertical slice through the sliding segment.

Let L_n and L_{n+1} equal the lateral reactions acting on sections n and n + 1 respectively. The difference between L_n and L_{n+1} is small and the effect of these forces can be ignored with little loss in accuracy.

Let the other forces acting on the slice be:

W = weight of slice
P = total normal force acting on base of slice
T = shear force acting on base of slice
z = height of slice
b = breadth of slice
l = length of BC (taken as a straight line)
α = angle between P and the vertical
x = horizontal distance from centre of slice to centre of rotation, O.

In terms of effective stress, the shear strength mobilized is

$$\tau = \frac{c' + (\sigma_n - u) \tan \phi'}{F}$$

Total normal stress on base of slice, $\sigma_n = \dfrac{P}{l}$

i.e. $\tau = \dfrac{1}{F}\left(c' + \left[\dfrac{P}{l} - u\right] \tan \phi'\right)$

Shear force acting on base of slice, $T = \tau l$

For equilibrium, disturbing moment = restraining moment

i.e. $\Sigma Wx = \Sigma TR = \Sigma \tau l R$

$$= \frac{R\Sigma}{F} [c'l + (P - ul) \tan \phi']$$

$$\therefore F = \frac{R}{\Sigma Wx} \Sigma [c'l + (P - ul) \tan \phi']$$

If we ignore the effects of L_n and L_{n+1} the only vertical force acting on the slice is W.

Hence $P = W \cos\alpha$

$$\therefore F = \frac{R}{\Sigma Wx} \Sigma [c'l + (W \cos\alpha - ul) \tan \phi']$$

Putting $x = R \sin\alpha$

$$F = \frac{1}{\Sigma W \sin\alpha} \Sigma [c'l + (W \cos\alpha - ul) \tan \phi']$$

If we express u in terms of the pore pressure ratio, r_u:

$$u = r_u \gamma z = r_u \frac{W}{b}$$

Now $b = 1 \cos\alpha$ $\therefore u = \dfrac{r_u W}{1 \cos\alpha} = \dfrac{r_u W}{1} \sec\alpha$ *[this will be different α for each slice]*

$$\therefore F = \frac{1}{\Sigma W \sin\alpha} \Sigma \left[c'1 + W(\cos\alpha - r_u \sec\alpha) \tan \phi' \right]$$

This formula gives a solution generally known as the conventional method which allows rapid determination of F when sufficient slip circles are available to permit the determination of the most critical. For analysing the stability of an existing tip it should prove perfectly adequate.

Numerical value for F.

In the case of an earth embankment F is usually considered to be satisfactory if it is not less than 1.25, and for economic reasons it should not be designed for a greater F value than 1.5. The assessment of an existing coal spoil heap, however, involves the consideration of various imponderables: for instance, the characteristics of the materials in the tip may vary considerably, depending upon the type of material that was being mined at certain periods while it was being created, and a site investigation that is to be kept within reasonable costs cannot be expected to pick up every variation within the tip. The use of a higher factor of safety seems to be called for, and until a code of practice appears with positive guidance on this point the author feels that any tip with an F value of less than 1.5 (based on the conventional method, using results from a normal site investigation) should be regarded as unstable.

Effective stress analysis by the rigorous method

The formula for the conventional method of analysis can give errors of up to 15 per cent in the value of F obtained, although the error is on the safe side since it gives a lower value than is the case. In the construction of new embankments and earth dams, however, this error can lead to unnecessarily high costs and becomes particularly pronounced with a deep slip circle where the variations of α over the slip length are large.

Returning to the equation:

$$F = \frac{R}{\Sigma Wx} \Sigma \left[c'1 + (P - ul) \tan \phi' \right]$$

Let the normal effective force, $(P - ul) = P'$
Resolving forces vertically:

$$W = P \cos\alpha + T \sin\alpha$$

Now $$P = P' + ul$$

and $$T = \frac{1}{F}(c'l + P' \tan\phi')$$

$$W = ul \cos\alpha + P' \cos\alpha + \frac{P' \tan\phi'}{F}\sin\alpha + \frac{c'l}{F}\sin\alpha$$

$$= ul \cos\alpha + \frac{c'l \sin\alpha}{F} + P'\left(\cos\alpha + \frac{\tan\phi'}{F}\sin\alpha\right)$$

$$= l\left(u \cos\alpha + \frac{c'}{F}\sin\alpha\right) + P'\left(\cos\alpha + \frac{\tan\phi'}{F}\sin\alpha\right)$$

$$\therefore \quad P' = \frac{W - l\left(u \cos\alpha + \dfrac{c'}{F}\sin\alpha\right)}{\cos\alpha + \dfrac{\tan\phi'\sin\alpha}{F}}$$

Substituting P' for $(P - ul)$ in the original equation:

$$F = \frac{R}{\Sigma Wx}\Sigma[c'l + (P - ul)\tan\phi']$$

$$F = \frac{R}{\Sigma Wx}\Sigma\left[\frac{c'l + \left(W - ul \cos\alpha - \dfrac{c'l}{F}\sin\alpha\right)\tan\phi'}{\cos\alpha + \dfrac{\tan\phi'\sin\alpha}{F}}\right]$$

and substituting $x = R\sin\alpha$, $b = l\cos\alpha$ and $\dfrac{ub}{W} = \dfrac{u}{\gamma z} = r_u$:

$$F = \frac{1}{\Sigma W \sin\alpha}\Sigma\left[(c'b + W(1 - r_u)\tan\phi')\frac{\sec\alpha}{1 + \dfrac{\tan\phi'\tan\alpha}{F}}\right]$$

The final analysis of forces acting on a vertical slice is best carried out by tabulating the calculations:

Slice No.	z(m)	b(m)	W = γzb	α°	sinα	$W_{\sin\alpha}$ (1)	c'b (2)	$W(1-r_u)\tan\phi'$ (3)	2 + 3 (4)	secα	tanα	(5) $\dfrac{\sec\alpha}{1+\dfrac{\tan\phi'\tan\alpha}{F}}$		4 × 5 (6)	
												F =	F =	F =	F =

Rapid determination of F for a homogeneous, regular slope with a constant pore pressure ratio

If on a trial slip circle the value of F is determined for various values of r_u and the results are plotted, a linear relationship is found between F and r_u (see example 5.6). The usual values or r_u encountered in practice range from 0.0 to 0.7 and it has been established that this linear relationship between F and r_u applies over this range. The factor of safety, F, may therefore be determined from the expression:

$$F = m - nr_u$$

in which m is the factor of safety with respect to total stresses (i.e. when no pore pressures are assumed) and n is the coefficient which represents the effect of the pore pressures on the factor of safety. These terms m and n are known as stability coefficients and were evolved by Bishop & Morgenstern (1960); they depend upon $c'/\gamma H$ (the stability number with c' equalling cohesion with respect to effective stress), cot β (the cotangent of the slope angle, e.g. a 5:1 slope means 5 horizontal to 1 vertical), and ϕ' (the angle of friction with respect to effective stresses).

Bishop & Morgenstern prepared charts of m and n for three sets of $c'/\gamma H$ values (0.0, 0.025, 0.05) that are reproduced at the end of this chapter and cover slopes from 2:1 (26½°) to 5:1 (11½°). Extrapolation, within reason, is possible for a case outside this range.

Graphs to cover depth factor values (D) up to 1.5 were produced for $\dfrac{c'}{\gamma H} = 0.05$, but for the other two cases D values greater than 1.25 were not calculated as such values are not critical in these instances. As in Taylor's analysis, the effect of tension cracks has not been included.

Determination of an average value for r_u

Generally r_u will not be constant over the cross section of an embankment and the following procedure can be used to determine an average value.

In Fig. 5.18 the stability of the downstream slope is to be determined.

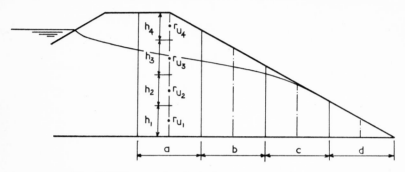

Fig. 5.18 Determination of average r_u value

From the centre line of the cross section divide the base of the dam into a suitable number of vertical slices, and on the centre line of each slice determine r_u values for a series of points as shown. Then the average pore pressure ratio on the centre line of a particular slice,

$$r_u = \frac{h_1 r_{u1} + h_2 r_{u2} + h_3 r_{u3} + \ldots}{h_1 + h_2 + h_3 + \ldots}$$

The average r_u for whole cross section

$$= \frac{A_a r_{ua} + A_b r_{ub} + A_c r_{uc} + \ldots}{A_a + A_b + A_c + \ldots}$$

where A_a = area of the slice a and r_{ua} = average r_u value in slice a.

EXAMPLES ON CHAPTER 5

Total stress analysis

Example 5.1

Figure 5.19 gives details of an embankment made of cohesive soil with $\phi = 0$ and $c = 20$ kN/m². The unit weight of the soil is 19 kN/m³.

For the trial circle shown, determine the factor of safety against sliding. The weight of the sliding sector is 346 kN acting at an eccentricity of 5 m from the centre of rotation. What would the factor of safety be if the

shaded portion of the embankment was removed? In both cases assume
that no tension crack develops.

Solution.

Disturbing moment = 346 × 5 = 1730 kNm

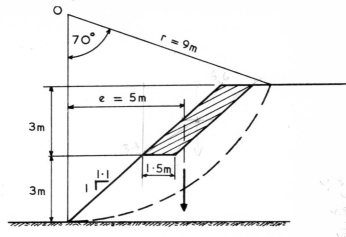

Fig. 5.19 Example 5.1

Restraining moment = $cr^2\theta$ = 20 × 9² × $\dfrac{70}{180}$ × π = 1980 kNm

$$\therefore F = \frac{1980}{1730} = 1.14$$

Area of portion removed = 1.5 × 3 = 4.5 m²

Weight of portion removed = 4.5 × 19 = 85.5 kN

Eccentricity from 0 = 3.3 + $\dfrac{3.3 + 1.5}{2}$ = 5.7 m

Relief of disturbing moment = 5.7 × 85.5 = 490 kNm

$$\therefore F = \frac{1980}{1730 - 490} = 1.6$$

Example 5.2

The embankment in Fig. 5.20 is made up from a soil with $\phi = 20°$ and

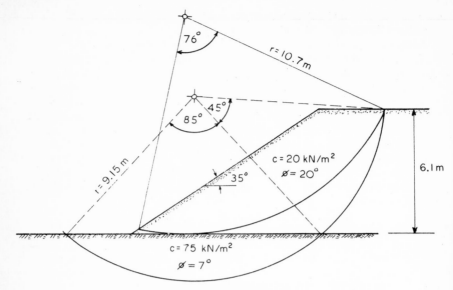

Fig. 5.20 Example 5.2

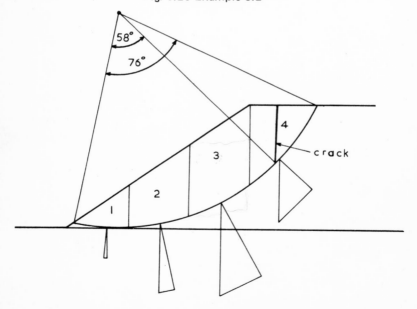

Fig. 5.21 Example 5.2: slip circle tangential to lower layer

$c = 200 \ kN/m^2$. The soil on which the embankment sits has a ϕ of $7°$ and $c = 750 \ kN/m^2$. For both soils $\gamma = 19.3 \ kN/m^2$.

Determine the factors of safety for the two slip circles shown.

Solution. This example is the classic case of an embankment resting on a stiff layer. The slip circle tangential to the lower layer (Fig. 5.21) will give a lower factor of safety, the example being intended to illustrate this effect. The sliding sector of soil is conveniently divided into four equal vertical slices. To determine the area of a particular slice its mid-height is multiplied by its breadth, and then the weight of the slice is obtained (density × area) and set off as a vector below it. The triangle of forces for the normal and tangential components is then drawn.

The procedure is repeated for each slice, after which the algebraic sum of the tangential forces and the numerical sum of the normal forces is obtained and F evaluated.

The calculations are best set out in tabular form.

Slice no.	Area m²	Weight W (kN)	Normal component N (kN)	Tangential component T (kN)
1	3.7	71	71	−7
2	8.5	164	163	42
3	11.6	224	191	116
4	7.4	143	104	106

$$\Sigma N = 529 \qquad \Sigma T = 257$$

$$\Sigma N \tan \phi = 529 \times 0.364 = 192 \ kN$$

$$cr\theta = 20 \times 10.7 \times \frac{76}{180} \times \pi = 284 \ kN$$

$$F = \frac{cr\theta + \Sigma N \tan \phi}{\Sigma T}$$

$$= \frac{192 + 284}{257} = 1.85$$

If a tension crack is allowed for:

$$hc = \frac{2c}{\gamma}\tan\left(45° + \frac{\phi}{2}\right) = \frac{40}{19.3} \times 1.43 = 2.96 \text{ m}$$

θ becomes 58°

$$\therefore \; cr\theta = 20 \times 10.7 \times \frac{58}{180} \times \pi = 217 \text{ kN}$$

$$F = \frac{192 + 217}{257} = 1.59$$

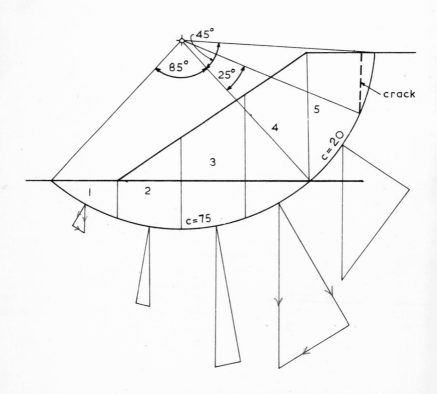

Fig. 5.22 Example 5.2—Deep slip circle

The deep circle is shown in Fig. 5.22.

Slice no.	Area (m^2)	Weight W (kN)	Normal component N (kN)	Tangential component T (kn)
1	3.7	71	61	−36
2	9.6	185	184	−33
3	16.3	314	316	52
4	19.2	370	322	186
5	13.9	268	182	254

$$\Sigma T = 423$$

$$\Sigma N \quad \text{Upper layer} \quad = \quad 182 \text{ kN}$$
$$\text{Lower layer} \quad = \quad 883 \text{ kN}$$

$$\Sigma N \tan \phi = 182 \times 0.364 + 883 \times 0.123 = 175 \text{ kN}$$

$$cr\theta = 75 \times 9.15 \times \frac{85}{180} \times \pi + 20 \times 9.15 \times \frac{45}{180} \times \pi = 1163 \text{ kN}$$

$$F = \frac{1163 + 175}{423} = 3.16$$

If a tension crack is allowed for, F becomes 2.95.

Example 5.3
An embankment has a slope of 1 vertical to 2 horizontal. The properties of the soil are: c = 25 kN/m^2, ϕ = 20°, γ = 16 kN/m^3, and H = 31 m.
   Using Taylor's charts, determine the F value for the slope.
   Solution. From the charts it will be seen that a slope with ϕ = 20° and an inclination of 26°30′ has a stability number of 0.017. This means that, if the factor of safety for friction was unity, the cohesion which must be developed would be found from the expression:

$$\frac{c}{\gamma H} = 0.017$$

i.e. c = 16 × 31 × 0.017 = 8.43 kN/m^2

$$\therefore \text{Factor of safety, with respect to cohesion,} = \frac{25}{8.43} = 2.96$$

This is not the factor of safety used in slope stability, which is:

$$F = \frac{\text{shear strength}}{\text{disturbing shear}}$$

i.e. $$F = \frac{c + \sigma \tan \phi}{\tau}$$

This safety factor applies equally to cohesion and to friction.

F can be found by successive approximations:

$$\tau = \frac{c}{F} + \frac{\sigma \tan \phi}{F}$$

so try F = 1.5

$$\frac{\tan \phi}{F} = \frac{0.364}{1.5} = 0.242 = \text{tangent of angle of } 13\tfrac{1}{2}°$$

Use this value of ϕ to establish a new N value from the charts

$$N = 0.047 \qquad \text{Stability no}$$

$$\therefore c = 0.047 \times 16 \times 31 = 23.3$$

$$\therefore \qquad F \text{ (for c)} = \frac{25}{23.3} = 1.07$$

Try F = 1.3

$$\frac{\tan \phi}{F} = \frac{0.364}{1.3} = 0.28 \ (\phi = 15\tfrac{3}{4}°)$$

From the charts N = 0.036 $\therefore F_c = \frac{25}{17.8} = 1.4$

Try F = 1.35   *close* $\therefore$ *or*

$$\frac{\tan \phi}{F} = \frac{0.364}{1.35} = 0.27 \ (\phi = 15°)$$

From the charts N = 0.037 $\therefore F_c = \frac{25}{18.3} = 1.37 \ (= F_\phi)$

Factor of safety for slope = 1.35

Example 5.4

Slope = 1 vertical to 4 horizontal, c = 12.5 kN/m², H = 31 m, ϕ = 20°, γ = 16 kN/m³.

Solution. Angle of slope = 14°, so obviously the slope is safe as it is less than the angle of friction. With this case N from the charts = 0.

The procedure is identical with example 5.3.

Try F = 1.5

$$\frac{\tan \phi}{F} = \frac{0.364}{1.5} = 0.24 \ (\phi = 13\tfrac{1}{2}°)$$

From the charts N = 0.005 ∴ $F_c = \dfrac{12.5}{0.005 \times 31 \times 16} = 5.05$

Try F = 2.0

$$\frac{\tan \phi}{F} = \frac{0.364}{2.0} = 0.182 \ (\phi = 10\tfrac{1}{4}°)$$

From the charts N = 0.016 ∴ $F_c = \dfrac{12.5}{7.95} = 1.57$

Try F = 1.9

$$\frac{\tan \phi}{F} = \frac{0.364}{1.9} = 0.192 \ (\phi = 11°)$$

From the charts N = 0.013 ∴ $F_c = \dfrac{12.5}{6.45} = 1.94$ (acceptable)

Factor of safety for slope = 1.9

Effective stress analysis

Example 5.5

The cross section of an earth dam sitting on an impermeable base is shown in Fig. 5.23. The stability of the downstream slope is to be investigated using the slip circle shown and given the following information:

$$\gamma_{sat} = 19.2 \text{ kN/m}^3$$
$$c' = 10 \text{ kN/m}^2$$
$$\phi' = 20°$$
$$R = 9.15 \text{ m}$$

Angle subtended by arc of slip circle, θ = 89°.

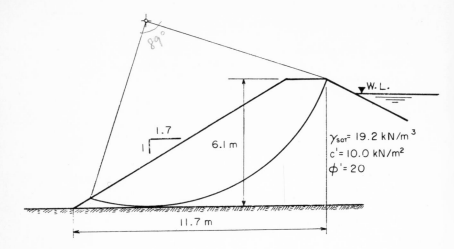

Fig. 5.23 Example 5.5

For this circle determine the factor of safety (a) with the conventional method and (b) with the rigorous method.

Solution. The first step in the analysis is to divide the sliding sector into a suitable number of slices and determine the pore pressure ratio at the mid-point of the base of each slice.

The phreatic surface must be drawn, using the method of Casagrande. A rough form of the flow net must then be established so that the equipotentials through the centre points of each slice can be inserted. Five slices is a normal number (Fig. 5.24).

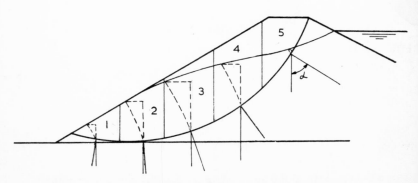

Fig. 5.24 Working diagram for example 5.5

The determination of the r_u values is required for both methods and will be considered first.

Slice no.	h_w (m)	u (kN/m^2)	z (m)	r_u
1	0.654	6.42	0.95	0.352
2	1.958	19.21	2.44	0.41
3	2.440	23.90	3.32	0.375
4	2.020	19.82	3.50	0.295
5	0.246	2.41	1.74	0.072

The calculations for the conventional method are set out in Fig. 5.25A:

$$\theta = 89°$$
$$\therefore c'1 = c'R\theta = 10 \times 9.15 \times \frac{\pi}{180} \times 89 = 142 \text{ kN}$$

$$F = \frac{101.2 + 142}{208.2} = 1.17$$

The rigorous method calculations are set out in Fig. 5.25B.

With the first approximation $F = \frac{267.7}{208.2} = 1.29$

This value was obtained by assuming a value for F of 1.5 in the expression:

$$\frac{\sec\alpha}{1 + \dfrac{\tan\phi'\tan\alpha}{F}}$$

of column (5).

To be accurate, columns 5 and 6 should be recalculated using an F value near to the one obtained from the first approximation. In the example F was put equal to 1.3 and the final value for F was

$$\frac{261.7}{208.2} = 1.26$$

This is near enough to the assumed value of 1.3 to be taken as correct, so the factor of safety for the slope is 1.26.

slice	z (m)	b (m)	W (kN)	$\alpha°$	$\cos \alpha$	$\sec \alpha$	$\cos \alpha - r_u \sec$	$W (\cos \alpha - r_u \sec \alpha) \tan \phi'$	$\sin \alpha$	$W \sin \alpha$
1	0.95	2.35	43	−10	.985	1.015	.627	9.9	−.174	−7.5
2	2.44	"	110	4	.998	1.001	.588	23.5	.070	7.7
3	3.32	"	149	20	.940	1.063	.54	29.3	.342	51
4	3.50	"	158	35	.819	1.208	.463	26.6	.574	91
5	1.74	"	79	57	.545	1.835	.413	11.9	.839	66
								$\Sigma 101.2$		$\Sigma 208.2$

(A) Conventional Method

slice	z (m)	b (m)	W (kN)	$\alpha°$	$\sin \alpha$	$W \sin \alpha$ (1)	$c'b$ (2)	$W(1 - r_u) \tan \phi'$ (3)	2 + 3 (4)	$\sec \alpha$	$\tan \alpha$	(5) $\dfrac{\sec \alpha}{1 + \dfrac{\tan \phi' \tan \alpha}{F}}$		(6) 4 × 5	
												F = 1.5	F = 1.3	F = 1.5	F = 1.3
1	0.95	2.35	43	−10	−.174	−7.5	23.5	10.1	33.6	1.015	−.176	.98	.97	32.9	32
2	2.44	"	110	4	.070	7.7	"	23.4	46.9	1.001	.07	.99	.984	46.4	46
3	3.32	"	149	20	.342	51	"	33.8	57.3	1.063	.364	.97	.965	55.5	55
4	3.50	"	158	35	.574	91	"	40.3	63.8	1.208	.70	1.03	1.01	65.7	64
5	1.74	"	79	57	.839	66	"	26.7	50.2	1.835	1.54	1.34	1.28	67.2	63
						$\Sigma 208.2$								$\Sigma 267.7$	26

(B) Rigorous Method

Fig. 5.25 Example 5.5

Only rarely are more than two approximations necessary, and often the procedure need only be carried out once if the assumed value for F was close to the final value obtained.

Example 5.6

Figure 5.26 gives details of the cross section of an embankment. The soil has

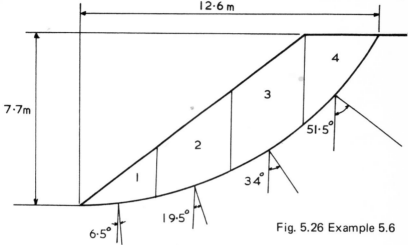

Fig. 5.26 Example 5.6

the following properties: $\phi' = 35°$, $c' = 10 \text{ kN/m}^2$, $\gamma = 16 \text{ kN/m}^3$.

For the slip circle shown, determine the factor of safety for the following values of r_u: 0.2, 0.4 and 0.6.

Plot the variation of F with r_u.

Solution. The calculations were based on the rigorous method and are shown in Fig. 5.27.

Example 5.7

An embankment has a slope of 1 vertical to 2 horizontal. The properties of the soil are: $c' = 25 \text{ kN/m}^2$, $\phi' = 20°$, $\gamma = 16 \text{ kN/m}^3$. The height of the embankment is 31 m and the average pore pressure ratio is 0.4.

Using Bishop & Morgenstern's charts, determine the factor of safety for the slope.

Solution. On the charts of n values are plotted a series of dotted lines labelled r_{ue}. The authors have shown that if the relevant r_{ue} value is less than the actual design r_u then the set of charts with the next highest depth factor should be used. The procedure therefore becomes:

Calculate $c'/\gamma H$ and, using the chart with D = 1.0, check that r_u is less than r_{ue}. If it is, then this is the correct chart to use: if r_u is not less than r_{ue} select the next chart (D = 1.25). In the case of $c'/\gamma H = 0.05$, r_{ue} should again be checked and if r_u is greater than this value then the chart for D = 1.5 should be used.

$r_u = 0.2$

slice	z (m)	b (m)	W (kN)	α°	sin α	W sin α (1)	c'b × 10⁻² (2)	$W(1-r_u)\tan\phi'$ (3)	2 + 3 (4)	sec α	tan α	(5) $\dfrac{\sec\alpha}{1+\dfrac{\tan\phi'\tan\alpha}{F}}$	4 × 5 (6)
												F = 1.5	F = 1.5
1	1.0	3.15	50.5	6.5	.113	5.7	31.5	28.2	59.7	1.007	.114	.954	57.0
2	3.08	,,	155.0	19.5	.334	51.7	,,	87.0	118.5	1.06	.354	.91	108.0
3	4.0	,,	202.0	34.0	.559	113.0	,,	113.0	144.5	1.207	.675	.917	132.5
4	2.7	,,	136.0	51.5	.783	106.5	,,	76.1	107.6	1.605	1.257	1.012	109.0

$$\Sigma 276.9 \qquad\qquad \Sigma 406.5$$

$$F = \frac{406.5}{276.9} = 1.47$$

$r_u = 0.4$

$W(1-r_u)\tan\phi'$ (3)	2 + 3 (4)	(5) $\dfrac{\sec\alpha}{1+\dfrac{\tan\phi'\tan\alpha}{F}}$		4 × 5 (6)	
		F = 1.3	F =1.1	F = 1.1	F = 1.1
21.2	52.7	.948	.939	50.0	49.5
65.1	96.6	.89	.865	86.0	83.6
84.9	116.4	.885	.844	103.0	93.2
57.1	88.6	.958	.893	83.9	79.1

$$\Sigma 322.9 \quad 305.4$$

$$F = \frac{322.9}{276.9} = 1.16 \qquad F = \frac{305.4}{276.9} = 1.1$$

$r_u = 0.6$

$W(1-r_u)\tan\phi'$ (3)	2 + 3 (4)	(5) $\dfrac{\sec\alpha}{1+\dfrac{\tan\phi'\tan\alpha}{F}}$		4 × 5 (6)	
		F = 0.7	F = 0.75	F = 0.7	F = 0.75
14.1	45.6	.883	.912	40.2	41.5
43.4	74.9	.768	.783	57.4	58.6
56.6	88.1	.721	.72	63.5	63.4
38.1	69.6	.711	.71	49.5	49.4

$$\Sigma 210.6 \quad 212.9$$

$$F = \frac{210.6}{276.9} = 0.76 \qquad F = \frac{212.9}{276.9} = 0.77$$

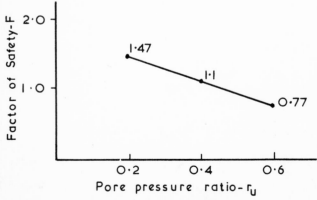

Fig. 5.27 Example 5.6

In the example (which is example 5.3 with an r_u value):

$$\frac{c'}{\gamma H} = \frac{25}{16 \times 31} = 0.05$$

Select the chart with D = 1.0

$\quad$ r_{ue} $\quad = \quad 0.6\overset{x}{4}$ ∴ this chart is acceptable ($r_{ue} > r_u$)

$\quad$ m $\quad = \quad 1.39$ (compare with Taylor's method = 1.35)

$\quad$ n $\quad = \quad 1.07$

∴ F $\quad = \quad 1.39 - 0.4 \times 1.07 = 0.75$

$\quad\quad = \quad m - ru \times n$

Example 5.8

Slope = 1 vertical to 4 horizontal, $c' = 12.5$ kN/m², $\phi' = 20°$, $\gamma = 16$ kN/m³, H = 31 m, $r_u = 0.35$.

$\quad$ Find F.

Solution. This is example 5.4 with an r_u value.

$$\frac{c'}{\gamma H} = \frac{12.5}{16 \times 31} = 0.025$$

Using D = 1.0, $r_{ue} = 0.0$ ($r_{ue} \not> r_u$).

Use chart for D = 1.25:

$\quad$ m $\quad = \quad 1.97$ (compare with Taylor's method = 1.9)

$\quad$ n $\quad = \quad 1.78$

$\quad$ F $\quad = \quad 1.97 - 0.35 \times 1.78 = 1.35$

Example 5.9

Slope angle = 24°, $c' = 20$ kN/m², $\gamma = 21$ kN/m³, $\phi' = 30°$, $r_u = 0.3$, H = 50 m. Find F.

Solution. Slope (24°) = 1 vertical to 2¼ horizontal.

$$\frac{c'}{\gamma H} = \frac{20}{21 \times 50} = 0.019$$

Chart $\dfrac{c'}{\gamma H} = 0.025$; D = 1.0

$\quad$ m $\quad = \quad 1.76$

$\quad$ n $\quad = \quad 1.68$

$\quad$ F $\quad = \quad 1.76 - 0.3 \times 1.68 = 1.26$

Chart $\dfrac{c'}{\gamma H} = 0.00$

$$m = 1.3$$
$$n = 1.54$$
$$F = 1.3 - 0.3 \times 1.54 = 0.84$$

The actual F value can be found by interpolation:

$$F = 0.84 + (1.26 - 0.84)\,\dfrac{0.019}{0.025}$$

$$= 0.84 + 0.32 = 1.16$$

NOTE: It is preferable to calculate the two F values and then interpolate rather than to determine the m and n values by interpolation.

EXERCISES ON CHAPTER 5

5.1 A proposed cutting is to have the dimensions shown in Fig. 5.28.

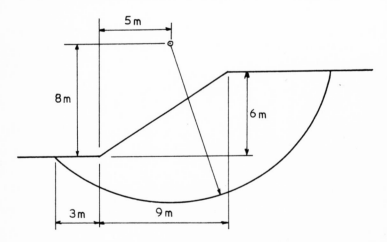

Fig. 5.28 Exercise 5.1

The soil has the following properties: $\phi = 15°, c = 13.5 \text{ kN/m}^2$
$\gamma = 19.3 \text{ kN/m}^3$

Determine the factor of safety against slipping for the slip circle shown (i) ignoring tension cracks and (ii) allowing for a tension crack.

Answer   (i) 1.7   (ii) 1.6

5.2 Investigate the stability of the embankment shown in Fig. 5.29.

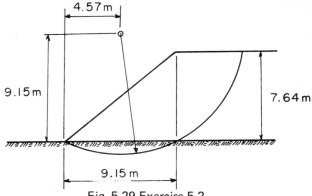

Fig. 5.29 Exercise 5.2

The embankment consists of two soils, both with bulk densities of 19.3 kN/m^3; the upper soil has c = 7.2 kN/m^2 and ϕ = 30°, whilst the lower soil has c = 32.5 kN/m^2 and ϕ = 0°.

Analyse the slip circle shown (ignore tension cracks).

Answer   F = 1.2

5.3 The surface of a granular soil mass is inclined at 25° to the horizontal. The soil is saturated throughout with a moisture content of 15.8 per cent particle specific gravity of 2.65 and an angle of internal friction of 38°.

At a depth of 1.83 m water is seeping through the soil parallel to the surface.

Determine the factor of safety against slipping on a plane parallel to the surface of the soil at a vertical depth of 3.05 m below the surface.

Answer   1.38

What would be the factor of safety for the same plane if the level of the seeping water lifted up to the surface of the soil?

Answer   0.91

5.4 Using Taylor's curves, determine the factor of safety for the following slopes (assume D = 1.0):

H = 30.5 m, β = 40°, c = 10.8 kN/m^2, ϕ = 35°, γ = 14.4 kN/m^3
Answer   Approximately 1.25

H = 15.25 m, β = 20°, c = 24.0 kN/m^2, ϕ = 0°, γ = 19.3 kN/m^3
Answer   0.8

H = 22.8 m, β = 30°, c = 9.6 kN/m^2, ϕ = 25°, γ = 16.1 kN/m^3
Answer   1.2

5.5 In the stability analysis of an earth embankment the slip circle shown in

Fig. 5.30 Exercise 5.5

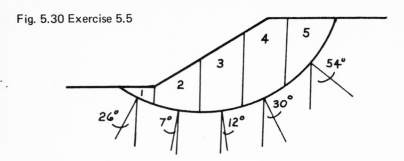

Fig. 5.30 was used and the following figures obtained:

Slice no.	Breadth b (m)	Weight W (kN)	α (Degrees)
1	5.65	372.	−26
2	5.65	656	−7
3	5.65	1070	12
4	5.65	1220	30
5	5.65	686	54

With the values, and using the conventional method, determine the safety factor of the slope at the end of construction assuming the pore pressure ratio to be 0.45 and the cohesion of soil and the angle of friction (with regard to effective stresses) to be 19.1 kN/m² and 25° respectively.
    Answer   1.15

Fig. 5.31 Exercise 5.6

123 m

135 m

23·4m

5.6 Using the slip circle shown in Fig. 5.31, determine the F values for $r_u = 0.4, 0.6$, and 0.8. Plot r_u against F. $\gamma = 23.3$ kN/m³, $c' = 17.1$ kN/m² $\phi = 37\frac{1}{2}°$.

Answer By rigorous method F 1.5   1.0   0.5
 r_u 0.4   0.6   0.8

5.7 Using Bishop & Morgenstern's curve, determine the factors of safety for the following slopes:

(i) $r_u = 0.5$, $c' = 5.37$ kN/m², $\phi' = 40°$, $\gamma = 14.4$ kN/m³, H = 15.2 m, slope = 3:1

Answer 1.6

(ii) $r_u = 0.3$, $c' = 7.2$ kN/m², $\phi' = 39°$, $\gamma = 12.8$ kN/m³, H = 76.4 m, slope = 2:1

Answer 1.9

(iii) $r_u = 0.5$, $c' = 20$ kN/m², $\gamma = 17.7$ kN/m³, $\phi' = 25°$, H = 25 m, angle of slope = 20°

Answer 1.2

REFERENCES

Bishop, A. W.
$\qquad$ The use of pore-pressure coefficients in practice. *Géotechnique* (1954).
$\qquad$ The use of slip circle for stability analysis. *Géotechnique* (1955).
Bishop, A. W., & Morgenstern, N.
$\qquad$ Stability coefficients for earth slopes. *Géotechnique* (1960).
Bishop, A. W., & Henkel, D. J.
$\qquad$ *The measurement of soil properties in the triaxial test* (2nd edn., Edward Arnold, 1962).
Fellenius, W.
$\qquad$ Calculation of stability of earth dams. *Trans 2nd Congress on Large Dams (1936)*.
Jumikis, A. R.
$\qquad$ *Soil Mechanics* (Van Nostrand, 1962).
Skempton, A. W.
$\qquad$ The pore pressure coefficients A and B. *Géotechnique* (1954).
Taylor, D. W.
$\qquad$ *Fundamentals of soil mechanics* (John Wiley, 1948).

STABILITY COEFFICIENTS FOR EARTH SLOPES
by A. W. BISHOP and NORBERT MORGENSTERN

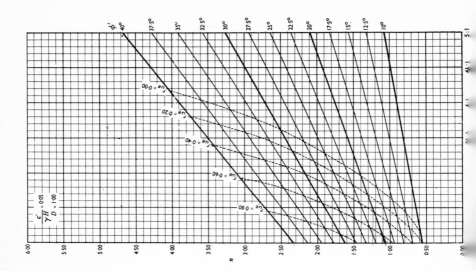

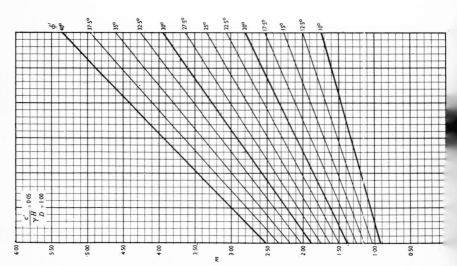

'Stability Coefficients for Earth Slopes' on pages 164–169 are reproduced from *Géotechnique*, December 1960 by permission of the Council of the Institution of Civil Engineers.

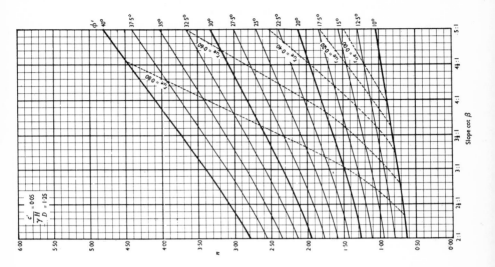

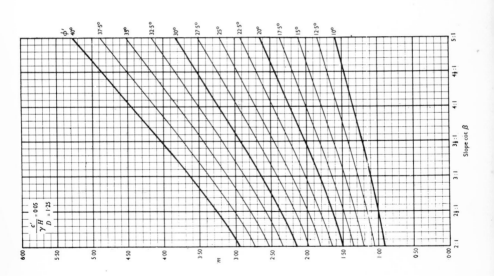

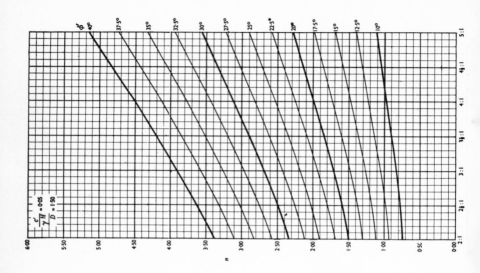

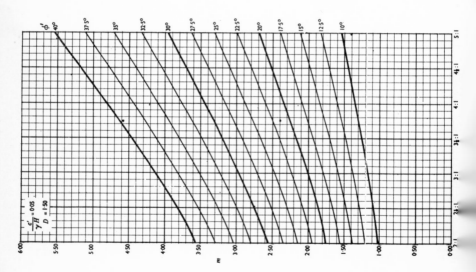

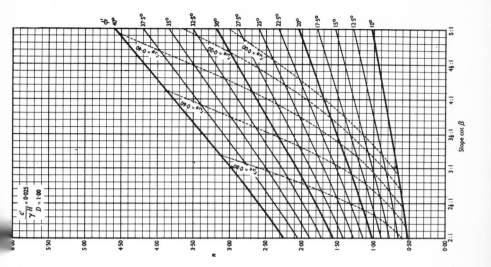

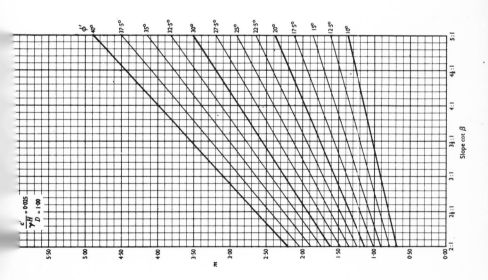

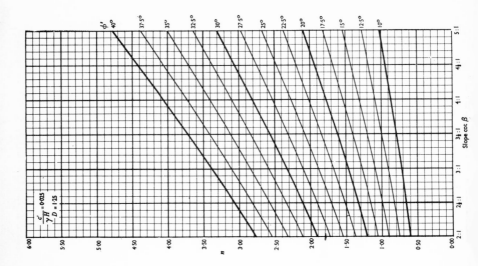

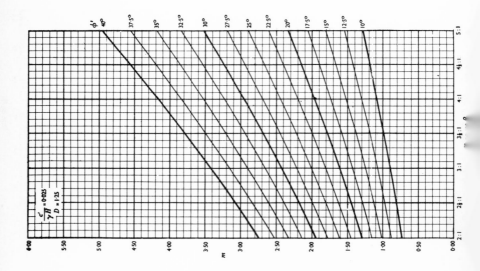

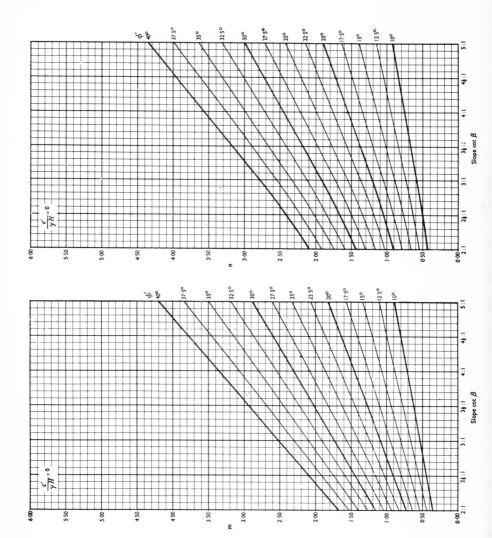

6. Earth Pressure

EARTH PRESSURE AT REST

Consider a mass of soil with a horizontal upper surface and let this soil be completely at rest, undisturbed by any forces other than its own weight. If the unit weight of the soil is γ then an element at a depth h below the surface will be subjected to a vertical pressure γh. This stress is a major principal stress, i.e. $\sigma_1 = \gamma h$, and it will induce a horizontal or minor principal stress σ_3.

The ratio σ_3/σ_1 for soil at rest is given the symbol K_0 and is called the coefficient of earth pressure at rest, i.e. lateral pressure in a soil at rest = $K_0 \gamma h$ (Fig. 6.1). It has been shown experimentally that for granular soils

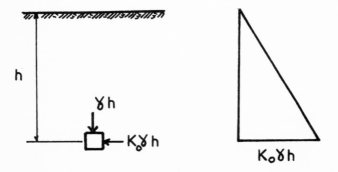

Fig. 6.1 Earth pressure at rest

and normally consolidated clays:

$$K_0 \doteq 1 - \sin \phi' \text{ (Bishop, 1958)}$$

ACTIVE AND PASSIVE EARTH PRESSURE

Consider now a smooth vertical wall supporting a mass of soil at rest in which the lateral pressure on the wall = $K_0 \gamma h$. If the wall is allowed to yield, i.e. move forward slightly, there will be an immediate reduction in the value of lateral stress, but if the wall is pushed slightly into the soil there will be an increase in the value of lateral pressure.

If we assume that the value of vertical pressure remains unchanged at γh

during these operations, then the minimum and maximum values of lateral earth pressure that will be achieved can be obtained from the Mohr circle diagram (Fig. 6.2).

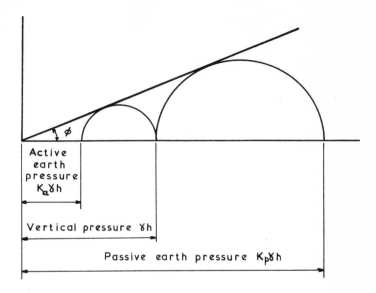

Fig. 6.2. Active and passive earth pressures

The lateral pressure can reduce to a minimum value at which the stress circle is tangential to the strength envelope of the soil; this minimum value is known as the active earth pressure and equals $K_a \gamma h$ where K_a = the coefficient of active earth pressure. The lateral pressure can rise to a maximum value (with the stress circle again tangential to the strength envelope) known as the passive earth pressure, which equals $K_p \gamma h$ where K_p = coefficient of passive earth pressure.

It can be seen from Fig. 6.2 that when considering active pressure the vertical pressure due to the soil weight (γh) is a major principal stress and that when considering passive pressure the vertical pressure due to the soil weight (γh) is a minor principal stress.

Active pressure in granular soils
Rankine's theory (soil surface horizontal)
Imagine a smooth, vertical retaining wall holding back a cohesionless soil with an angle of internal friction ϕ. The top of the soil is horizontal and level with the top of the wall. Consider a point in the soil at a depth h below the

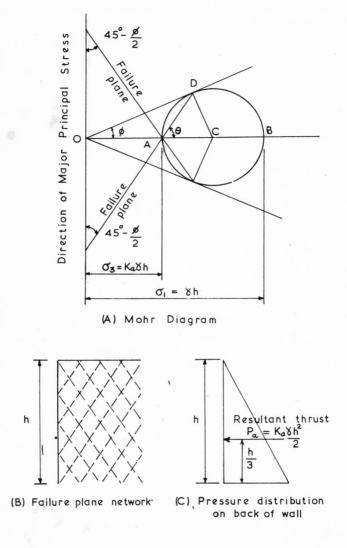

(A) Mohr Diagram

(B) Failure plane network

(C) Pressure distribution on back of wall

Fig. 6.3 Active pressure for a cohesionless soil with a horizontal upper surface

top of the wall (Fig. 6.3), assuming that the wall has yielded sufficiently to satisfy active earth pressure conditions.

In the Mohr diagram: $DC = $ radius $= AC$.

$$\frac{\sigma_3}{\sigma_1} = \frac{OA}{OB} = \frac{OC - AC}{OC + CB} = \frac{OC - DC}{OC + DC} = \frac{1 - \dfrac{DC}{OC}}{1 + \dfrac{DC}{OC}} = \frac{1 - \sin \phi}{1 + \sin \phi}$$

It can be shown by trigonometry that $\dfrac{1 - \sin \phi}{1 + \sin \phi} = \tan^2\left(45° - \dfrac{\phi}{2}\right)$

Hence $$K_a = \frac{1 - \sin \phi}{1 + \sin \phi} = \tan^2\left(45° - \frac{\phi}{2}\right)$$

Rankine's theory (soil surface sloping at angle β)
This problem is illustrated in Fig. 6.4. The evaluation of K_a may be carried

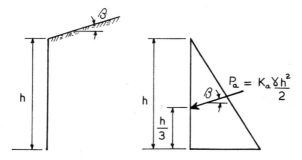

Fig. 6.4 Active pressure for a cohesionless soil with its surface sloping upwards at angle β to the horizontal

out in a similar manner to the previous case, but the vertical pressure will no longer be a principal stress. The pressure on the wall is assumed to act parallel to the surface of the soil, i.e. at angle β to the horizontal.

The active pressure, p_a, is still given by the expression:

$$p_a = K_a \gamma h \text{ where } K_a = \cos \beta \cdot \frac{\cos \beta - \sqrt{\cos^2 \beta - \cos^2 \phi}}{\cos \beta + \sqrt{\cos^2 \beta - \cos^2 \phi}}$$

if $\beta = \phi$.

$K_a = \cos \phi$

Limitations of the Rankine theory

Rankine's theory only applies to vertical backed walls. Most walls are in this category, but where the wall is battered an allowance can be made (example 6.5).

The theory does not allow for friction between the soil and the wall which occurs when the wall yields and the soil moves (downwards for active pressures and upwards for passive pressures); the friction forces have a relieving effect on the wall that can be allowed for, but as the error is on the safe side it is not usually evaluated.

Coulomb's wedge theory

Instead of considering the equilibrium of an element in a stressed mass, Coulomb's theory considers the soil as a whole. If a wall supporting a granular soil is suddenly removed the soil will slump down to its angle of friction, ϕ, on the plane BC in Fig. 6.5A. It is therefore reasonable to assume

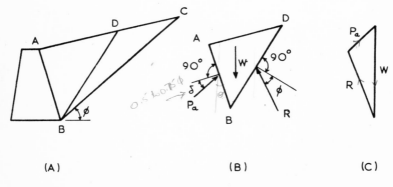

Fig. 6.5 Wedge theory for granular soils

that if the wall only moved forward slightly a rupture plane BD would develop somewhere between AB and BC: the wedge of soil ABD would then move down the base of the wall AB and along the rupture plane BD. These wedges do in fact exist and have failure surfaces approximating to planes. The theory is very adaptable to graphical solution, and the effects of wall friction and batter are automatically allowed for.

The procedure is to select a series of trial wedges and find the one that exerts the greatest thrust on the wall. A wedge is acted upon by three forces:

W, the weight of the wedge,
P_a, the reaction from the wall,
R, the reaction on the plane of failure.

At failure, the reaction on the failure plane will be inclined at maximum obliquity, ϕ, to the normal to the plane. If the angle of wall friction is δ then the reaction from the wall will be inclined at δ to the normal to the wall (δ cannot be greater than ϕ). As active pressures are being developed the wedge is tending to move downwards, and both R and P_a will consequently be on the downward sides of the normals (Fig. 6.5B). W is of known magnitude (area ABD × unit weight) and direction (vertical) and R and P_a are both of known direction, so the triangle of forces can be completed and the magnitude of P_a found (Fig. 6.5C). The value of the angle of wall friction, δ, can be obtained from tests, but if test values are not available δ is usually assumed as 0.5 to 0.75 ϕ.

In Fig. 6.6 the total thrust on the wall due to earth pressure is to be

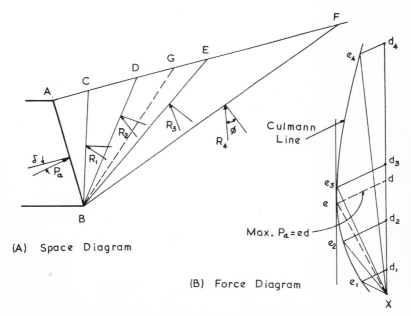

Fig. 6.6 Culmann line construction for a cohesionless soil

evaluated, four trial wedges having been selected with failure surfaces BC, BD, BE and BF. At some point along each failure surface a line normal to it is drawn, after which a second line is constructed at ϕ to the normal. The resulting four lines give the lines of action of the reactions on each of the trial planes of failure. The direction of the wall reaction is similarly obtained by drawing a line normal to the wall and then another line at angle δ to it.

The weight of each trial slice is next obtained, and starting at a point X these weights are set off vertically upwards as points d_1, d_2, etc. such that Xd_1 represents the weight of slice 1 to some scale, Xd_2 represents the weight of slice 2, and so on.

A separate triangle of forces is now completed for each of the four wedges, the directions of the corresponding reaction on the failure plane and of P_a being obtained from the space diagram. The point of intersection of R and P_a is given the symbol e with a suffix that tallies with the wedge analysed, e.g. the point e_1 represents the intersection of P_{a1} and R_1.

The maximum thrust on the wall is obviously represented by the maximum value of the length ed. To obtain this length a smooth curve (the Culmann line) is drawn through the points e_1, e_2, e_3 and e_4. A tangent to the Culmann line which is parallel to Xd_4 will cut the line at point e; hence the line ed can be drawn on the force diagram and the length ed represents the thrust on the back of the wall due to the soil.

If required the position of the actual failure plane can be plotted on the space diagram, the angle $e_3 Xe_2$ on the force diagram equalling the angle EBD on the space diagram whilst the angle eXe_2 similarly equals the angle GBD where BG = failure plane.

Passive pressure in granular soils
Rankine's theory (soil surface horizontal)
In this case the vertical pressure due to the weight of the soil, γh, is acting as a minor principal stress. Figure 6.7A shows the Mohr circle diagram representing these stress conditions and drawn in the usual position, i.e. with the axis OX (the direction of the major principal plane) horizontal. Figure 6.7B shows the same diagram correctly orientated with the major principal stress, $K_p \gamma h$, horizontal and the major principal plane vertical. The Mohr diagram, it will be seen, must be rotated through $90°$.

In the Mohr diagram:

$$\frac{\sigma_1}{\sigma_3} = \frac{OB}{OA} = \frac{OC + DC}{OC - DC} = \frac{1 + \sin \phi}{1 - \sin \phi} = \tan^2 \left(45° + \frac{\phi}{2}\right)$$

Hence
$$K_p = \frac{1 + \sin \phi}{1 - \sin \phi} = \tan^2 \left(45° + \frac{\phi}{2}\right)$$

As with active pressure, there is a network of shear planes inclined at $(45° - \phi/2)$ to the direction of the major principal stress, but this time the soil is being compressed as opposed to expanded.

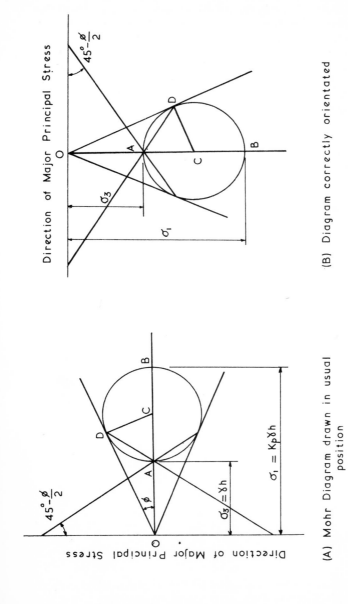

Direction of Major Principal Stress

$45° - \dfrac{\phi}{2}$

σ_3

σ_1

O

A

C

D

B

(B) Diagram correctly orientated

$45° - \dfrac{\phi}{2}$

ϕ

$\sigma_3 = \gamma h$

$\sigma_1 = K_p \gamma h$

Direction of Major Principal Stress

O

A

C

D

B

(A) Mohr Diagram drawn in usual position

Fig. 6.7 Passive earth pressure for a cohesionless soil with a horizontal upper surface

Rankine's theory (soil surface sloping at angle β)
The directions of the principal stresses are not known, but we assume that
the passive pressure acts parallel to the surface of the slope. The analysis
gives:

$$K_p = \cos \beta \cdot \frac{\cos \beta + \sqrt{\cos^2 \beta - \cos^2 \phi}}{\cos \beta - \sqrt{\cos^2 \beta - \cos^2 \phi}}$$

Coulomb's wedge theory
The assumption that the surface of rupture is a plane cannot be accepted for
passive pressures unless δ is not greater than $\phi/3$. Generally the failure surface
is a pronounced curve and this form of failure can therefore be analysed in a
similar manner to a problem of slope stability, although in most cases a
solution by the Rankine theory is sufficient.

Surcharges

The extra loading carried by a retaining wall is known as a surcharge and
can be a uniform load (roadway, stacked goods etc.), a line load (trains
running parallel to a wall), or an isolated load (column footing).

Uniform load
In the analytical solution the load is considered as equivalent to an extra
height of soil.
Equivalent height is given by the expression:

$$h_e = \frac{w_s}{\gamma} \frac{\sin \theta}{\sin(\theta + \beta)}$$

where　γ =　unit weight of soil
　　　　w_s =　intensity of uniform load/unit area
　　　　θ =　angle of back of wall to horizontal
　　　　β =　angle of inclination of retained soil.

The surcharge can therefore be regarded as an extra height of soil, h_e,
placed on the top of the wall.
Pressure due to the surcharge, $p_u = K_a \gamma h_e$, is distributed uniformly over the
back of the wall with its centre of pressure acting at half the wall's height
(Fig. 6.8). When the surface of the fill is horizontal, $\beta = 0$ and $h_e = w_s/\gamma$.
In Fig. 6.8, P_u = thrust on wall due to surcharge and P_a = thrust on wall
due to earth pressure; P_a and P_u can be combined to give the magnitude
and point of application of the resultant thrust.
With the Culmann line construction the weight of surcharge on each slice
is merely added to the weight of the slice. The weight of each wedge plus its
surcharge is plotted as Xd_1, Xd_2, etc. and the procedure is as described
before.

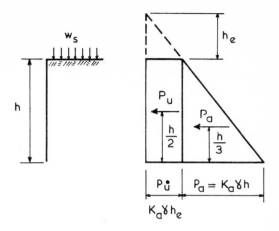

Fig. 6.8 Effect of uniform surcharge on a retaining wall

Line load
An approximate mathematical solution for line loads is described in Civil Engineering Code of Practice no. 2, *Earth retaining structures* (Institution of Civil Engineers, London).

In Fig. 6.9 the line load, W_L, affects the wall as if it were a horizontal force

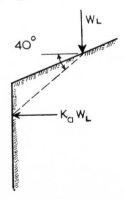

Fig. 6.9 Line load effect (From Code of Practice "Earth Retaining Structures")

of magnitude $K_a W_L$. Its point of application is obtained from the procedure shown in the illustration.

With the Culmann line construction the weight of W_L is simply added to the trial wedges affected (Fig. 6.10).

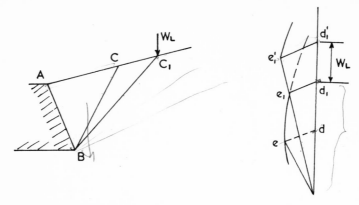

Fig. 6.10 Culmann line construction for a line load

The Culmann line is constructed as before, ignoring the line load. On this basis the failure plane would be BC, and P_a would have a value ed to some force scale.

Slip occurring on BC_1 and all planes further from the wall will be due to the wedge weight plus W_L. For plane BC_1, set off $(W_1 + W_L)$ from X to d_1' and continue the construction of the Culmann line as before (i.e. for every trial wedge to the right of plane BC_1, add W_L to its weight.) The Culmann line jumps from e_1 to e_1' and then continues to follow a similar curve.

The wall thrust is again determined from the maximum ed value by drawing a tangent, the maximum value of ed being in this case $e_1' d_1'$. If W_L is located far enough back from the wall it may be that ed is still greater than $e_1' d_1'$; in this case W_L is taken as having no effect on the wall.

Isolated loads

Neither the Rankine theory nor the Coulomb wedge theory can be adapted for this case as they cannot allow for the spread of the load through the soil, but it can be solved by application of the elastic theory of which a solution is given in Civil Engineering Code of Practice no. 2, *Earth retaining structures.*

The effect of cohesion under active pressure

A cohesive soil is partially self-supporting and it will therefore exert a smaller pressure on a retaining wall than a cohesionless soil having the same angle of friction and density.

Consider two such soils with their surfaces horizontal. The Mohr circle diagrams for both are shown superimposed upon each other in Fig. 6.11.

At depth h both soils are subjected to the same major principal stress $\sigma_1 = \gamma h$. The minor principal stress for the cohesionless soil is σ_3 but for

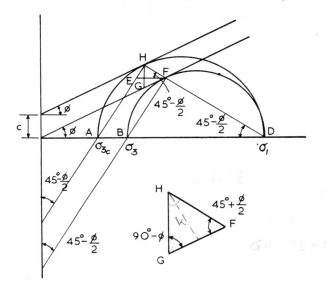

Fig. 6.11 The effect of cohesion on active pressure

the cohesive soil is only σ_{3c}, the difference being due to the cohesive strength, c, that is represented by the length AB or EF.

Consider triangle HGF

$$\frac{HF}{GH} = \frac{HF}{c} = \frac{c \sin\left(90° - \phi\right)}{c \sin\left(45° + \dfrac{\phi}{2}\right)} = 2\frac{\sin\left(45° - \dfrac{\phi}{2}\right)\cos\left(45° - \dfrac{\phi}{2}\right)}{\cos\left(45° - \dfrac{\phi}{2}\right)}$$

Or

$$HF = 2c \sin\left(45° - \frac{\phi}{2}\right)$$

Difference between σ_3 and σ_{3c}

$$= EF = \frac{HF}{\cos\left(45° - \dfrac{\phi}{2}\right)}$$

$$= 2c\frac{\sin\left(45° - \dfrac{\phi}{2}\right)}{\cos\left(45° - \dfrac{\phi}{2}\right)} = 2c \tan\left(45° - \frac{\phi}{2}\right)$$

Hence the horizontal pressure at depth h in a cohesive soil with a horizontal upper surface is:

$$p_a = K_a \, \gamma \, h - 2c \tan \left(45° - \frac{\phi}{2}\right)$$

$$= Ka \, \gamma h - 2c \sqrt{Ka}$$

The pressure diagram obtained from such a soil is shown in Fig. 6.12.

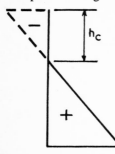

h_c

$+$

Fig. 6.12 Active pressure diagram
for a cohesive-frictional soil

The negative values of p_a between the range h = 0 and h = h_c indicate a suction effect, but soils cannot really withstand tensile stresses and suction is therefore unlikely. For design purposes the pressure in this range is consequently taken simply as zero.

Tension cracks

In Fig. 6.12 the depth of the tensile zone was given the symbol h_c. It is possible for cracks to develop over this depth and a value for h_c is often necessary.

If p_a in the expression $p_a = K_a \, \gamma \, h_c - 2c \tan\left(45° - \frac{\phi}{2}\right)$ is put equal to zero we can obtain an expression for h_c:

$$K_a \, \gamma \, h_c = 2c \tan \left(45° - \frac{\phi}{2}\right)$$

i.e. $$\tan^2 \left(45° - \frac{\phi}{2}\right) \gamma h_c = 2c \tan \left(45° - \frac{\phi}{2}\right)$$

$\therefore$ $$h_c = \frac{2c}{\gamma} \frac{1}{\tan \left(45° - \frac{\phi}{2}\right)}$$

$$= \frac{2c}{\gamma} \tan \left(45° + \frac{\phi}{2}\right)$$

When $\phi = 0°$, $h_c = \dfrac{2c}{\gamma}$

Actual measured values indicate that the 2 in these formulae is nearer 1.5.

The wedge theory

This is of wider application than the analytical solution and assumes that there is a zone of soil of depth

$$\frac{2c}{\gamma}\tan\left(45° + \frac{\phi}{2}\right)$$

within which there is no adhesion or friction along the back of the wall or along the plane of rupture (Fig. 6.13).

There are now five forces acting on the wedge:

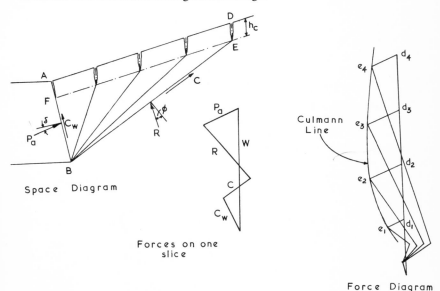

Fig. 6.13 Culmann line construction adapted to allow for cohesion

R, reaction on plane of failure,
W, weight of whole wedge ABED,
P_a, resultant thrust on wall,
C_w, cohesion along length of wall BF (C_w = c_wBF),
C, cohesion along rupture plane BE (C = cBE).

The unit wall cohesion, c_w, cannot be greater than the unit cohesion, c. In the absence of tests c_w can be taken as equal to c for soils up to c = 50 kN/m². For soils with a cohesion value greater than this, c_w should be taken as 50 kN/m².

The value of W is obtained as before, so there are only two unknown forces: R and P_a.

In order to draw the Culmann line a polygon of forces must be constructed. The weights of the various wedges are set off as before, vertically up from the point X. As the force C_w is common to all polygons it is drawn next, and the C force is then plotted. The direction of P_a is drawn from point d and the direction of R is drawn from the end of force C; these two lines cross at the point e on the Culmann line.

Point of application of resultant active thrust

If required the point of application can be found by taking moments of forces about some convenient point on the space diagram. For most practical cases it is sufficiently accurate to assume that the line of active thrust cuts the back of the wall at one third of its vertical height above the base.

Passive pressure

Rankine's theory has been developed by Bell (1915) for the case of a frictional/cohesive soil

His solution for a soil with a horizontal surface is:

$$p_p = \gamma h \tan^2 \left(45° + \frac{\phi}{2}\right) + 2c \tan \left(45° + \frac{\phi}{2}\right)$$

The wedge theory is not applicable for this case and, as with a cohesionless soil, analysis must be carried out by considering the analysis of a curved rupture surface.

Influence of wall yield on design

A wall can yield in one of two ways: either by rotation about its lower edge (Fig. 6.14B) or by sliding forward (Fig. 6.14C). Provided that the wall yields sufficiently, a state of active earth pressure is reached and the thrust on the back of the wall is in both cases about the same (P_a).

The pressure distribution that gives this total thrust value can be very different in each instance, however. For example, consider a wall that is unable to yield (Fig. 6.14A). The pressure distribution is triangular and is represented by the line AC.

Consider that the wall now yields by rotation about its lower edge until the total thrust = P_a (Fig. 6.14B). This results in conditions that approximate to the Rankine theory and is known as the totally active case.

Suppose, however, that the wall yields by sliding forward until active thrust conditions are achieved (Fig. 6.14C). This hardly disturbs the upper layers of soil so that the top of the pressure diagram is similar to the earth pressure at rest diagram. As the total thrust on the all is the same as in rotational yield, it means that the pressure distribution must be roughly similar to the line AE in Fig. 6.14C.

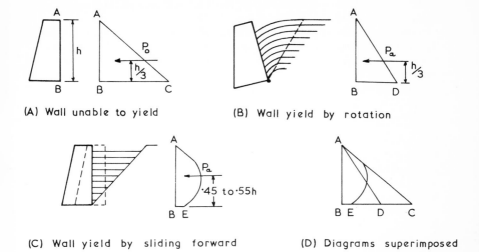

(A) Wall unable to yield   (B) Wall yield by rotation

(C) Wall yield by sliding forward   (D) Diagrams superimposed

Fig. 6.14 Influence of wall yield on pressure distribution

This type of yield gives conditions that approximate to the wedge theory, the centre of pressure moving up to between 0.45 and 0.55 h above the wall base, and is referred to as the arching-active case.

The differences between the various pressure diagrams can be seen in Fig. 6.14D where the three diagrams have been superimposed. It has been found that if the top of a wall moves 0.1 per cent of its height, i.e. a movement of 10 mm in a 10 m high wall, an arching-active case is attained. This applies whether the wall rotates or slides. In order to achieve the totally active case the top of the wall must move about 0.5 per cent, or 50 mm in a 10 m wall.

It can therefore be seen that if a retaining wall with a cohesionless backfill is held so rigidly that little yield is possible (e.g. if is joined to an adjacent structure) it must be designed to withstand earth pressure values much larger than active pressure values.

If such a wall is completely restrained it must be designed to take earth pressure at rest values, although this condition does not often occur; if a wall is so restrained that only a small amount of yielding can take place arching-active conditions may be achieved, as in the strutting of trench timbers. In this case the assumption of triangular pressure distribution is incorrect, the actual pressure distribution being indeterminate but roughly parabolic.

If the wall yields 0.5 per cent of its height then the totally active case is attained and the assumption of triangular pressure distribution is satisfactory.

Almost all retaining walls, unless propped at the top, can yield a considerable amount with no detrimental effects and attain this totally active state.

In the case of a wall with a cohesive backfill, the totally active case is reached as soon as the wall yields but due to plastic flow within the clay there is a slow build-up of pressure on the back of the wall, which will eventually yield again to re-acquire the totally active pressure conditions. This process is repetitive and over a number of years the resulting movement of the wall may be large. For such soils one can either design for higher pressure or, if the wall is relatively unimportant, design for the totally active case bearing in mind that the useful life of the wall may be short.

Pressure distribution on trench sheeting

When excavating a deep trench the insertion of shuttering to hold up the sides becomes necessary. The excavation is carried down first to some point, X, and rigidly strutted timbering is inserted between the levels D to X.

As further excavation is carried out, timbering and strutting are inserted in stages, but before the timbering is inserted the soil yields by an amount that tends to increase with depth (it is relatively small at the top of the trench).

In Fig. 6.15B the shape $A'B'C'D'$ represents, to an enlarged scale, the original form of the surface that has yielded to the position ABCD of Fig. 6.15A;

In Fig. (C):

   1 = Totally Active Pressure Distribution

   2 = Probable Pressure Distribution

   3 = Pressure Distribution assumed for
           design

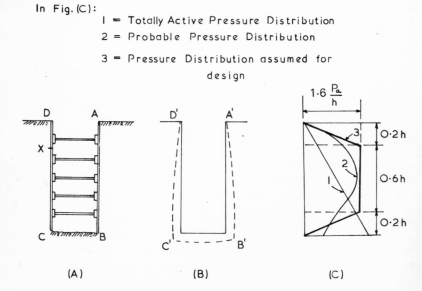

    (A)   (B)   (C)

Fig. 6.15 Pressure distribution on trench timbering

the resulting pressure on the back of the wall is roughly parabolic and is indicated in Fig. 6.15C.

For design purposes a trapezoidal distribution is assumed, of the form recommended by Civil Engineering Code of Practice no. 2 (Fig. 6.15C). The area of this assumed pressure diagram is some 44 per cent greater than the area of the pressure diagram for the totally active case and is intended to allow for any inequality between the loadings carried by the various struts. The total thrust is assumed to act at the mid-height of the trench and to be of magnitude $1.44 \, P_a$.

TYPES OF EARTH RETAINING STRUCTURES

Gravity walls

These walls depend on their weight for stability, the overturning effect of the earth pressure being resisted by the rebalancing moment due to the wall's weight. Walls up to 2 m in height are invariably gravity walls.

They can be built of mass concrete, brick, precast concrete, stone etc. Simplicity of construction and maintenance are obvious advantages; their heights are limited by the allowable bearing pressure on the soil beneath them.

Flexible walls

This term includes both reinforced concrete and sheet piled walls.
Reinforced concrete walls
Cantilever walls. These have a vertical or inclined stem monolithic with a base slab (Fig. 6.16A). Cantilevered reinforced concrete walls are suitable for heights up to about 7½ m.

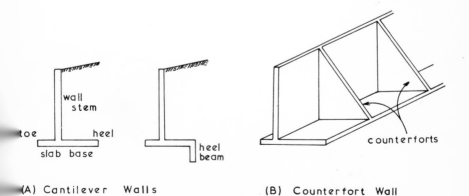

(A) Cantilever Walls   (B) Counterfort Wall

Fig. 6.16 Types of reinforced concrete retaining walls

Counterfort walls. A vertical or inclined stem is used in counterfort walls, supported by both the base slab and the counterforts with which it is monolithic (Fig. 6.16B).

Sheet piled walls

Cantilever walls. These are held in the ground by the passive resistance of the soil both in front of and behind them (Fig. 6.19A).

Anchored walls. An anchored wall is fixed at its base as a cantilever wall but supported by tie rods or struts near the top, sometimes using two rows of ties (Fig. 6.20).

COMMON CAUSES OF FAILURE IN EARTH RETAINING STRUCTURES

Failure in earth retaining structures may be due to various causes, of which the more common are as follows:

(1) By slip of the surrounding soil (Fig. 6.17A). This effect can occur in cohesive soils and can be analysed as for a slope stability problem.

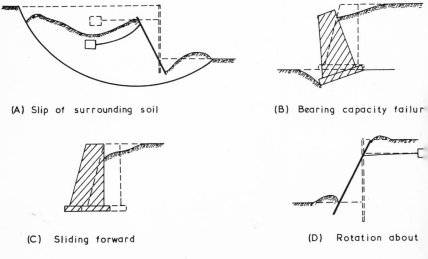

(A) Slip of surrounding soil   (B) Bearing capacity failur

(C)   Sliding forward   (D)   Rotation about

Fig. 6.17 Common causes of failure in earth retaining structures
Adapted from Code of Practice "Earth Retaining Structures"

(2) Bearing failure of the soil beneath the structure (Fig. 6.17B). The overturning moment from the earth's thrust causes high bearing pressures at the toe of the wall. These values must be kept within safe limits — usually not more than one-third of the supporting soil's ultimate bearing capacity.

(3) Overturning. For a wall to be stable the resultant thrust must be within the base. Most walls are so designed that the thrust is within the middle third of the base.

(4) By sliding forward (Fig. 6.17C). Caused by insufficient base friction or lack of passive resistance in front of the wall. The angle of friction between the wallbase and the soil may be taken as ϕ when the wall is cast in situ and as δ when the wall is precast or stone. For cohesive soils the cohesion between the base and the soil may be taken as equal to c_w.

It is doubtful whether the passive resistance of the soil in front of the wall should be taken into account. Often this soil is exposed to the elements and the effects of weathering and climatic changes can extend down to about a metre. The presence of roots and humus makes the soil so spongy that a considerable wall yield is required to create passive resistance.

(5) By rotation about a point near the top of the wall (Fig. 6.17D). This type of failure occurs mainly in sheet piled walls due to insufficient support in front of the wall. It can, however, occur in any type of wall which is held at the top, such as a bridge abutment.

(6) Structural failure caused by faulty design, poor workmanship, deterioration of materials, etc.

BEARING PRESSURES ON SOIL

The resultant of the forces due to the pressure of the soil retained and the weight of the wall subject the foundation to both direct and bending effects.

Let R be the resultant force on the wall, per unit length, and let R_v be its vertical component (Fig. 6.18A). Considering unit length of wall:

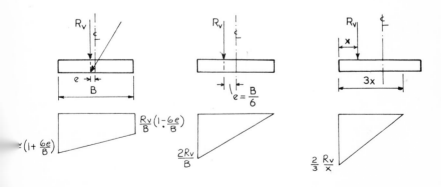

(A) Within middle third   (B) On middle third   (C) Outside middle third

Fig. 6.18 Bearing pressures due to a retaining wall foundation

Section modulus of foundation $= \dfrac{B^2}{6}$

Maximum pressure on base $=$ Direct pressure + pressure due to bending

$$= \dfrac{R_v}{B} + \dfrac{6R_v e}{B^2}$$

$$= \dfrac{R_v}{B}\left(1 + \dfrac{6e}{B}\right)$$

Minimum pressure on base $= \dfrac{R_v}{B}\left(1 - \dfrac{6e}{B}\right)$

The formulae only apply when R_v is within the middle third;

when R_v is on the middle third (Fig. 6.18B), then $e = \dfrac{B}{6}$

∴ Maximum pressure $= \dfrac{2R_v}{B}$, minimum pressure $= 0$

If the resultant R lies outside the middle third (Fig. 6.18C) the formulae become:

Maximum pressure $= \dfrac{2\,R_v}{3\,x}$; minimum pressure $= 0$

Sheet piled walls

Retaining walls of this type differ from other walls in that their weight is negligible compared with the remaining forces involved. Design methods usually neglect the effect of friction between the soil and the wall, but this omission is fairly satisfactory when determining active pressure values; it should be remembered, however, that the effect of wall friction can almost double the Rankine value of K_p. According to Terzaghi (1943), the value of K_p should be taken as twice the Rankine value for soils with a ϕ value equal to or greater than $25°$, whilst for soils with ϕ less than $25°$ the rapid fall-off in the effects of wall friction indicate that K_p should be taken as equal to the Rankine value.

Cantilever walls

Sheet piled walls are flexible and sufficient yield will occur in a cantilever wall to give totally active earth pressure conditions (Fig. 6.19A).

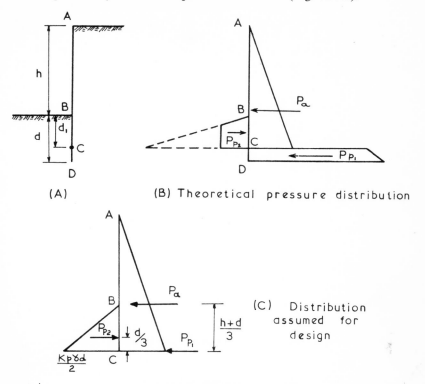

(A)   (B) Theoretical pressure distribution

(C) Distribution assumed for design

Fig. 6.19 Sheet-piled cantilever wall

Let the height of the wall be h, and suppose it is required to find the depth of penetration, d, that will make the wall stable. For equilibrium the active pressure on the back of the wall must be balanced by the passive pressure both in front of and behind the wall. If an arbitrary point C is chosen and it is assumed that the wall will rotate outwards about this point, the theoretical pressure distribution on the wall is as shown in Fig. 6.19B.

As has been discussed previously, it is very unlikely that the full passive resistance for the soil in front of the wall will be developed. Common practice is to divide the total theoretical value of thrust $K_p \gamma d^2/2$ by a factor of safety, usually taken as 2.0. The effective passive resistance in front of the wall is therefore assumed to have a magnitude of $K_p \gamma d^2/4$ and is of trapezoidal distribution, the centre of pressure of this trapezium lying between $d/2$ and $d/3$ above the base of the pile (for ease of calculation the value is generally taken as $d/3$). Calculations are considerably simplified if it is assumed that the passive resistance on the back of the wall, P_{p1}, acts as a concentrated load on the foot of the pile, leading to the pressure distribution shown in Fig. 6.19C from which d can be obtained by taking moments of thrusts about the base of the pile. The value of d obtained by this method is more nearly the value of d_1 in Fig. 6.19B, the customary practice being to increase the value of d by 20 per cent to allow for this effect.

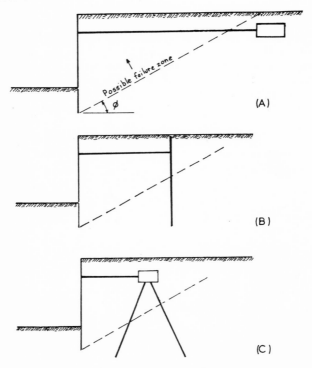

Fig. 6.20 Anchorage systems for sheet-piled walls

Anchored sheet piled wall

When the top of a sheet piled wall is anchored, a considerable reduction in the penetration depth can be obtained. Due to this anchorage the lateral yield in the upper part of the wall is similar to the yield in a timbered trench, whereas in the lower part the yield is similar to that of a retaining wall yielding by rotation. As a result the pressure distribution on the back of an anchored sheet pile is a combination of the totally active and the arching-active cases, the probable pressure distribution being indicated in Fig. 6.21B. In practice the pressure distribution is assumed to be totally active.

Anchorage can be obtained by the use of additional piling or by anchor blocks (large concrete blocks in which the tie is embedded). Any anchorage block must be outside the possible failure plane (Fig. 6.20A), and when space is limited piling becomes necessary (Fig. 6.20B); if bending is to be avoided in the anchorage pile, then a pair of raking piles can be used (Fig. 6.20C).

Penetration of piling for anchored walls

The penetration depth can be either the depth that is just sufficient to balance lateral forces without taking account of fixity (the free earth support method) or else the depth which gives full fixity at the base of the pile with an accompanying increase in penetration depth and a reduction in the bending moments on the pile (the fixed earth support method).

Free earth support method. The pressure distribution assumed in design is shown in Fig. 6.21A, the wall being considered free to rotate about its base

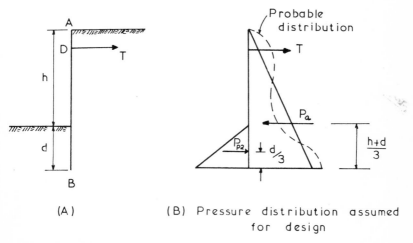

(A)   (B) Pressure distribution assumed for design

Fig. 6.21 Free earth support method for anchored sheet-piled walls

(the point B). By taking moments about the tie rod at D an expression for the penetration depth, d, can be obtained, the actual penetration depth being taken as equal to 1.2d).

Fixed earth support method. The pressure distribution assumed for design work is shown in Fig. 6.22, with a point of contraflexure, O, introduced by the assumption of fixity.

The wall can therefore be regarded as two walls, AO and OB, entirely

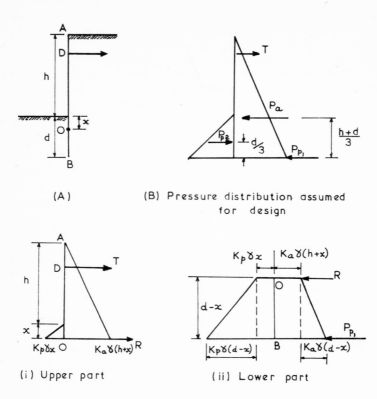

(A)

(B) Pressure distribution assumed
for design

(i) Upper part

(ii) Lower part

In (i) : Taking moments about D gives R

In (ii) : Taking moments about B eliminates P_{P_1} and gives d

(C) Equivalent Beam Analysis

Fig. 6.22 Fixed earth support method for anchored sheet-piled walls

separate from each other, this form of analysis being called the equivalent beam method.

Analysis by the elastic line method (Terzaghi, 1943) gives the following positions for O (depending upon the value of ϕ for the soil) where h is the height of the wall and x is the dimension shown in Fig. 6.22A.

ϕ	20°	25°	30°	35°
x	0.25h	0.15h	0.08h	0.035h

For most backfills the average value of ϕ is $30°$. Hence if x is assumed equal to 0.1h little error will generally be involved.

Graphical solutions for anchored sheet piled walls

In many problems the backfill is stratified and analytical solutions become tedious, but for most design work a graphical solution is within the possible range of accuracy and is much simpler.

Free earth support method. The procedure for this technique is as follows (Fig. 6.23):

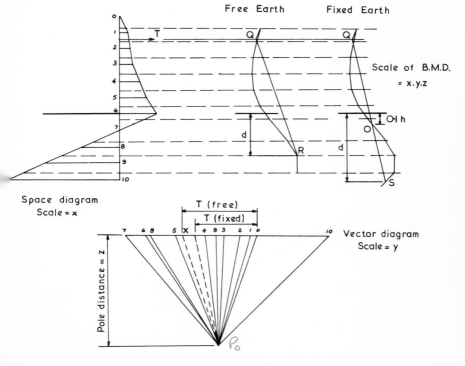

Fig. 6.23 Graphical method for anchored sheet-piled walls

(i) Draw the active and passive pressure diagrams acting on the wall for some assumed penetration depth.

(ii) Divide the length of the piling into a number of horizontal strips, 1, 2, 3, 4, etc., and calculate the total thrust on each strip.

(iii) Construct a vector diagram by plotting these thrust values along a base line.

(iv) Select a pole point, P_o, and draw rays P_o0, P_o1, P_o2, etc.

(v) Project horizontal lines through the centre of gravity of each strip (taken as the middle of the strip unless it is a triangle) and hence draw a funicular polygon of bending moment. Note that the line drawn parallel to ray P_o0 cuts the line of action of the tensile force T at the point Q.

(vi) From Q draw a base line tangential to the lower part of the funicular polygon to establish the point R.

(vii) Obtain the penetration depth d by projecting a horizontal line from R back to the wall (actual penetration depth = 1.2d).

Fixed earth support method. This procedure is similar to the free earth support method except that allowance must be made for the point of contraflexure O.

In Fig. 6.23 the base of the bending moment diagram (i.e. the line from Q) will cut the horizontal line from O to give the point of change-over from positive to negative bending. The distance x for the point O can be taken as 0.1h. Where the projection of the line QO cuts the bending moment diagram again, at the point S, the depth d can be determined (the actual penetration depth is again taken as 1.2d).

To find T, the tensile force per unit length of wall, merely draw a ray through the pole point, P_o, parallel to the base of the bending moment diagram to cut the vector line at X.

Distance OX = tensile force to the same scale as the vector diagram.

The value of T obtained (either graphically or analytically) is generally increased by 20 per cent.

The bending moment at any point in the pile can be read off directly from the bending moment diagram, which is to the scale of x.y.z. where:

$$x \ = \ \text{vertical scale of space diagram}$$
$$y \ = \ \text{scale of vector diagram}$$
$$z \ = \ \text{pole distance.}$$

Reinforced earth

The reinforced earth system is one of the most recent developments in soil mechanics and is a method of retaining soil where existing ground conditions do not allow construction by other, more conventional, methods. It can also be used where there is insufficient land space available to construct the battered side of a conventional embankment.

The system uses granular soil with little or no cohesive strength. This soil is split into elements by longitudinal reinforcing elements of high tensile strength interspersed throughout it. The granular elements between the reinforcement strips are linked to their adjacent granular elements by the frictional forces developed between the soil and the reinforcing material. At the free end of the structure a facing of standard sections called "skin elements" retains the soil.

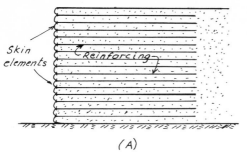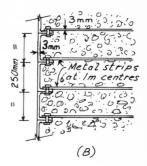

Fig. 6.24 Reinforced earth

A cross section through a typical reinforced earth structure is shown in Fig. 6.24A and is seen to be rectangular, generally with a width slightly wider than the height of earth supported. Strips and skin elements are generally of galvanised steel: a typical detail is shown in Fig. 6.24B.

The technique was developed by H. Vidal (1966) and has been used exclusively in France and North America. It was first used in the United Kingdom by Tarmac Construction in Edinburgh where a retaining wall, curved in plan, 100 m long with a maximum height of 6 m, was constructed in 1973. In this case the skin elements were of precast concrete panels.

PRESSURES ON TUNNELS AND CULVERTS

Arching in soil

This effect has already been discussed in connection with the arching active pressure distribution in trench timbering. If part of a support to a soil mass yields outwards, then the soil in contact with the yielding portion will also tend to move outwards from its neighbouring soil. This movement will create slip surfaces within the soil and there will be a development of shear forces along these surfaces trying to prevent further movement. The friction forces, in preventing movement, will reduce the pressure on the yielding part of the support, this pressure relief being transmitted as a pressure increase to the adjacent stationary parts of the foundation.

Transfer of pressure from the yielding part of a soil to the immobile parts is known as arching, and only occurs if the friction forces can be maintained (vibration in a granular soil will destroy it). Terzaghi analysed this problem in 1943.

Figure 6.25 represents a long strip of width 2B supporting a soil and a surcharge q. The thickness of the strip is dz and it is assumed that the strip is yielding vertically downwards. The soil immediately above AB tends to follow the yield, which causes movements in the soil. These soil movements

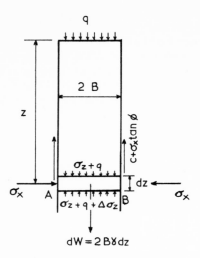

Fig. 6.25 Arching in soil

are resisted by friction forces on the sliding surfaces and the vertical pressure on AB is reduced by an amount equal to the vertical component of the shearing forces developed.

If the assumption is made that the sliding surfaces are vertical:

Normal stress on plane of sliding $= \sigma_x = K\sigma_z$, where $K = \sigma_x/\sigma_z$.

Shear forces on $dz = c + \sigma_x \tan \phi = c + K\sigma_z \tan \phi$.

Summating vertical forces per unit length of strip:

$$2\gamma Bdz + 2B(\sigma_z + q) - 2B(\sigma_z + q + \Delta\sigma_z) - 2cdz - 2K\sigma_z \tan \phi = 0$$

$$\therefore \ \gamma Bdz - B\Delta\sigma_z - cdz - K\sigma_z \tan \phi = 0$$

Hence
$$\frac{d\sigma_z}{dz} = \gamma - \frac{c}{B} - K\sigma_z \frac{\tan \phi}{B}$$

and
$$\sigma_z = q \text{ when } z = 0$$

It can therefore be shown that:

$$\sigma_z = \frac{B\left(\gamma - \dfrac{c}{B}\right)}{K \tan \phi} \left(1 - e^{-K\frac{z}{B} \tan \phi}\right) + qe^{-K\frac{z}{B} \tan \phi}$$

Terzaghi showed that K has a value of about 1.0 immediately above centre line of the strip and that this value increases with elevation to a maximum value of something like 1.5 at a height of approximately 2B above the yielding strip. For routine calculations K is generally taken as 1.0.

The vertical yield has virtually no effect on the state of stress in the soil at elevations of about 5B above the yielding strip. This phenomenon can be allowed for by assuming that the weight of soil above this elevation acts as a surcharge of intensity q on the yielding mass of soil of depth 5B below it.

The problem can therefore be divided into two sections (Fig. 6.26). Over

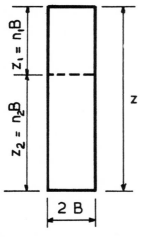

Fig. 6.26

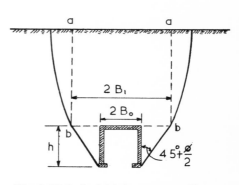

Fig. 6.27 Soil yield due to tunnelling

the depth $n_1 B$ no shear stresses are developed in the soil on the vertical sliding faces, and for values of n_2 less than or equal to 5.0 it may be taken that q is zero. The expression for σ_z can therefore be written:

$$\sigma_z = \frac{B\left(\gamma - \dfrac{c}{B}\right)}{K \tan \phi}\left(1 - e^{-K n_2 \tan \phi}\right) + q e^{-K n_1 \tan \phi}$$

with the proviso that q = O when $n_2 \leqslant 5$.

Tunnels and tunnel excavations

A tunnel excavation tends to lead to a soil yield similar to that shown in Fig. 6.27.

The vertical pressure on the top of the tunnel can be worked out by assuming that the yielding strip is bounded by the two vertical faces ab.

$$B_1 \doteq B_0 + h \tan \left(45° + \frac{\phi}{2}\right)$$

and the expression for σ_z becomes:

$$\sigma_z = \frac{B_1 \left(\gamma - \dfrac{c}{B_1}\right)}{K \tan \phi} \left(1 - e^{-K \frac{z}{B_1} \tan \phi}\right) + qe^{-K \frac{z}{B} \tan \phi}$$

Thus σ_z on section bb (and hence on the tunnel roof) can be obtained, and the value of σ_z is seen to be zero when $B_1 \leqslant c/\gamma$.

The pressures on the side of the tunnel can be determined if it is realized that σ_z acts as a surcharge on surfaces cb, enabling the pressures to be evaluated as for a retaining wall with a surcharge.

It should be pointed out that the expression was obtained by assuming that in the area of arching the normal stresses on a horizontal plane are equal, but the surfaces of equal normal pressure are in reality more nearly arched and the zero pressure surface is itself arch shaped to meet the vertical centre line of the tunnel at some height above the roof. Between this zero pressure surface and the tunnel roof the soil is in tension and could fall out into the tunnel, so unlined tunnels should always have arched roofs.

Application of the arching theory to actual tunnels

The foregoing theory is based on the assumption that both the roof of the tunnel and its walls are capable of yielding (Fig. 6.28A). With such a tunnel

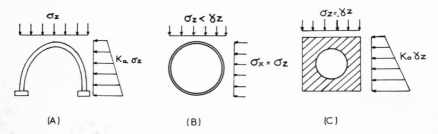

Fig. 6.28 Pressure distribution on tunnels

the steel ribs are capable of inward deflections and the foundations on which they sit can settle under load, so that K will lie between K_a and 1.0.

Figure 6.28B illustrates a tunnel lined with a flexible steel tube, the roof of which is therefore capable of vertical yield that will be accompanied by lateral bulging; under these conditions K should be taken as 1.0, but with stress relaxation (see below) it is possible for both the horizontal and vertical stresses to attain values approximately equal to γz; the use of $K = 1.0$ is therefore only advisable when the supports are temporary. The pressure increase due to stress relaxation in flexible tunnels occurs at a slow rate and a temporary structure may be defined as one in use for two or three years.

In the case of a semi-rigid tunnel (Fig. 6.28C) little yield is possible, with the result that σ_z may eventually almost equal γz and the lateral pressure on the sides of the tunnel could be $K_0 \gamma z$.

Stress relaxation

With most soils, even in undrained conditions, a set of applied stresses will produce a time dependent strain effect known as creep. If a certain strain value is applied to a soil and kept constant, then the stress induced by this strain often tends to decline with the passage of time. Yield will eventually cease in tunnels and it is therefore possible for the shear stress along the sliding planes to decrease. This will have the opposite effect of arching and will tend to increase both the vertical and the horizontal stresses on the tunnel.

EXAMPLES ON CHAPTER 6

Example 6.1

Using the Rankine theory, determine the total active thrust on a vertical retaining wall 10 m high if the soil retained has the following properties: $\phi = 35°; \gamma = 19 \text{ kN/m}^3$

What is the increase in horizontal thrust if the soil slopes up from the top of the wall at an angle of $35°$ to the horizontal?

Solution A: Soil surface horizontal

$$K_a = \frac{1 - \sin 35°}{1 + \sin 35°} = 0.27$$

Maximum p_a = $19 \times 10 \times 0.27 = 51.3 \text{ kN/m}^2$

Thrust = area of pressure diagram

$$= \frac{51.3 \times 10}{2} = 257 \text{ kN}$$

$$K_a = \frac{Cos\,\beta - \sqrt{Cos^2\beta - Cos^2\phi}}{Cos\,\beta + \sqrt{Cos^2\beta - Cos^2\phi}}$$

Solution B: Soil sloping at 35°

In this case $\beta = \phi$. When this happens the formula for K_a reduces to

$K_a = \cos \phi$

Hence $\qquad\qquad\qquad K_a = \cos 35° = 0.819$

$$\text{Thrust} = \gamma\,K_a\frac{h^2}{2} = 0.819 \times 19 \times \frac{10^2}{2} = 778 \text{ kN}$$

This thrust is assumed to be parallel to the slope, i.e. at 35° to the horizontal.

$\qquad\qquad$ Horizontal component = $778 \times \cos 35° = 635$ kN

Increase in horizontal thrust = 378 kN/m length of wall

Example 6.2

A smooth backed vertical wall is 6 m high and retains a soil with a bulk unit weight of 20 kN/m^3 and $\phi = 20°$. The top of the soil is level with the top of the wall and is horizontal. If the soil surface carries a uniformly distributed load of 50 kN/m^2, determine the total thrust on the wall/linear metre of wall, and its point of application.

Solution

Figure 6.29 shows the problem (A) and the resultant pressure diagram (B).

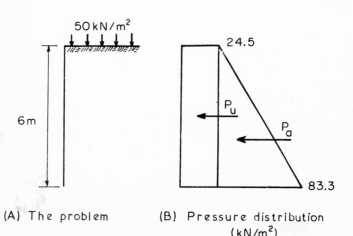

(A) The problem$\qquad$(B) Pressure distribution (kN/m^2)

Fig. 6.29 Example 6.2

$$K_a = \frac{1 - \sin 20°}{1 + \sin 20°} = 0.49$$

$$h_e = \frac{w_s}{\gamma} = \frac{50}{20} = 2.5 \text{ m} \quad \text{equivalent height of wall.}$$

$$p_u = K_a \, \gamma \, h_e = 0.49 \times 20 \times 2.5 = 24.5 \text{ kN/m}^2$$

At the base of the wall the equivalent height of the soil $\quad = \quad 6 + 2.5$
$$\hspace{9.5cm} = \quad 8.5 \text{ m}$$

Pressure at base $= 0.49 \times 20 \times 8.5 = 83.3 \text{ kN/m}^2$

The pressure diagram is now plotted (Fig. 6.29B)

$$\text{Total thrust} \quad = \quad \text{area of diagram}$$

$$= \quad P_u + P_a \qquad\qquad P_a = \delta h K$$

$$= 24.5 \times 6 + 58.8 \times \frac{6}{2} = 323.4 \text{ kN}$$

The point of application of this thrust is obtained by taking moments of forces about the base of the wall, i.e.:

$$323.4 \times h = 147 \times 3 + 176.4 \times \frac{6}{3}$$

$$\therefore h = \frac{793.8}{323.4} = 2.45 \text{ m}$$

Resultant thrust acts at 2.45 m above base of wall.

Example 6.3
  Details of the soil retained behind a wall are given in Fig. 6.30. Draw the diagram of the pressure distribution on the back of the wall.

p_a at top of wall $= p_{a7.5} = 0$

$p_{a4.5}$ Consider upper soil layer:

$$K_a = \frac{1 - \sin 30}{1 + \sin 30} = 0.333$$

$$p_{a4.5} = 0.33 \times 16 \times 3 = 16 \text{ kN/m}^2$$

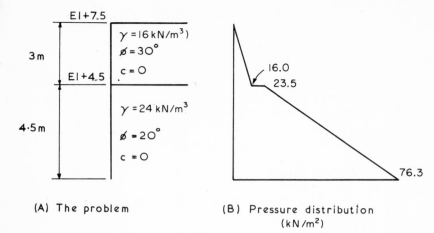

(A) The problem   (B) Pressure distribution (kN/m²)

Fig. 6.30 Example 6.3

Consider lower soil layer:

$$K_a = \frac{1 - \sin 20}{1 + \sin 20} = 0.49$$

$$h_e = \frac{w_s}{\gamma} = \frac{\text{Weight of upper soil}}{\text{unit weight of lower soil}} = \frac{16 \times 3}{24} = 2.0 \text{ m}$$

$$\therefore p_{u4.5} = 0.49 \times 24 \times 2 = 23.5 \text{ kN/m}^2$$

The pressure value at elevation +4.5 jumps from 16 to 23.5 kN/m²

For p_{ao}: $h_e = 2 + 4.5 = 6.5$ m   (at base)

$$p_{ao} = 0.49 \times 24 \times 6.5 = 76.3 \text{ kN/m}^2 \text{ (see Fig. 6.30B).}$$

Example 6.4

A vertical wall 9 m high is retaining soil which is saturated and has a unit weight of 22.5 kN/m³. The angle of friction of the soil is 35° and the surface of the soil is horizontal and level with the top of the wall. Ground water level occurs 3 m down from the top of the wall.

Calculate the significant pressure values and draw the diagram of pressure distribution on the back of the wall.

Solution

Figure 6.31A illustrates the problem and Figs. 6.31B and 6.31C show the pressure distribution due to the soil and the water.

$$K_a = \frac{1 - \sin 35}{1 + \sin 35} = 0.27$$

Although there is the same soil throughout there is a change in density at elevation +6 m. The problem can therefore be regarded as two layers of different soil, the upper having a unit weight of 22.5 kN/m^3 and the lower $(22.5-10) = 12.5$ kN/m^3.

Consider the upper soil:

$$p_{a_6} = K_a \, \gamma \, h = 0.27 \times 22.5 \times 3 = 18.2 \text{ kN/m}^3$$

Consider the lower soil:

$$h_e = \frac{w_s}{\gamma} = \frac{22.5 \times 3}{12.5} = 5.4 \text{ m}$$

$$p_{u_6} = K_a \, \gamma \, h_e = 0.27 \times 12.5 \times 5.4 = 18.2 \text{ kN/m}^3$$

(Note that at the junction of two soil layers the pressure values are the same if the ϕ values are equal.)

For p_{a_0}: $h_e = 5.4 + 6 = 11.6$ m

$$p_{a_0} = 0.27 \times 12.5 \times 11.6 = 39.2 \text{ kN/m}^2$$

Water pressures

At El. +6, the water pressure $= 0$
At El. 0, the water pressure $= 9.81 \times 6 = 58.9$ kN/m^3

The two pressure diagrams are shown in Figs. 6.31B and C; the resultant pressure diagram is the addition of these two drawings.

The same result would not have been obtained if the soil had been regarded as saturated throughout, since in this case the reduction factor K_a would have been applied to the water pressure and given a lower answer.

A situation in which there is a water table immediately behind a retaining wall should not arise. Where such a possibility is likely to occur either a drain should be placed behind the wall to lower the water level, or else (in the case of an outside wall) weep holes must be inserted so that the

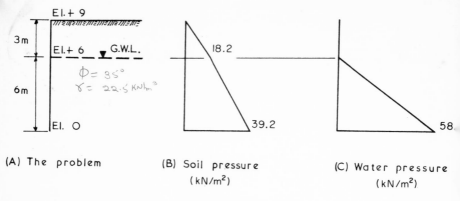

(A) The problem

(B) Soil pressure
(kN/m²)

(C) Water pressure
(kN/m²)

Fig. 6.31 Example 6.4

water seeps through the wall instead of building up a pressure behind it.

A further point that arises from this problem is that most earth pressure calculations are carried out in terms of total stress, the strength parameters of the soil being taken as the undrained ones, c and ϕ. If water forces are to be taken into account the calculations must be in terms of effective stress, as in the example when the submerged unit weight of the soil was used for the soil weight below the water table. In this particular case the water table could only have been established after a period of seepage and for these types of problems the strength parameters that should be used are the drained values c' and ϕ'.

Standing water behind a retaining wall is usually prevented by placing a filter drain down the back of the wall, but it is still possible for seepage to take place through the soil (from the top into the drain) when there is heavy rain and the top of the soil is a form of catchment area. If this condition is to be analysed the Coulomb wedge theory is used.

The failure plane will now be acted on by an additional force, P_w, (due to water pressure) that acts upwards at right angles to the plane. First a flow net is drawn (Fig. 6.32A), in which for simplicity the flow lines are usually taken as being at right angles to the drain (this is not always so but the error involved is of little account). For a particular trial plane of failure the pore pressures along it can be evaluated and plotted as a curve, the area bounded by the curve and the plane representing the force P_w. The triangle of forces for the Culmann line construction now becomes a polygon of forces as illustrated in Fig. 6.32B, and apart from allowing for this extra force the construction is as previously described, the Culmann line being drawn and the value of the maximum active thrust determined.

In theory the polygon of forces for a cohesive-frictional soil will be like that shown in Fig. 6.32C, but with such soils there is little chance of

obtaining saturated continuous flow conditions due to the permeability
of the soil and the length of time of the rainfall.

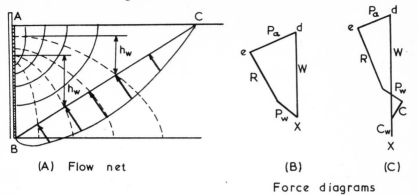

(A) Flow net   (B)   (C)

Force diagrams

Fig. 6.32 Seepage forces behind a retaining wall during heavy rain

Example 6.5

The proposed retaining wall shown in Fig. 6.33 is to be constructed in
masonry of weight 24 kN/m^3. The unit weight of the soil will be 17.6
kN/m^3, $\phi = 33°$ and $c = 0$. The safe bearing capacity of the soil is 215
kN/m^2 and the coefficient of base friction = 0.65.

Check the stability of the proposed arrangement.

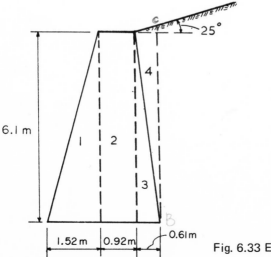

Fig. 6.33 Example 6.5

Solution

The first step is to determine the active thrust on the back of the wall by Rankine's method:

$$K_a = \cos \beta \; \frac{\cos \beta - \sqrt{\cos^2 \beta - \cos^2 \phi}}{\cos \beta + \sqrt{\cos^2 \beta - \cos^2 \phi}}$$

$$= 0.401$$

Let BC = vertical surface from heel of wall to top of soil:

$$\text{Thrust on} \quad BC = \frac{K_a \, \gamma \, BC^2}{2}$$

Now BC = 0.61 tan 25° + 6.1 = 6.39 m

$$\text{Thrust on} \quad BC = \frac{0.401 \times 17.6 \times 6.39^2}{2} = 144 \text{ kN}$$

The thrust acts parallel to the surface of the backfill, so that:

Horizontal component $= P_a \cos 25° = 0.9063 \times 144 = 131$ kN
Vertical component $\quad = P_a \sin 25° = 0.4226 \times 144 = 61$ kN

Part	Vertical force (kN)	Horizontal force (kN)	Lever arm from B (m)	Moment about B (mkN)
1	112.0	—	2.037	228
2	134.5	—	1.07	144
3	44.7	—	0.407	18.2
4	33.3	—	0.204	6.8
P_{av}	60.8	—	0	0
P_{ah}		131	2.13	279

$$\Sigma V = R_v = 385.3 \text{ kN}, \quad \Sigma H = 131 \text{ kN}, \quad \Sigma M = \underline{676}$$

If R_v acts at x from B then:

$$R_v x = 676$$

$$\therefore \; x = \frac{676}{385.3} = 1.76 \text{ m}$$

Eccentricity of R_v from centre of foundation = $1.76 - 1.53 = 0.23$ m so R is well within the middle third.

Maximum pressure on soil $= \dfrac{R_v}{B}\left(1 + \dfrac{6e}{B}\right)$

$$= \dfrac{385.3}{3.05}\left(1 + \dfrac{6 \times 0.23}{3.05}\right)$$

$$= 183 \text{ kN/m}^2 \qquad\qquad\qquad \text{(acceptable)}$$

Factor of safety against sliding

$$= \dfrac{\mu R_v}{P_{ah}} = \dfrac{0.65 \times 385.3}{131} = 1.9$$

This figure should not be less than 2.0, so the base of the wall should be widened slightly.

Example 6.6

A vertical sheet piled wall is shown in Fig. 6.34A. The properties of the soil both behind and in front of the wall are: $\gamma = 21$ kN/m^3, $\phi = 30°$, c = 0.

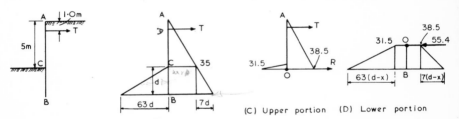

(A) The problem   (B) Free Earth Support   Fixed Earth Support

(C) Upper portion   (D) Lower portion

Fig. 6.34 Example 6.6

Determine the minimum penetration depth of the pile to achieve (i) free earth support conditions and (ii) fixed earth support conditions.
Solution: Free earth support
The conditions are shown in Fig. 6.34B. Active pressure at C = 0.33 × 21 × 5 = 35 kN/m^2.
At the base of the pile:

$$P_{p_1} = 3.0 \times 21 \times d = 63d$$
$$P_a = 0.333 \times 21 \times d + 35 = 35 + 7d$$

Taking moments about tie rod at D:

$$\left(63 - 7\right) \frac{d^2}{2} \left(4.0 + \frac{2d}{3}\right) = 35d \left(4.0 + \frac{d}{2}\right) + \frac{35 \times 5}{2} \left(\frac{2}{3} \times 5 - 1.0\right)$$

This reduces to:

$$d^3 + 5.06d^2 - 7.51d - 10.92 = 0$$

so that by substitution d = 1.90 m approximately.
Solution: Fixed earth support (Figs. 6.34C and D)
Assume x = 0.1h = 0.5 m.
Active pressure at 0 = 0.333 × 21 × 5.5 = 38.5 kN/m²
Passive pressure at 0 = 3 × 21 × 0.5 = 31.5 kN/m²
  Considering the upper portion of the wall (Fig. 6.34C) and taking moments about the tie rod at D:

$$\frac{38.5 \times 5.5}{2} \left(\frac{2}{3} \times 5.5 - 1.0\right) = \frac{31.5 \times 0.5}{2} \left(4.5 - \frac{1}{3} \times 0.5\right) + 4.5 \, R$$

Hence   R = 55.4 kN

Considering the lower portion (Fig. 6.34D), put k = (d − x).

Taking moments about B;

$$55.4 \, k + (38.5 - 31.5) \frac{k^2}{2} - (63 - 7) \frac{k^2}{2} \times \frac{k}{3} = 0$$

Hence $k^3 - 0.375k^2 - 5.94k = 0$

By substitution   k = (d − x) = 2.62 m

Hence   d = 3.12 m

Force in the tie: Free earth support

$$\begin{aligned} d \; &= \; 1.9 \text{ m} \\ p_{a_0} \; &= \; 0.333 \times 21 \times 6.9 = 48.3 \text{ kN/m}^2 \\ p_{p_{1_0}} \; &= \; 3.0 \times 21 \times 1.9 = 119.7 \text{ kN/m}^2 \end{aligned}$$

Summating forces horizontally:

$$T = 48.3 \times \frac{6.9}{2} - 119.7 \times \frac{1.9}{2} = 53.2 \text{ kN/m length of wall.}$$

Force in the tie: Fixed earth support
Considering upper portion of wall:

$$\text{Active thrust} = 38.5 \times \frac{5.5}{2} = 106 \text{ kN}$$

$$\text{Passive thrust} = 31.5 \times \frac{0.5}{2} = 78.8 \text{ kN}$$

$$\text{Reaction R} = 55.4 \text{ kN}$$

$$\therefore T = 106 - 7.88 - 55.4 = 42.7 \text{ kN/m length of wall.}$$

NOTE: In these calculations it may seem that the passive resistance has not been reduced by a factor of safety. Due to the high value of ϕ, K_p is approximately twice the Rankine value and as the calculations have used the Rankine value a factor of safety of two has been applied.

In Fig. 6.35 the graphical solution to the problem is given (in the fixed earth support x was again taken as 0.1h).

Free earth support: $d = 1.88$ m; $T = 53.6$ kN
Fixed earth support: $d = 3.15$ m; $T = 43.0$ kN

For design purposes the derived values would be increased by 20 per cent.

Example 6.7

Details of a retaining wall are given in Fig. 6.36A. Plot the pressure distribution on the back of the wall (i) without the surcharge and (ii) with the surcharge.

Solution: Without the surcharge
p_{a15} Consider the upper soil ($K_a = 0.333$)

$$p_{a15} = 0.333 \times 16 \times 3 = 16 \text{ kN/m}^2$$

Consider the lower soil:

$$h_e = \frac{48}{21} = 2.28 \text{ m}, \quad K_a = \frac{1 - \sin 10}{1 + \sin 10} = 0.704$$

$$p_{a15} = K_a \gamma h_e - 2c \tan\left(45° - \frac{\phi}{2}\right)$$

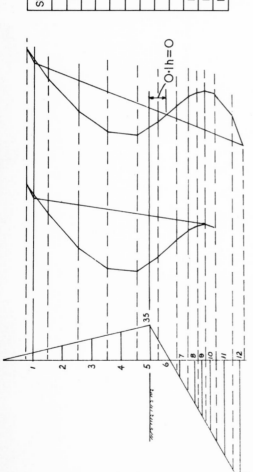

Slice	Thrust −kN	Total Thrust
1	3.5	3.5
2	10.5	14.0
3	17.5	31.5
4	24.5	56.0
5	31.5	87.5
6	10.9	98.4
7	−4.0	94.4
8	−16.5	77.9
9	−12.8	65.1
10	−15.8	49.3
11	−40.5	8.8
12	−52.5	−43.7

O'lh=O

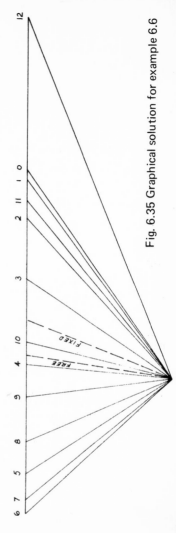

Free Earth
d=1.88m T=53.6kN

Fixed Earth
d=3.15m T=43.0kN

Fig. 6.35 Graphical solution for example 6.6

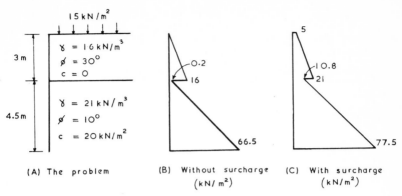

Fig. 6.36 Example 6.7

$$= 0.704 \times 21 \times 2.28 - 2 \times 20 \times \tan 40°$$

$$= 33.7 - 33.5 = 0.2 \text{ kN/m}^2$$

(If this value had been negative it would have been taken as zero.)

$$p_{a_0} = 0.704 \times 21 \times (2.28 + 4.5) - 33.5 = 66.5 \text{ kN/m}^2$$

Solution: With the surcharge

$p_{a_{25}}$ Consider the upper layer of soil:

$$h_e = \frac{15}{16} = 0.94 \text{ m}$$

$$p_{a_{25}} = 0.333 \times 16 \times 0.94 = 5 \text{ kN/m}^2$$

$p_{a_{15}}$ Consider the upper layer of soil:

$$p_{a_{15}} = 0.333 \times 16 \times 3.94 = 21.0 \text{ kN/m}^2$$

Consider the lower soil:

$$h_e = \frac{w_s}{\gamma} = \frac{15 + 48}{21} = 3.0 \text{ m}$$

$$p_{a_{15}} = 0.704 \times 21 \times 3 - 33.5 = 10.8 \text{ kN/m}^2$$

$$p_{a0} = 0.704 \times 21 \times (4.5 + 3) - 33.5 = 77.5 \text{ kN/m}^2$$

The pressure diagrams are given in Figs. 6.36B and 6.36C.

Example 6.8
Determine the maximum thrust on the wall shown in Fig. 6.37A.

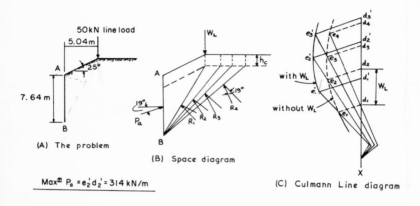

Fig. 6.37 Example 6.8

Properties of the soil are: $\gamma = 17.4 \text{ kN/m}^3$, $c = 9.55 \text{ kN/m}^2$, $\delta = \phi = 19°$.
Solution

$$h_c = \frac{2c}{\gamma} \tan\left(45° + \frac{\phi}{2}\right)$$

$$= \frac{2 \times 9.55}{17.4} \times \tan 54.5$$

$$= 1.52 \text{ m}$$

Wall adhesion $= (7.64 - 1.52)\,9.55 = 58.5 \text{ kN}$

Cohesion on failure planes:

$$
\begin{aligned}
1:&\ 9.93 \times 9.55 = 94.7 \text{ kN}\\
2:&\ 11.11 \times 9.55 = 106.0 \text{ kN}\\
3:&\ 12.20 \times 9.55 = 116.4 \text{ kN}\\
4:&\ 13.25 \times 9.55 = 126.5 \text{ kN}
\end{aligned}
$$

Weight of wedges:

$$1: \quad 22.6 \times 17.4 = 394 \text{ kN}$$
$$2: \quad 35.1 \times 17.4 = 610 \text{ kN}$$
$$3: \quad 43.8 \times 17.4 = 763 \text{ kN}$$
$$4: \quad 51.9 \times 17.4 = 903 \text{ kN}$$

Space and force diagrams are given in Figs. 6.37B and 6.37C.

$$\text{Maximum } P_a = e_2' d_2' = 314 \text{ kN/m}$$

Example 6.9

Calculate the vertical pressure on a long strip of width 1 m that yields vertically and is at a depth of 4 m in a soil with the following properties: $\gamma = 19 \text{ kN/m}^3$, $\phi = 30°$, $c = 0$ (Fig. 6.38).

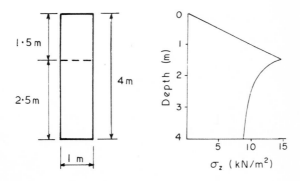

(A) The problem   (B) Vertical Stress
                           distribution

Fig. 6.38 Example 6.9

With $n_2 = 5$ then $n_2 B = 2.5$ m and the surcharge q will be equal to $1.5 \times 19 = 28.5 \text{ kN/m}^2$

Taking $K = 1.0$:

$$\sigma_z = \frac{B\gamma}{K \tan \phi} \left(1 - e^{-K n_2 \tan \phi} \right) + q \, e^{-K n_1 \tan \phi}$$

$$e^{-K n_2 \tan \phi} = e^{-0.5774 \times 5} = 0.0556$$

Tabulated values of e^{-x} are given in most books of mathematical tables.

$$\therefore \sigma_Z = \frac{0.5 \times 19 \times 0.944}{1 \times 0.577} + 28.5 \times 0.056$$

$$= 17.1 \text{ kN/m}^2$$

The vertical stress distribution throughout the soil is shown in Fig. 6.38B; the reader may like to work out these values.

EXERCISES ON CHAPTER 6

6.1 A 6 m high retaining wall with a smooth vertical back retains a mass of dry cohesionless soil that has a horizontal surface level with the top of the wall and carries a uniformly distributed load of 10 kN/m^2. The soil weighs 20 kN/m^3 and has an angle of internal friction of 36°. Determine the active thrust on the back of the wall per metre length of wall (i) without the uniform surcharge and (ii) with the surcharge.
Answer   (i) 93.6 kN   (ii) 109.2 kN

6.2 The back of a 10.7 m high wall slopes away from the soil it retains at an angle of 10° to the vertical. The surface of the soil slopes up from the top of the wall at a surcharge angle of 20°. The soil is cohesionless with a density of 17.6 kN/m^3 and a $\phi = 33°$.
If the angle of wall friction is 19° determine, by a graphical method, the maximum thrust on the wall.
Answer   478 kN/m

6.3 A 4 m high wall retains two horizontal layers of soil, both 2 m thick. The upper layer of soil has a unit weight of 18 kN/m^3 and $\phi = 30°$, c = 0; the lower layer of soil has a unit weight of 24 kN/m^3 and $\phi = 40°$, c = 0.
(i) Determine the pressure distribution on the back of the wall and hence find the maximum thrust on the wall.
(ii) Assuming that both soils are saturated, determine the total thrust on the wall if there is a standing water level (behind the wall) at an elevation of 1.5 m above the base.
Answer   (i) 38 kN/m   (ii) 43 kN/m

6.4 An anchored sheet piled wall is to retain soil to a height of 5.5 m
The soil, including that into which the piles will be driven, is cohesionless with an angle of internal friction of 30° and a bulk unit weight of 20.8 kN/m^3
The surface of the retained soil will be horizontal and level with the top of the wall. Tie rods, at 4.57 m centres, will be fixed to the wall at 1.83 m below the wall top.

Assuming 'free earth support' conditions, determine the minimum penetration depth and the force in a tie rod.

Answer   d = 1.98 m + 20 per cent   T = 327 kN + 20 per cent

6.5 A soil has the following properties: $\gamma = 16$ kN/m^3, $\phi = 30°$, c = 5 kN/m^2. The soil is retained behind a 6 m high vertical wall and has a horizontal surface level with the top of the wall.

(i) Draw the diagram of pressure distribution on the back of the wall and determine the total active thrust on the wall.

(ii) Determine the pressure distribution and total thrust if the surface of the soil carries a uniform load of 30 kN/m^2.

Answer   (i) 64.5 kN/m   (ii) 121.7 kN/m

6.6 Details of the soil to be retained behind a proposed anchored sheet piled wall are given in Fig. 6.39. Determine the penetration depth and tie force

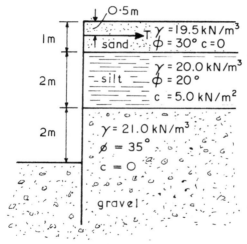

Fig. 6.39 Exercise 6

per metre length of wall for fixed earth support conditions.

Answer   d = 3.5 m + 20 per cent   T = 28 kN + 20 per cent

REFERENCES

Bell, A. L.
Lateral pressure and resistance of clay and the supporting power of clay foundations. *Minutes Proc. Instn civ. Engrs* (1915).

Bishop, A. W.
Test requirements for measuring the coefficient of earth pressure at rest. Brussels Earth Conference (1958).

Coulomb, C. A.
Essais sur une application des règles des maxims et minimis à quelques problemes de statique relatifs à l'architecture. *Mem. Acad. Roy. Pres. Divers,* Sav. 5, 7, Paris (1776).

Culmann, K.
Die Graphische Statik, Section 8, 'Theorie der Stutz und Futtermauern' (Meyer & Zeller, Zurich, 1866).

Institution of Civil Engineers
Code of Practice no. 2, *Earth retaining structures* (1951).

Rankine, W. J. M.
On the stability of loose earth *Proc. R. Soc.* (1857).

Terzaghi, K.
Theoretical soil mechanics (John Wiley, 1943).

Vidal, H.
La terre armée. *Annls Inst. tech. Bâtim.* 223 and 224 (1966).

7. Elements of Stress Analysis

Any load placed on a soil mass will induce stresses within the soil. In a three dimensional system there are six stress components induced on an elemental cube, comprising the normal stresses on each plane of the cube together with their accompanying shear stresses. Once these normal and shear stresses are known they can be compounded to give the values and directions of the principal stresses acting at the point considered using the theory of elasticity (Timoshenko & Goodier, 1951).

The assumption that a soil mass acts as an elastic medium obviously introduces errors but work carried out by Zienkiewicz, Cheung & Stagg (1966) has produced numerical methods based on finite elements which lead to more realistic computations. An elementary introduction to this important field in stress analysis has been prepared by Smith (1971).

Some modern methods of settlement analysis, such as those proposed by Lambe (1964, 1967), necessitate determining the increments of both major and minor principal stresses, but Jürgenson (1934) has prepared stress tables based on the elastic theory that can be very helpful in this and other aspects of stress analysis. In most foundation problems, however, it is only necessary to be acquainted with the increase in vertical stresses (for settlement analysis) and the increase in shear stresses (for shear strength analysis).

Boussinesq (1885) evolved equations that can be used to determine the six stress components that act at a point in a semi-infinite elastic medium due to the action of a vertical point load applied on the horizontal surface of the medium.

His expression for vertical stress is:

$$\sigma_z = \frac{3P}{2\pi} \frac{z^3}{(r^2 + z^2)^{5/2}}$$

where P = concentrated load
$r = \sqrt{x^2 + y^2}$ (see Fig. 7.1)

The expression has been simplified to:

$$\sigma_z = K \frac{P}{z^2}$$

where K is an influence factor.

Values of K against values of $\frac{r}{z}$ are shown in Fig. 7.1.

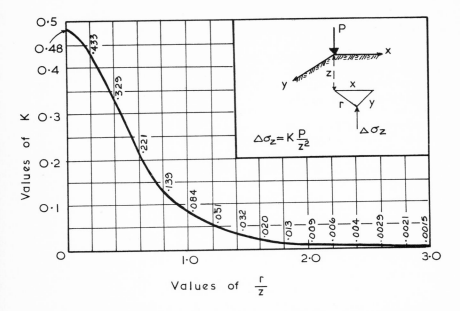

Fig. 7.1 Influence coefficients for vertical stress from a concentrated load (Boussinesq, 1885)

Example 7.1

A concentrated load of 400 kN acts on the surface of a soil. Determine the vertical stress increments at points directly beneath the load to a depth of 10 metres.

Solution

For points below the load r = 0 and at all depths $\frac{r}{z}$ = 0, whilst from Fig. 7.1 it is seen that K = 0.48.

z (metres)	z^2	$\dfrac{P}{z^2}$	$\Delta\sigma_z = \dfrac{KP}{z^2}$ (kN/m^2)
0.5	0.25	1600	758
1.0	1.0	400	192
2.5	6.25	64	30.7
5.0	25	16	7.7
7.5	56.2	7.1	3.4
10.0	100	4	1.9

This method is only applicable to a point load, which is a rare occurrence in soil mechanics, but the method can be extended by the principle of superposition to cover the case of a foundation exerting a uniform pressure on the soil. A plan of the foundation is prepared and this is then split into a convenient number of geometrical sections. The force due to the uniform pressure acting on a particular section is assumed to be concentrated at the centroid of the section, and the vertical stress increments at the point to be analysed due to all the sections are now obtained. The total vertical stress increment at the point is the summation of these increments.

Steinbrenner's method (1934)

If a foundation of length L and width B exerts a uniform pressure on the soil of p, then the vertical stress increment due to the foundation at a depth z below one of the corners is given by the expression:

$$\sigma_z = pI_\sigma$$

where I_σ is an influence factor depending upon the relative dimensions of L, B and z.

I_σ can be evaluated by the Boussinesq theory and values of this factor (which depend upon the two coefficients $m = B/z$ and $n = L/z$) were prepared by Fadum in 1941 (Fig. 7.2).

With the use of this influence factor the determination of the vertical stress increment at a point under a foundation is very much simplified, provided that the foundation can be split into a set of rectangles or squares with corners that meet over the point considered.

Example 7.2

A 4.5 m square foundation exerts a uniform pressure of 200 kN/m^2 on a soil. Determine (i) the vertical stress increments due to the foundation load to a depth of 10 m below its centre and (ii) the vertical stress increment at a point 3 m below the foundation and 4 m from its centre along one of the axes of symmetry.

Solution

(i) The square foundation can be divided into four squares whose corners meet at the centre 0 (Fig. 7.3A).

z (m)	$m = \dfrac{B}{z}$	$n = \dfrac{L}{z}$	I_σ	$4I_\sigma$	σ_z (kN/m²)
2.5	0.9	0.9	.163	.652	130
5.0	0.45	0.45	.074	.296	59
7.5	0.3	0.3	.04	.16	32
10.0	0.23	0.23	.025	.1	20

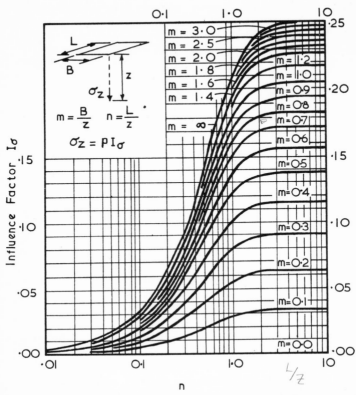

Fig. 7.2 Influence factors for the vertical stress beneath the corner of a rectangular foundation (Fadum, 1941)

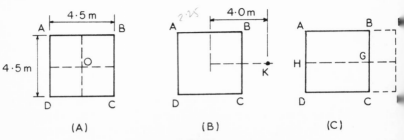

Fig. 7.3 Example 7.2

(ii) This example illustrates how the method can be used for points outside the foundation area (Fig. 7.3B). The foundation is assumed to extend to the point K (Fig. 3.7C) and is now split into two rectangles, AEKH and HKFD.

For both rectangles:

$$m = \frac{B}{z} = \frac{2.25}{3} = 0.75; n = \frac{L}{z} = \frac{6.25}{3} = 2.08$$

From Fig. 7.2: $I_\sigma = 0.176$, ∴ $\sigma_z = 0.176 \times 2 \times 200 = 70.4$ kN/m². The effect of rectangles BEGK and KGCF must now be subtracted.

For both rectangles:

$$m = \frac{2.25}{3} = 0.75; n = \frac{1.75}{3} = 0.58$$

From Fig. 7.2, $I_\sigma = 0.122$ (stricly speaking m is 0.58 and n is 0.75, but m and n are interchangeable in Fig. 7.2).

Hence $\sigma_z = 0.122 \times 2 \times 200 = 48.8$ kN/m²

Therefore the vertical stress increment due to foundation

$$= 70.4 - 48.8 = 21.6 \text{ kN/m}^2$$

Circular foundations can also be solved by Steinbrenner's method, and according to Jürgenson (1934) the stress effects from such a foundation may be found approximately by assuming that it is the same as for a square foundation of the same area.

Example 7.3 A

A circular foundation of diameter 100 m exerts a uniform pressure on the soil of 450 kN/m². Determine the vertical stress increments for depths up to 200 m below its centre.

Solution

$$\text{Area of foundation} = \frac{\pi \times 100^2}{4} = 7\,850 \text{ m}^2$$

Length of side of square foundation of same area = $\sqrt{7\,850} = 88.5$ m. This imaginary square can be divided into four squares as in example 7.2(i). Length of sides of squares = 44.25 m.

z (m)	$n = m = \dfrac{B}{z}$	I_σ	$4I_\sigma$	σ_z kN/m^2
10	4.43	0.248	0.992	446
25	1.77	0.221	0.884	398
50	0.89	0.16	0.64	288
100	0.44	0.071	0.284	128
150	0.3	0.04	0.16	72
200	0.22	0.024	0.096	43

Influence charts for vertical stress increments

It may not be possible to employ Fadum's method for irregularly shaped foundations and a numerical solution is then only possible by the use of Boussinesq's coefficients, K, and the principle of superposition.
An alternative method that removes the numerical work is to utilize the influence charts devised by Newmark in 1942 (Fig. 7.4).

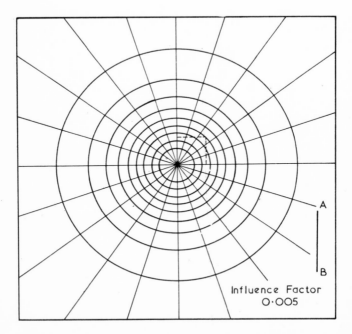

Influence Factor
0·005

Fig. 7.4 The Newmark chart for vertical stress under a foundation

It can be shown that at a point at a depth z, vertically below a uniformly loaded circular foundation and a horizontal distance r from its centre, the vertical stress is given by the expression:

$$\sigma_z = p\left(1 - \frac{1}{\left[1 + \left(\dfrac{r}{z}\right)^2\right]^{3/2}}\right)$$

where p = the contact pressure between the foundation and the soil. This expression may be rewritten as:

$$\frac{r}{z} = \sqrt{\left(1 - \frac{\sigma_z}{p}\right)^{-\frac{2}{3}} - 1}$$

If a series of values are assigned for the ratio σ_z/p (say 0, 0.1, 0.2 etc.) then a corresponding set of numbers for the ratio r/z can be obtained.

$\dfrac{\sigma_z}{p}$	$\dfrac{r}{z}$
0.0	0.00
0.1	0.27
0.2	0.40
0.3	0.52
0.4	0.64
0.5	0.77
0.6	0.92
0.7	1.11
0.8	1.39
0.9	1.91
1.0	∞

If a particular depth is chosen for z then a series of concentric circles can be drawn. In theory there will be ten circles, but one has an infinite radius, so that in practice only nine circles can therefore be drawn. If a set of equally spaced rays, say n in number, are now drawn emanating from the centre of the circles there will be 10n enclosed areas or influence units. Each area will contribute $\sigma_z/10n$ where σ_z is the total vertical stress. If, for example, n = 8 then each influence unit contributes $\sigma_z/80 = 0.0125\,\sigma_z$. The influence factor is 0.0125.

Construction of a Newmark chart
   Choose a convenient dimension for z (say z = 20 m); the radii of the circles are then 5.4, 8.0, 10.4, 12.8 m, etc. Establish a scale (say 1:100) and draw the circles. Select a suitable number of rays (20 is the usual figure) and construct them at equally spaced intervals. The resulting diagram is shown in Fig. 7.4; on it is drawn a vertical line, AB, representing z to the scale used (AB = 200 mm). With n = 20, the influence factor is 1/200 = 0.005.
   The diagram can be used for other values of z by simply assuming that the scale to which it is drawn alters: thus if z is to be 10 m the line AB now represents 10 m and the scale is therefore 1:50 (similarly if z = 40 m the scale becomes 1:200).
   1 in = 5 ft (similarly if z = 40 ft the scale becomes 1 in = 20 ft).

Operation of a Newmark chart
   The chart can be used for any uniformly loaded foundation of whatever shape. First a scale drawing is made of the foundation, generally on tracing paper, using a scale that corresponds with the length AB on the chart; the point at which the vertical stress is required is then placed over the centre of the circles and the number of influence units contained within the boundaries of the foundation, including fractions of units, are added together to give a total number of units N. σ_z is simply equal to $N \times p \times$ influence factor.

Example 7.4
   With the Newmark chart in Fig. 7.4, determine the vertical stress increment at a depth of 5 m in example 7.2.
Solution
As z is 5 m, the distance AB on the chart represents 5 m to the same scale as that to which the foundation must be drawn. Due to the symmetry only a quarter of the foundation need be considered (Fig. 7.4), the number of influence units enclosed by this quarter being 13.9.

$$\therefore \sigma_z = 4 \times 13.9 \times 200 \times 0.005 = 56 \text{ kN/m}^2$$

   This method is simple but can become very tedious; it is used for peculiarly shaped foundations and may well have an application for coal spoil heaps.

Bulbs of pressure
   If points of equal vertical pressure are plotted on a cross section through the foundation, a diagram of the form shown in Figs. 7.5A and 7.5B is obtained.

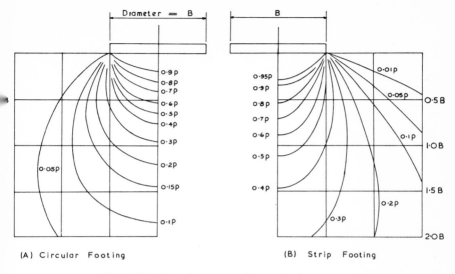

Fig. 7.5 Bulbs of pressure for vertical stress

These diagrams are known as bulbs of pressure and constitute another method of determining vertical stresses at points below a foundation that is of regular shape, the bulb of pressure for a square footing being obtainable approximately by assuming that it has the same effect on the soil as a circular footing of the same area.

In the case of a rectangular footing the bulb pressure will vary at cross sections taken along the length of the foundation, but the vertical stress at points below the centre of such a foundation can still be obtained from the charts in Fig. 7.5 by either (i) assuming that the foundation is a strip footing or (ii) determining σ_z values for both the strip footing case and the square footing case and combining them by proportioning the length of the two foundations.

From a bulb of pressure one has some idea of the depth of soil affected by a foundation. Significant stress values go down roughly to 2.0 times the width of the foundation, and Fig. 7.6 illustrates how the results from a plate loading test may give quite misleading results if the proposed foundation is much larger: the soft layer of soil in the diagram is unaffected by the plate loading test but would be considerably stressed by the foundation.

Boreholes in a site investigation should therefore be taken down to a depth at least 1.5 times the width of the proposed foundation or until rock is encountered, whichever is the lesser.

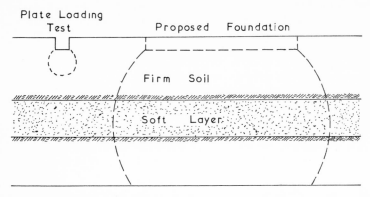

Fig. 7.6 Illustration of how a plate loading test may give misleading results

Small foundations will act together as one large foundation (Fig. 7.7) unless the foundations are at a greater distance apart (c/c) than five times their width, which is not usual. Boreholes for a building site investigation should therefore be taken down to a depth of approximately 1.5 times the width of the proposed building.

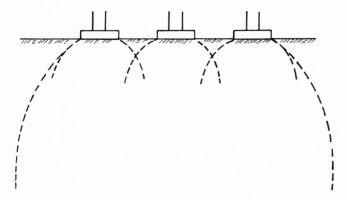

Fig. 7.7 Overlapping of pressure bulbs

SHEAR STRESSES

In normal foundation design procedure there is not much call for a knowledge of shear stresses, but Jürgenson obtained solutions for the case of a circular footing and for the case of a strip footing (Fig. 7.8A). It may be noted that, in the case of a strip footing, the maximum stress

induced in the soil is p/π, this value occurring at points lying on a
semi-circle of diameter equal to the foundation width B. Hence the
maximum shear stress under the centre of a continuous foundation
occurs at a depth of B/2 beneath the centre.

Shear stresses under a rectangular foundation

It is sometimes necessary to evaluate the shear stresses beneath a
foundation in order to determine a picture of the likely overstressing
in the soil.

Unfortunately a large number of foundations are neither circular nor
square but rectangular, but Figs. 7.8A and 7.8B can be used to give a rough
estimate of shear stress under the centre of a rectangular footing.

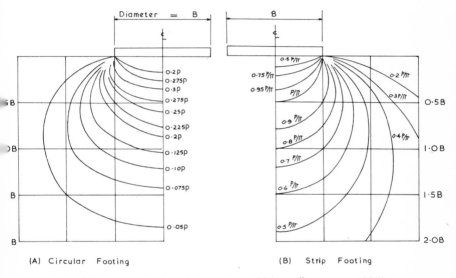

Fig. 7.8 Pressure bulbs of shear stress (After Jürgenson, 1934)

Example 7.5

A rectangular foundation has the dimensions 15 m × 5 m and exerts
a uniform pressure on the soil of 600 kN/m². Determine the shear
stress induced by the foundation beneath the centre at a depth of 5 m.
Solution
Strip footing

$$\frac{z}{B} = \frac{5}{5} = 1.0$$

From Fig. 7.8B:

$$\tau = \frac{0.81 \times 600}{\pi} = 155 \text{ kN/m}^2$$

Square footing

$$\text{area} = 5 \times 5 = 25 \text{ m}^2$$

Diameter of circle of same area =

$$\sqrt{\frac{25 \times 4}{\pi}} = 5.64 \text{ m}$$

Hence the shear stress under a 5 m square foundation can be obtained from the bulb of pressure of shear stress for a circular foundation of diameter 5.64 m.

$$\frac{z}{B} = \frac{5}{5.64} = 0.89$$

From Fig. 7.8A:

$$\tau = 0.2 \times 600 = 120 \text{ kN/m}^2$$

These values can be combined if we proportion them to the respective areas (or lengths)

$$\tau = 120 + (155 - 120) \frac{15}{15 + 5} = 146 \text{ kN/m}^2$$

The method is approximate but it does give an indication of the shear stress values.

CONTACT PRESSURE

Contact pressure is the actual pressure transmitted from the foundation to the soil. In all the foregoing discussions it has been assumed that this contact pressure value, p, is uniform over the whole base of the foundation, but a uniformly loaded foundation will not necessarily transmit a uniform contact pressure to the soil. This is only possible if the foundation is perfectly flexible. The contact pressure distribution of a rigid foundation depends upon the type of soil beneath it. Figures 7.9A and 7.9B show

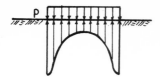
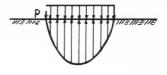

(A) Cohesive soil

(B) Cohesionless soil

Fig. 7.9 Contact pressure distribution under a rigid foundation loaded with a uniform pressure, p

the form of contact pressure distribution induced in a cohesive soil (A) and in a cohesionless soil (B) by a rigid, uniformly loaded, foundation.

On the assumption that the vertical settlement of the foundation is uniform, it is found from the elastic theory that the stress intensity at the edges of a foundation on cohesive soils is infinite. Obviously local yielding of the soil will occur until the resultant distribution approximates to Fig. 7.9A.

For a rigid surface footing sitting on sand the stress at the edges is zero as there is no overburden to give the sand shear strength, whilst the pressure distribution is roughly parabolic (Fig. 7.9B). The more the foundation is below the surface of the sand the more shear strength there is developed at the edges of the foundation, with the result that the pressure distribution tends to be more uniform.

In the case of cohesive soil, which is at failure when the whole of the soil is at its yield stress, the distribution of the contact pressure again tends to uniformity.

A reinforced concrete foundation is neither perfectly flexible nor perfectly rigid, the contact pressure distribution depending upon the degree of rigidity. This pressure distribution should be considered when designing for the moments and shears in the foundation, but in order to evaluate shear and vertical stresses below the foundation the assumption of a uniform load inducing a uniform pressure is sufficiently accurate.

Contact pressures of a coal spoil heap

A coal soil heap, even if compacted, is flexible as far as the supporting soil is concerned. Most existing heaps are of non-uniform section and the stresses induced in the soil below the tip can be approximately determined by superposition in which the tip is divided into a set of equivalent layers. Each layer is assumed to act in turn on the surface of the soil and the total induced stresses are obtained by addition (Fig. 7.10). The method can be extended to include earth embankments.

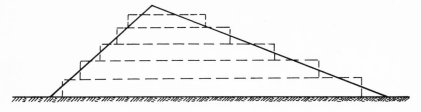

Fig. 7.10 Method for determining subsoil stresses beneath a coal spoil heap (the effect of slope is of course three-dimensional)

EXERCISES ON CHAPTER 7·

7.1 A raft foundation subjects its supporting soil to a uniform pressure of 268 kN/m². The dimensions of the raft are 6.1 m by 15.25 m. Determine the vertical stress increments due to the raft at a depth of 4.58 m below it (i) At the centre of the raft and (ii) At the central points of the short edges.
   Answer   (i) 177 kN/m²   (ii) 91.2 kN/m²

7.2 A concentrated load of 85 kN acts on the horizontal surface of a soil. Plot the variation of vertical stress increments due to the load on horizontal planes at depths of 1 m, 2 m and 3 m directly beneath it.
   Answer   Fig. 7.11

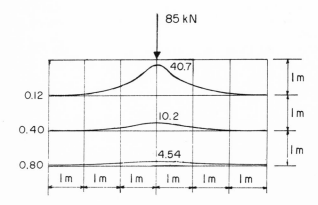

Vertical stress increments (kN/m²)

Fig. 7.11 Exercise 2

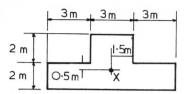
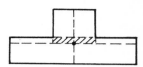

(A) The problem   (B) Selection of rectangles

Fig. 7.12 Exercise 7.3

7.3 The plan of a foundation is given in Fig. 7.12A. The uniform pressure on the soil is 40 kN/m². Determine the vertical stress increment due to the foundation at a depth of 5 m below the point X, using Fig. 7.2.

NOTE In order to obtain a set of rectangles whose corners meet at a point, a section of the foundation area is sometimes included twice and a correction made. For this particular problem the foundation area must be divided into six rectangles (Fig. 7.12B); the effect of the shaded portion will be included twice and must therefore be subtracted once.

Answer   11.2 kN/m²

7.4 Solve exercise 7.3 using the Newmark chart in Fig. 7.4.

7.5 With the use of figs. 7.8A and 7.8B, determine an approximate value for the shear stress at a depth of 1.52 m below the centre of a rectangular foundation (B = 1.52 m, L = 6.1 m) uniformly loaded with a pressure of 161 kN/m².

Answer   45 kN/m²

REFERENCES

Boussinesq, J.
Application des potentials à l'étude de l'équilibre et de mouvement des solids élastiques. (Gauthier–Villars, Paris, 1885.)

Fadum, R. E.
Influence values for vertical stresses in a semi-infinite solid due to surface loads. School of Engineering, Harvard University (1941).

Jürgenson, L.
The application of theories of elasticity and plasticity to foundation problems. *Proc. Boston Soc. Civ. Engrs.* (1934).

Lambe, T. W.
Methods of estimating settlement. *Proc. Am. Soc. Civ. Engrs.* (1964).
Stress path method. *Proc. Am. Soc. Civ. Engrs.* (1967).

Newmark, N. M.
Influence charts for computation of stresses in elastic foundations. *Bull. Ill. Univ. Engng Exp. Stn* no. 338 (1942).

Smith, G. N.
An introduction to matrix and finite element methods in civil engineering. (App. Science Pub. Ltd, London, 1971.)

Steinbrenner, W.
Tafeln zur Setzungsberechnung *Strasse* (1934).

Timoshenko, S. P., & Goodier, J. N.
Theory of elasticity (2nd edn, 1951).

Zienkiewicz, O. C., Cheung, Y. K., & Stagg, K. G.
Stresses in anisotropic media with particular reference to problems of rock mechanics. *J. strain Anal.* (1966).

8. Bearing Capacity of Soils

BEARING CAPACITY TERMS

The following terms are used in bearing capacity problems.
Ultimate bearing capacity
The value of the average contact pressure between the foundation and the soil which will produce shear failure in the soil.
Maximum safe bearing capacity
The maximum value of contact pressure to which the soil can be subjected without risk of shear failure. This is based solely on the strength of the soil and is simply the ultimate bearing capacity divided by a suitable factor of safety.
Allowable bearing pressure
The maximum allowable nett loading intensity on the soil allowing for both shear and settlement effects.

DETERMINATION OF ULTIMATE BEARING CAPACITY FROM LABORATORY TESTS

If the strength parameters of a soil are know, then the ultimate bearing capacity of a foundation can be obtained by using one of the following methods.
Earth pressure theory
Consider an element of soil under a foundation (Fig. 8.1). The vertical

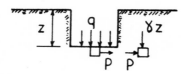

Fig. 8.1 Earth pressure conditions immediately below a foundation

downward pressure of the footing, q, is a major principal stress causing a corresponding Rankine active pressure, p. For particles beyond the edge of the foundation this lateral stress can be considered as a major principal stress (i.e. passive resistance) with its corresponding vertical minor principal stress γz (the weight of the soil).

235

$$\text{Now} \quad p = q \ \frac{1 - \sin \phi}{1 + \sin \phi}$$

$$\text{Also} \quad p = \gamma z \ \frac{1 + \sin \phi}{1 - \sin \phi}$$

$$\therefore q = \gamma z \left(\frac{1 + \sin \phi}{1 - \sin \phi} \right)^2$$

This is the formula for the ultimate bearing capacity, q. It will be seen that it is not satisfactory for shallow footings because when z = 0 then according to the formula q also = 0.

Bell's development of the Rankine solution for $c - \phi$ soils gives the following equation:

$$q = \gamma z \left(\frac{1 + \sin \phi}{1 - \sin \phi} \right)^2 + 2c \sqrt{\left(\frac{1 + \sin \phi}{1 - \sin \phi} \right)^3} + 2c \sqrt{\frac{1 + \sin \phi}{1 - \sin \phi}}$$

For $\phi = 0°$, q = γz + 4c
or   q = 4c for a surface footing.

Slip circle methods

With slip circle methods the foundation is assumed to fail by rotation about some slip surface, usually taken as the arc of a circle. Almost all foundation failures exhibit rotational effects and Fellenius (1927) showed that the centre of rotation is slightly above the base of the foundation and to one side of it. He found that in a cohesive soil the ultimate bearing capacity for a surface footing is

$$q = 5.52c$$

To illustrate the method we will consider a foundation failing by rotation about one edge and founded at a depth z below the surface of the soil (Fig. 8.2).

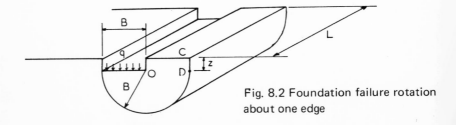

Fig. 8.2 Foundation failure rotation about one edge

Disturbing moment about 0:

$$q \times LB \times \frac{B}{2} = \frac{qLB^2}{2} \qquad \ldots (1)$$

Resisting moments about 0

Cohesion along cylindrical sliding surface $= c\pi LB$

$$\therefore \text{Moment} = \pi cLB^2 \qquad \ldots (2)$$

Cohesion along CD $= czL$

$$\therefore \text{Moment} = czLB \qquad \ldots (3)$$

Weight of soil above foundation level $= \gamma zLB$

$$\therefore \text{Moment} = \frac{\gamma zLB^2}{2} \qquad \ldots (4)$$

For limit equilibrium $(1) = (2) + (3) + (4)$

$$\text{i.e.} \ \frac{qLB^2}{2} = \pi cLB^2 + czLB + \frac{\gamma zLB^2}{2}$$

$$\therefore q = 2\pi c + \frac{2cz}{B} + \gamma z$$

$$= 2\pi c \left(1 + \frac{1}{\pi} \frac{z}{B} + \frac{1}{2\pi} \frac{\gamma z}{c} \right)$$

$$= 6.28c \left(1 + 0.32 \frac{z}{B} + 0.16 \frac{\gamma z}{c} \right)$$

Cohesion of end sectors. The above formula only applies to a strip footing, and if the foundation is of finite dimensions then the effect of the ends must be included.

To obtain this it is assumed that when the cohesion along the perimeter of the sector has reached its maximum value, c, the value of cohesion at some point on the sector at distance r from 0 is $c_r = cr/B$.

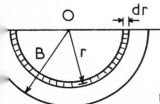

Rotational resistance of an elemental ring, dr, thick

$$= \frac{cr}{B} \times \pi r \, dr \ (\text{Fig. 8.3})$$

Fig. 8.3

Moment about $0 = \dfrac{cr}{B} \times \pi r\, dr \times r = \pi \dfrac{c}{B} r^3\, dr$

Total moment of both ends $= 2 \displaystyle\int_0^B \pi \dfrac{c}{B} r^3\, dr$

$$= 2\pi \dfrac{c}{B} \times \dfrac{B^4}{4} = \pi \dfrac{cB^3}{2} \qquad \ldots (5)$$

This analysis ignores the cohesion of the soil above the base of the foundation at the two ends, but unless the foundation is very deep this will have little effect on the value of q. The term (5) should be added into the original equation.

For a surface footing the formula for q is:

$$q = 6.28c$$

This value is high since the centre of rotation is actually above the base, but in practice a series of rotational centres are chosen and each circle is analysed (as for a slope stability problem)until the lowest value for q has been obtained. The method can be extended to allow for frictional effects but is considered most satisfactory when used for cohesive soils; it has been extended by Wilson (1941) who prepared a chart (Fig. 8.4) which gives the

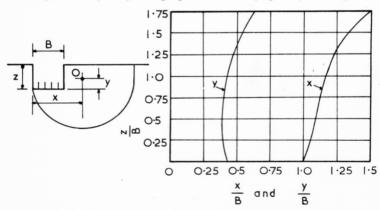

Fig. 8.4 Location of centre of critical circular for use with Fellenius's method (Wilson)

centre of the most critical circle for cohesive soils (his technique is not applicable to other categories of soil or to surface footings).

The slip circle method is useful when the soil properties beneath the foundation vary, since an approximate position of the critical circle can be obtained from Fig. 8.4 and then other circles near to it can be analysed. When the soil conditions are uniform Wilson's critical circle gives

$$q = 5.52c \text{ for a surface footing.}$$

Plastic failure theory (Prandtl's analysis)
Prandtl (1921) was interested in the plastic failure of metals and one of his solutions (for the penetration of a punch into metal) can be applied to the case of a foundation penetrating downwards into a soil with no attendant rotation. Under these conditions (Fig. 8.5) the triangular wedge of soil (I)

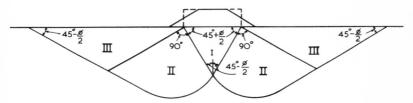

Fig. 8.5 Prandtl's analysis for ultimate bearing capacity

immediately below the footing is assumed to go down with the footing and to suffer no deformation, thereby creating an area of plastic flow (II) which is prevented from moving outwards by the passive resistance of wedge (III).

The analysis gives solutions for various values of ϕ, and for a surface footing with $\phi = 0$, Prandtl obtained

$$q = 5.14c$$

Terzaghi's formula
Working on similar lines to Prandtl's analysis, Terzaghi (1943) produced a formula for q which allows for the effects of cohesion and friction between the base of the footing and the soil and is also applicable to shallow ($z/B \leqslant 1$) and surface foundations. His solution for a strip footing is:

$$q = cN_c + \gamma zN_q + 0.5 \gamma BN_\gamma$$

The coefficients N_c, N_q and N_γ depend upon the soil's angle of internal friction and can be obtained from Fig. 8.6.

When $\phi = 0°$, $N_c = 5.7$; $N_q = 1.0$; $N_\gamma = 0$

$$\therefore q = 5.7c + \gamma z$$

or $\quad q = 5.7c$ for a surface footing.

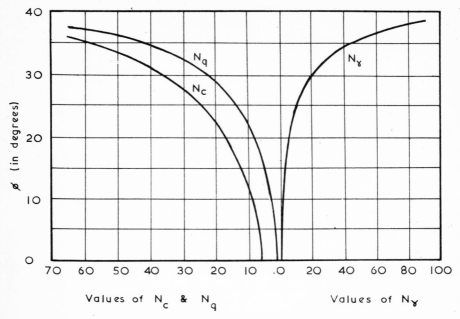

Fig. 8.6 Terzaghi's bearing capacity coefficients

Terzaghi's solution for a circular footing is:

$$q = 1.3cN_c + \gamma zN_q + 0.3\gamma BN_\gamma \text{ (where B = diameter)}$$

and for a square footing:

$$q = 1.3cN_c + \gamma zN_q + 0.4\gamma BN_\gamma$$

Skempton (1951) showed that for a cohesive soil ($\phi = 0°$) the value of the coefficient N_c increases with the value of z. His suggested values for N_c are given in Fig. 8.7.

Summary of bearing capacity formula

It will thus be seen that Rankine's theory does not give satisfactory results, and for variable subsoil conditions the slip surface analysis of Fellenius provides the best solution. For normal soil conditions Terzaghi's formulae are generally used and they may be applied to foundations at any depth in c/ϕ soils and to shallow footings in cohesive soils; they can be modified by using the suggested N_c value of Skempton for deep footings in cohesive soil.

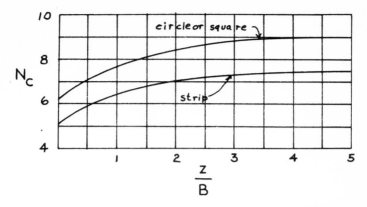

Fig. 8.7 Variation of the coefficient N_c with depth (Skempton)

IN SITU TESTING FOR ULTIMATE BEARING CAPACITY

The plate loading test
In this test an excavation is made to the expected foundation level of the proposed structure and a steel plate, usually from 300 to 750 mm square, is placed in position and loaded by means of a kentledge. During loading the settlement of the plate is measured and a curve similar to that illustrated in Fig. 8.8 is obtained.

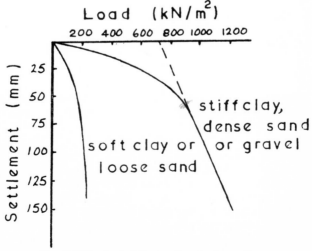

Fig. 8.8 Typical plate loading test results

On dense sands and gravels and stiff clays there is a pronounced departure from the straight line relationship that applies in the initial stages of loading and the value of q then is determined by extrapolating backwards (as shown in the figure). With a soft clay or a loose sand the plate experiences a more or less constant rate of settlement under load and no definite failure point can be established.

In spite of the fact that a plate loading test can only assess the upper few feet of a soil layer, the method can be extremely helpful in stoney soils where undisturbed sampling is not possible providing it is preceded by a boring programme, to prove that the soil does not exhibit significant variations.

The test can give erratic results in sands when there is a variation in density over the site and several tests should be carried out to determine a sensible average. This procedure is costly, particularly if the ground water level is near the foundation level and ground water lowering techniques consequently become necessary.

Estimation of allowable bearing pressure from the plate loading test. As would be expected, the settlement of a square footing kept at a constant pressure increases as the size of the footing increases.

Terzaghi & Peck (1948) investigated this effect and produced the relationship

$$S = S_1 \left(\frac{2B}{B + 0.3} \right)^2$$

where S_1 = settlement of a loaded area 0.305 m square under a given loading intensity p and

S = settlement of a square or rectangular footing of width B (in metres) under the same pressure p.

In order to use plate loading test results the designer must first decide upon an acceptable value for the maximum allowable settlement. Unless there are other conditions to be taken into account it is generally accepted that maximum allowable settlement = 25 mm.

The method for determining the allowable bearing pressure for a foundation of width B m is apparent from the formula. If S is put equal to 25 mm and the numerical value of B is inserted in the formula, S_1 will be obtained. From the plate loading test results we have the relationship between S_1 and p (Fig. 8.8), so the value of p corresponding to the calculated value of S_1 is the allowable bearing pressure of the foundation subject to any adjustment that may be necessary for certain ground water conditions. The adjustment procedure is the same as that employed to obtain the allowable bearing pressure from the standard penetration test.

Standard penetration test

This test is generally used to determine the bearing capacity of sands or gravels and is conducted with a split spoon sampler sometimes known as the Raymond spoon sampler after the piling firm that evolved the test (Fig. 8.9).

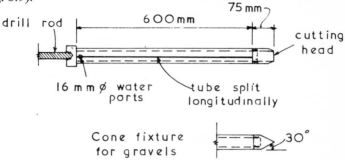

Fig. 8.9 The Raymond spoon sampler

The sampler is lowered down the borehole until it rests on the layer of cohesionless soil to be tested. It is then driven into the soil for a length of 450 mm by means of a 63.3 kg hammer free falling 760 mm for each blow. The number of blows required to drive the last 300 mm is recorded and this figure is designated as the N value of the soil (the first 150 mm of driving is ignored because of possible loose soil in the bottom of the borehole from the boring operations). After the tube has been removed from the borehole it can be opened and its contents examined.

In gravelly soils damage can occur to the cutting head and a solid cone, evolved by Palmer & Stuart (1957), is fitted in its place. The N value derived from such soils appears to be of the same order as that obtained when the cutting head is used in finer soils.

Terzaghi & Peck (1948) evolved a qualitative relationship between the relative density of the soil tested and the number of blows from the standard penetration test (N). Gibbs & Holtz (1957) put figures to this relationship which are given in the table below:

	Relative density	
N	Terzaghi & Peck	Gibbs & Holtz
0-4	very loose	0-15%
4-10	loose	15-35
10-30	medium	35-65
30-50	dense	65-85
over 50	very dense	85-100

Gibbs and Holtz's figures are plotted in Fig. 8.10B.

In order that the test can be carried out the overburden on the soil to be tested must be removed. Terzaghi & Peck make no reference to the effects that this can have, but Gibbs & Holtz examined the effects of most of the variables involved and concluded that the significant factors affecting the N value are the relative density of the soil and the value of the effective overburden pressure removed.

Coffman (1960) interpreted Gibbs & Holtz's results in a simpler form, his diagram of their figures being given in Fig. 8.10A.

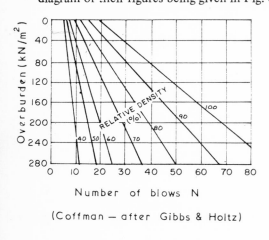

Number of blows N

(Coffman — after Gibbs & Holtz)

(A) Relation between effective over-burden pressure, N and R.D.

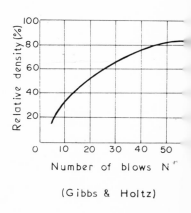

Number of blows N'

(Gibbs & Holtz)

(B) Relation between N and

Fig. 8.10 Estimation of N' from the test value N

The use of Figs. 8.10A and 8.10B is illustrated in example 8.1.

Terzaghi & Peck point out that in saturated (i.e. below the water table) fine and silty sands the N value can be altered by the low permeability of the soil. If the void ratio of the soil is higher than that corresponding to its critical density, the penetration resistance is less than in a larger grained soil of the same relative density. Conversely, if the void ratio is less than that corresponding to critical density the penetration resistance is increased. An empirical rule suggested by Terzaghi & Peck for such soils is:

$$N' = 15 + \tfrac{1}{2}(N - 15)$$

where N = actual number of blows obtained from the test

   N' = number of blows to be assumed for design purposes.

If, in example 8.1, the soil tested had been a fine sand:

$$N' = 15 + \tfrac{1}{2}(38 - 15) = 26$$

Estimation of allowable bearing pressure from the standard penetration test. Having obtained N', the determination of the allowable bearing pressure is generally based upon an empirical relationship evolved by Terzaghi & Peck (1948) that is based on the measured settlements of various foundations on sand (Fig. 8.11). The allowable bearing pressure for these curves

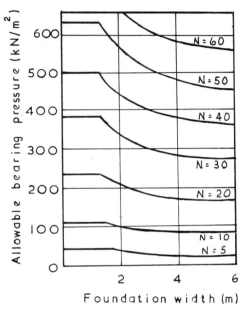

Fig. 8.11 Allowable bearing pressure from the standard penetration test (after Terzaghi & Peck)

(which are applicable to both square and rectangular foundations) was defined by Terzaghi & Peck as the pressure that will not cause a settlement greater than 25 mm.

When several foundations are involved the normal design procedure is to determine an average value for N from all the boreholes. The allowable bearing pressure for the widest foundation is then obtained with this figure and this bearing pressure is used for the design of all the foundations. The procedure generally leads to only small differential settlements, but even in extreme cases the differential settlement between any two foundations will not exceed 20 mm.

The curves of Fig. 8.11 apply to unsaturated soils, i.e. when the water table is at a depth of at least 1.0B below the foundation. When the soil is submerged the value of allowable bearing pressure obtained from the curves is halved, but although standard practice this procedure may be over cautious; Meyerhof (1956) suggests that the influence of the water table is already included in the observed penetration resistance and therefore need not be allowed for again.

If settlement is of no consequence it is possible to think in terms of ultimate bearing capacity and Peck, Hanson & Thorburn (1953) give an approximate relationship between N' and ϕ. From their curve (Fig. 8.12),

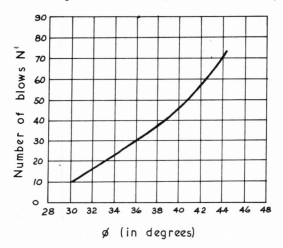

Fig. 8.12 Approximate relationship between N and φ (Peck, Hanson & Thorburn)

ϕ can be obtained and the Terzaghi coefficients N_γ and N_q evaluated, the ultimate bearing capacity being obtained from Terzaghi's formula. This procedure is not, however, generally adopted.

Correlation between the plate loading and the standard penetration tests
Meigh & Nixon (1961) compared the results of plate loading tests with those of standard penetration tests carried out at the same sites by determining from both sets of results the allowable bearing pressure (p, defined as the pressure causing 25 mm settlement of the foundation) for a 3.05 m square foundation. The differences were quite marked: for fine and silty sands the plate loading test led to values of p about 1.5 times the value obtained from the standard penetration test results, whilst for gravels the plate loading test gave values of p that were from 4 to 6 times greater.

It should be pointed out that Meigh and Nixon used the uncorrected N test values in their calculations, and when Sutherland (1963) examined Meigh & Nixon's results he showed that the disparity between the allowable bearing pressures calculated from the two tests became much less when the corrected N' value (in which overburden is allowed for) was used, thus confirming that Gibbs & Holtz's method of correcting for N is worthy of serious consideration.

The static cone penetration test

This penetrometer (often called the Dutch cone) is pushed, as opposed to being driven, into the soil from the surface without any boring. During the test it is possible to split the penetration resistance into its two components of end bearing and side friction.

Static cone penetration is widely used on the continent of Europe and is useful not only for soft clays but also for loose sandy soils where boring operations tend to disturb the in situ density values. In Britain the Dutch cone test has not proved so popular as the standard penetration test — probably unjustly. The correlation between the two tests is discussed in chapter 9.

The choice of a suitable safety factor

Except for values obtained from Terzaghi & Peck's curves (Fig. 8.11), a factor of safety must be applied to the value of q determined from any of the other methods discussed. Generally F is never less than 3 (except when the structure is relatively unimportant) and can sometimes be as much as 5. At first glance these values seem high, but the necessity for them is illustrated in example 8.2 which demonstrates the effect on q of a small variation in ϕ. The factor of safety should be applied to the nett ultimate bearing capacity, the nett load that the soil will be subjected to being the value above that of the original overburden load (which has to be removed so that the foundation can be constructed).

The original overburden pressure is γz, and this term should therefore be subtracted in Terzaghi's equations to give, for a strip footing:

$$q_{nett} = cN_c + \gamma z(N_q - 1) + 0.5\gamma BN_\gamma$$

The safe bearing capacity is therefore this expression divided by the factor of safety plus the term γz; in the case of a surface footing founded on cohesive soil the nett bearing capacity is of course cN_c.

The effect of ground water on bearing capacity

Water table below the foundation level

If the water table is at a depth of not less than B below the foundation, the expression for nett ultimate bearing capacity is the one given above, but when the water table rises to a depth of less than B below the foundation the expression becomes:

$$q_{nett} = cN_c + \gamma z(N_q - 1) + 0.5\gamma_{sub} BN_\gamma$$

where γ = unit weight of soil above ground water level

and γ_{sub} = submerged unit weight

For cohesive soils ϕ is small and the term $0.5\,\gamma_{sub}BN_\gamma$ is of little account, the value of the bearing capacity being virtually unaffected by ground water. With sands, however, the term cN_c is zero and the term $0.5\gamma_{sub}BN_\gamma$ is about one half of $0.5\gamma BN_\gamma$, so that ground water has a significant effect.
Water table above the foundation level
For this case Terzaghi's expressions are best written in the form:

$$q_{nett} = cN_c + p_0'(N_q - 1) + 0.5\gamma_{sub}BN_\gamma$$

where p_0' = effective overburden pressure removed.

From the expression it will be seen that, in these circumstances, the bearing capacity of a cohesive soil can be affected by ground water.

Overstressing due to high contact pressures

In the case of variable soil conditions the analysis for bearing capacity values should be carried out using the Fellenius method. This procedure can take time and designs based on one of the various bearing capacity formulae are consequently quite often used.

At first glance a safe way of determining the bearing capacity of a foundation might be to base it on the shear strength of the weakest soil below it, but such a procedure can be uneconomical, particularly if the weak soil is overlain by much stronger soil. A more suitable method is to calculate the safe bearing capacity using the shear strength of the stronger material and then to check the amount of overstressing that this will cause in the weaker layers. The method is shown in example 8.4, which illustrates a typical problem that may arise during the selection of a site for a new coal spoil heap.

For structural foundations the factor of safety against bearing capacity failure is generally not less than 3.0, but for coal spoil heaps this factor can be reduced to 2.0.

Safe bearing capacities

Below are set out a selection of safe bearing capacities, based on approximate values, given in Civil Engineering Code of Practice no. 4, *Foundations*. These are given in kN/m^2 for horizontal foundations at 0.6 m depth below the ground surface and have been based on the following assumptions:
(i) The site and adjoining sites are reasonably level.
(ii) The ground strata are reasonably level.
(iii) There is no softer layer below the foundation stratum.
(iv) The site is protected from deterioration.
Rocks

Igneous	10 000
Hard sandstone	4 000
Hard shale	2 000
Clay shale	1 000

Cohesionless soils (figures to be halved if soil submerged)

        Compact, well graded sand or gravel   400–600

        Compact uniform sand   200–400

Cohesive soils

Stiff boulder clays	400–600
Stiff clays	200–400
Firm clays	100–200
Soft clays	50–100

PILED FOUNDATIONS

The use of sheet piling, which can be of timber, concrete or steel, for earth retaining structures has been described in Chapter 6. Piled foundations form a separate category and are generally used:

   (i) to transmit a foundation load to a solid soil stratum

  (ii) to support a foundation by friction of the piles against the soil

 (iii) to resist a horizontal or uplift load

 (iv) to compact a loose layer of granular soil.

Classification of piles

There are two main classes of piles.

End bearing (Fig. 8.13A). Derive most of their carrying capacity from the penetration resistance of the soil at the toe of the pile. The pile behaves as an ordinary column and should be designed as such except that, even in weak soil, a pile will not fail by buckling and this effect need only be considered if part of the pile is to be in water.

Friction (Fig. 8.13B). Carrying capacity is derived mainly from the adhesion or friction of the soil in contact with the shaft of the pile.

Combination of the two (Fig. 8.13C). Really an extension of the end bearing pile when the bearing stratum is not hard, such as a firm clay. The pile is driven far enough into the lower material to develop adequate frictional resistance. A further variation of the end bearing pile is piles with enlarged bearing areas. This is achieved by forcing a bulb of concrete into the soft stratum immediately above the firm layer to give an enlarged base.

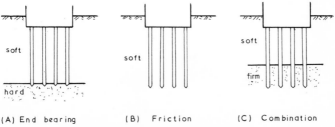

(A) End bearing   (B) Friction   (C) Combination

Fig. 8.13 Classification of piles

Driven piles

Timber. Used from earliest recorded times and still used for permanent work where timber is plentiful. In Britain, timber piles are used mainly in sea defences, piers and fenders. Timber piles can have a useful life of up to 25 years in reasonable conditions but can deteriorate quickly if used in ground in which water level varies. Pressure creosoting is the usual method of protection.

Precast concrete. Usually of square or octogonal section. Reinforcement is necessary within the pile to help withstand both handling and driving stresses. Prestressed concrete piles are also used and are becoming more popular than ordinary precast as less reinforcement is required.

Steel piles: tubular, box or H-section. Suitable for handling and driving in long lengths. They have a relatively small cross sectional area and penetration is easier than with other types. Risk from corrosion is not as great as one might think although tar coating or cathodic protection can be employed in permanent work.

Pile Driving

The essentials of a standard pile driving rig are shown in Fig. 8.14. The frames are of steel construction and vary in height from 10 to 25 m. Obviously, much more complicated, and larger, arrangements than that illustrated are available.

To guide the hammer, and the pile as it is driven into the ground, a pair of steel members, called leaders, extend the full height of the piling frame. The winch is generally driven by steam or diesel, although petrol and electric motors are available. The reader is referred to *The B.S.P. Pocket Book* (British Steel Piling Co. Ltd.) where he will find comprehensive information on both piling equipment and techniques.

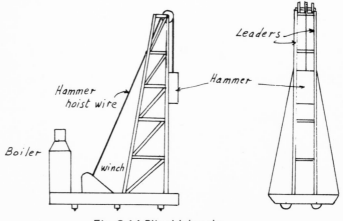

Fig. 8.14 Pile driving rig

In the case of a simple drop hammer, as illustrated in Fig. 8.14, a hammer, of a mass between 2000 to 10 000 kg, is raised by the winch and then released by some form of clutch arrangement and allowed to fall on to the pile. With this relatively simple equipment the rate of driving is very slow. A more satisfactory technique is to mount, directly above the pile, a single acting hammer consisting of a cylinder in which a heavy steel block, referred to as the ram or hammer, can slide up and down. Steam or compressed air is driven into the cylinder so that the ram is lifted some 1.5 m. When the hammer is in its raised position a valve may be opened and the hammer allowed to fall. Alternatively, the cylinder itself is made to lift up and fall down around a fixed ram. The order of blows is some 50 to 60 per minute.

An even more efficient system is that employing a double acting hammer in which the steam or air is used to both lift and then drive the ram downwards. The frequency of blows may be as high as 500 per minute.

Protection of top of pile during driving

In order that the top of the pile is not damaged during driving it is protected by packing material, generally layers of hard wood, over which is placed a steel cap or dolly. The determination of the correct form of packing and dolly for the driving conditions is a highly specialized task.

Measurement of set

Piles are either driven to a specified depth or to a specified set. The set of a pile is the amount of downward movement of the pile per blow and need only be measured during the final stages of driving.

To measure the set an arrangement similar to that shown in Fig. 8.15A can be used. A paper sheet is attached to the pile and a straight edge,

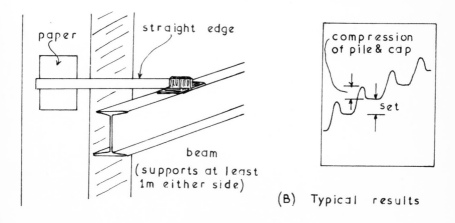

(A) Arrangement

Fig. 8.15 Measurement of set

supported by a beam, is arranged to lie over the paper. As driving proceeds a pencil is drawn along the straight edge and a graph, similar to that shown in Fig. 8.15B, is obtained.

The total downward movement of the pile following a blow consists of the set plus the temporary elastic compression of the pile and its protecting cap.

Jetting of piles

When driving piles in non-cohesive soils the penetration resistance can often be considerably reduced by jetting a stream of high pressured water into the soil just below the pile. There have been cases where piles have been installed by jetting alone. The method requires an adequate supply of water and considerable experience, particularly when near to existing foundations.

Vibration of piles

As an alternative to jetting, vibration techniques can be used to place piles in granular soils. Vibrators are not efficient in clays but can be used if piles are to be extracted.

Driven and cast-in-place piles

Two of the main types of this pile, used in Britain, are described below.

West's shell pile

Precast, reinforced concrete tubes, about 1 m long, are threaded onto a steel mandrel and driven into the gound after a concrete shoe has been placed at the front of the shells. Once the shells have been driven to specification the mandrel is withdrawn and reinforced concrete inserted in the core. Diameters vary from 325 to 600 mm. Details of the pile and the method of installation are shown in Fig. 8.16.

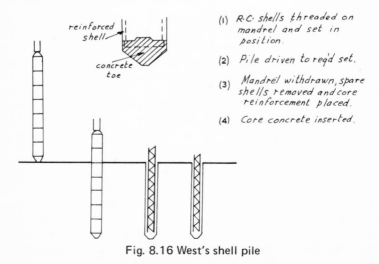

(1) R.C. shells threaded on mandrel and set in position.

(2) Pile driven to req'd set.

(3) Mandrel withdrawn, spare shells removed and core reinforcement placed.

(4) Core concrete inserted.

Fig. 8.16 West's shell pile

Franki pile

A steel tube is erected vertically over the place where the pile is to be driven, and about a metre depth of gravel is placed at the end of the tube. A drop hammer, 1500 to 4000 kg mass, compacts the aggregate into a solid plug which then penetrates the soil and takes the steel tube down with it. When the required set has been achieved the tube is raised slightly and the aggregate broken out. Dry concrete is now added and hammered until a bulb is formed. Reinforcement is placed in position and more dry concrete is hammered until the pile top comes up to ground level. The sequence of operations is illustrated in Fig. 8.17.

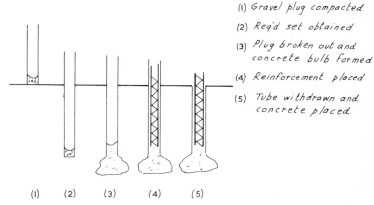

(1) *Gravel plug compacted*

(2) *Req'd set obtained*

(3) *Plug broken out and concrete bulb formed*

(4) *Reinforcement placed*

(5) *Tube withdrawn and concrete placed*

Fig. 8.17 Installation of a Franki pile

Advantages and disadvantages of the driven and cast-in-place pile

The pile can be adapted more readily than the conventional driven pile for a varying level of bearing stratum. The bulb end that is formed with some types can be of advantage in some conditions. The disadvantages are that vibration and ground displacement may damage green concrete in adjacent piles, and waisting or necking (extrusion of concrete from the pile into soft spots in the ground) may occur in swelling ground. Concrete shells may be displaced and, as the concrete is not placed under ideal conditions, it may be porous.

Bored and cast-in-place piles   *Angered cast-in-place pile*

The hole for the pile is made by a normal well-boring technique. The sides of the bore are supported by a casing or by boring mud (bentonite suspension). At the required depth the boring is stopped and the hole is filled with concrete. If required, a cage of reinforcement can be lowered before the concrete is placed. The proprietary 'Pressure Pile' compacts the concrete by compressed air as the casing is withdrawn. The method can lead to waisting, but this is not necessarily a disadvantage provided that the pile shaft itself is maintained full of concrete. The 'Prestcore Pile' is similar in principle but permanent precast units are used for lining.

The advantages are the elimination of vibration and the fact that such piles can be placed in limited headroom (only 2 m required). They are useful for underpinning and are readily adjustable in length. They have the disadvantage that they are expensive in bouldery ground and the concrete is liable to be porous, with the risk of waisting or washout from artesian water.

Composite piles

Piles may consist of two materials, timber and concrete or steel and concrete. Such piles are termed composite piles. The idea is to combine the cheapness of one material with the greater corrosion resistance of the other. Typical examples are a timber pile with the lower half, extending below the ground water level, in concrete, or a steel pile extending up to G.W.L. with a concrete section above it.

Large diameter bored piles

The driven or bored and cast-in-place piles discussed previously generally have maximum diameters in the order of 0.6 m and are capable of working loads round about 2 MN. With modern buildings column loads in the order of 20 MN are not uncommon. A column carrying such a load would need about ten conventional piles, placed in a group and capped by a concrete slab, probably some 25 m^2 in area.

A consequence of this problem has been the increasing use, over the past twenty years, of the large diameter bored pile. This pile has a minimum shaft diameter of 0.75 m and may be under-reamed to give a larger bearing area if necessary. Such a pile is capable of working loads in the order of 25 MN and, if taken down through the soft to the hard material, will minimise settlement problems so that only one such pile is required to support each column of the building. Large bored diameter piles have been installed in depth down to 60 m.

Determination of the bearing capacity of a pile by load tests

The load test is the only really reliable means of determining a pile's load capacity, but it is expensive, particularly if the ground is variable and a large number of piles must therefore be tested.

Full scale piles should be used and these should be driven in the same manner as those placed for the permanent work.

Fig. 8.18 gives rough indications of how a test pile may be loaded. A large mass of dead weight is placed on a platform supported by the pile. The load is applied in increments and the settlement is recorded when the rate of settlement has reduced to 0.25 mm in an hour, at which stage a further increment can be applied (Fig. 8.18A). The method has the disadvantage that the platform must be balanced on top of the pile and there is always the risk of collapse. An alternative, and better, technique is to jack the pile against a kentledge using an arrangement similar to Fig. 8.18B.

Sometimes the piles to be used permanently can be used to test a pile as shown in Fig. 8.18C.

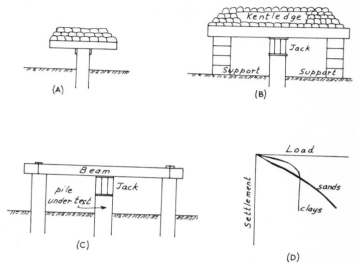

Fig. 8.18 Methods for testing a pile

The form of load to settlement relationship obtained from a loading test is shown in Fig. 8.18D. Loading is continued until failure occurs, except for large diameter bored piles which, having a working load of some 25 MN, would require massive kentledges if failure loads were to be achieved. General practice has become to test load these piles to the working load plus fifty per cent.

Definition of failure of a pile

The Civil Engineering Code of Practice No. 4 defines the ultimate load of a pile as being either the load at which the load/settlement curve approaches the vertical or, when there is no definite failure point, as the load at which the rate of settlement continues undiminished without further loading. This latter definition is not very satisfactory and it has become general practice to use Terzaghi's definition, which is that the ultimate load is that which causes a settlement of one tenth of the pile diameter or width.

The figure of one tenth was intended for normal sized piles and, if applied to large diameter bored piles, could lead to excessive settlements if a factor of safety of 2.5 were adopted. This, of course, only applies to large diameter piles resting on soft rocks. In the case of a large diameter bored pile resting on hard rock the ultimate load depends upon the ultimate stress in the concrete.

Determination of the bearing capacity of a pile by soil mechanics

A pile is supported in the soil by the resistance of the toe to further penetration plus the frictional or adhesive forces along its embedded length.

Ultimate bearing capacity = ultimate base resistance + ultimate skin friction:

$$\dot{Q}_u = Q_b + Q_s$$

Cohesionless soils

Q_b can be calculated from Terzaghi's equation for a square or circular foundation:

$$Q_b = p_0' (N_q - 1) + 0.3 \, \gamma_{sub} B N_\gamma$$

Usually the pile diameter or breadth is small compared with its length and the last term may be ignored.

Hence $Q_b = p_0' (N_q - 1) A_b$

where p_0' = effective stress at base level

              N_q = bearing capacity coefficient (see Fig. 8.6)

              A_b = area of base

Meyerhof (1953) suggested that the ultimate unit skin friction, f, may be evaluated from the expression:

$$f = K_s \, p_0' \tan \delta$$

where K_s = a constant depending upon the soil type (varies from 0.5 for loose to 1.0 for dense sands)

              δ = angle of wall friction

Hence $Q_s = K_{sp_0}' \tan \delta \, (A_s)$ *something wrong!*

where   d   = diameter of shaft

              A_s = surface area of embedded length of shaft

Hence $Q_u = A_b p_0' (N_q - 1) + K_s p_0' \tan \delta \, dA_s$

Values of ϕ can be obtained from standard penetration tests, and N_q obtained. The angle of wall friction, δ, depends upon the material of which the pile is made (a rough guide is 0.6ϕ for steel to 0.9ϕ for in situ placed concrete).

An alternative method is to use the results of the Dutch cone test (described in Chapter 9) when Q_b and Q_s can be obtained more or less directly. Typical results from a Dutch cone test are shown in Fig. 8.19 and are given in the form of a plot showing the variation of the cone penetration resistance with depth.

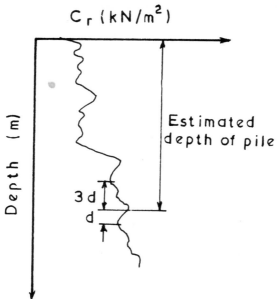

Fig. 8.19 Typical results from a Dutch cone test

For the ultimate base resistance C_r, the cone resistance, is taken as being the average value of C_r over the depth 4d as shown.

Then $\quad Q_b = C_r A_b$

The ultimate unit skin friction is taken as $\dfrac{\overline{C}_r}{200}$ where $\overline{C}_r$ is the average cone resistance over the embedded length of the pile.

Then $\quad Q_s = \dfrac{\overline{C}_r}{200} d\, A_s$

And, as before, $Q_u = Q_b + Q_s$

The factor of safety applied to Q_u is generally taken as 2.5.

NOTE. The above formulae are applicable to driven piles and to driven and cast-in-place piles. For bored and cast-in-place piles an estimation of the reduction of ϕ due to the loosening effects during boring must be made.

Cohesive soils

Q_b for piles in cohesive soils is based on Meyerhof's equation (1951)

$$Q_b = N_c \times c_b \times A_b$$

where N_c = bearing capacity factor, widely accepted as equal to 9.0

               c_b = undisturbed shear strength of the soil at base of pile

Q_s is given by the equation:

$$Q_s = \alpha \times \bar{c} \times A_s$$

where α = adhesion factor

               $\bar{c}$ = average undisturbed shear strength of soil adjoining pile

Hence $Q_u = c_b N_c A_b + \alpha \bar{c} A_s$

The adhesion factor α

Most of the bearing capacity of a pile in cohesive soil is derived from its shaft resistance, and the problem of determining the ultimate load resolves into determining a value for α. For soft clays α can be equal to or greater than 1.0 as, after driving, soft clays tend to increase in strength. In over-consolidated clays α has been found to vary from 0.3 to 0.6 – the usual value assumed for design purposes is 0.45.

Negative skin friction

If a soil subsides or consolidates around a group of piles these piles will tend to support the soil and there can be a considerable increase in the load on the piles.

The main causes for this state of affairs are:

(i) bearing piles have been driven into recently placed fill
(ii) fill has been placed around the piles after driving.

If negative friction effects are likely to occur then the piles must be designed to carry the additional load. In extreme cases the value of negative skin friction can equal the positive skin friction but, of course, this maximum value cannot act over the entire bedded length of the pile, being virtually zero at the top of the pile and reaching some maximum value at its base.

Action of pile groups

As indicated in the previous paragraph, piles are usually driven in groups (see Fig. 8.20).

In the case of end bearing piles the pressure bulbs of the individual piles will overlap (if spacing $<$ 5d ⁓ the usual condition). Provided that the bearing strata are firm throughout the affected depth of this combined bulb then the bearing capacity of the group will be equal to the summation of the individual strengths of the piles. However, if there is a compressible soil layer beneath the firm layer in which the piles are founded, care must be taken to ensure that this weaker layer is not overstressed.

Pile groups in cohesionless soils

Pile driving in sands and gravels compacts the soil between the piles. This compactive effect can make the bearing capacity of the pile group greater

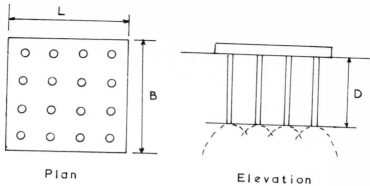

Plan   Elevation

Fig. 8.20 A typical pile group

than the sum of the individual pile strengths. Spacing of piles is usually from 2 to 3 times the diameter, or breadth, of the piles.

Pile groups in cohesive soils

A pile group placed in a cohesive soil has a collective strength which is considerably less than the summation of the individual pile strengths which compose it.

One characteristic of pile groups in cohesive soils is the phenomenon of 'block failure'. If the piles are placed very close together (a common temptation when dealing with a limited site area), the strength of the groups may be governed by its strength at block failure. This is when the soil fails along the perimeter of the group.

For block failure $Q_u = 2D(B + L) \times \bar{c} + 1.3\, c_b N_c BL$

where

D = depth of pile penetration

L = length of pile group

B = breadth of pile group

N_c = bearing capacity coefficient (taken generally as 9.0)

Whitaker (1957), in a series of model tests, showed that block failure will not occur if the piles are spaced at not less than 1.5d apart. General practice is to use 2 to 3d spacings.

In such cases $Q_u = E\, n\, Q_{up}$

where E = efficiency of pile group (0.7 for spacings 2 – 3d)

Q_{up} = ultimate bearing capacity of single pile

Settlement effects in pile groups

Quite often it is the allowable settlement, rather than the safe bearing capacity, that decides the working load that a pile group may carry.

For bearing piles the total foundation load is assumed to act at the base of the piles on a foundation of the same size as the plan of the pile group. With this assumption it becomes a simple matter to examine settlement effects.

With friction piles it is virtually impossible to determine the level at which the foundation load is effectively transferred to the soil. An approximate method, often used in design, is to assume that the effective transfer level is at a depth of $\frac{2}{3}D$ below the top of the piles. It is also assumed that there is a spread of the total load, one horizontal to four vertical. The settlement of this equivalent foundation (Fig. 8.21) can then be determined by the normal methods.

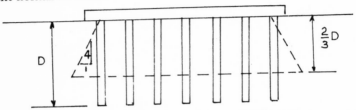

Fig. 8.21 Transference of load in friction piles

EXAMPLES ON CHAPTER 8

Example 8.1

A granular soil at a depth of 3 m was subjected to a standard penetration test. Ground water level occurred at a depth of 1.5 m below the surface of the soil, which was saturated with an average unit weight of 19.3 kN/m³. Determine a truer estimate for N if the test result was N = 15.

Solution

Effective overburden pressure = 3 × 19.3 − 1.5 × 9.81 = 43.2 kN/m²

From Fig. 8.10A: for an effective overburden of 432 kN/m² and N = 15, R.D. $\doteq$ 74 per cent

From Fig. 8.10B: an R.D. of 74 per cent corresponds to N = 38

Therefore the corrected value of N, N′, = 38

Example 8.2

A strip footing is 2 m wide and founded at a depth of 3 m in a soil of unit weight 19.3 kN/m³ and a cohesion of 10 kN/m².

Determine the variation in the value of the ultimate bearing capacity of the foundation for $\phi = 30°$ and $\Phi = 25°$.

Solution

If $\phi = 30°$ then, from Terzaghi's charts (Fig. 8.6):

$$N_c = 37, \; N_q = 22, \; N_\gamma = 20$$

For a strip footing:

$$q = cN_c + \gamma z N_q + 0.5\gamma BN_\gamma$$

$$= 10 \times 37 + 19.3 \times 3 \times 22 + 0.5 \times 19.3 \times 2 \times 20$$

$$= 2030 \text{ kN/m}^2$$

If $\phi = 25°$: $N_c = 25$, $N_q = 13$, $N_\gamma = 10$

$$q = 10 \times 25 + 19.3 \times 3 \times 13 + 0.5 \times 19.3 \times 2 \times 10$$

$$= 1200 \text{ kN/m}^2$$

The ultimate bearing capacity is reduced by some 40 per cent for a 16 per cent difference in the value of ϕ.

Example 8.3

Assuming a factor of safety of 3.0, determine the safe bearing capacities for the two values of ϕ in Example 8.2.

Solution

When $\phi = 30°$: safe bearing capacity $= \dfrac{2030 - 19.3 \times 3}{3} + 19.3 \times 3$

$$= 720 \text{ kN/m}^2$$

Similarly, when $\phi = 25°$, safe bearing capacity $= 440$ kN/m^2.

Example 8.4

The effective width of a proposed spoil heap will be about 61 m. The subsoil conditions on which the tip is to be built are shown in Fig. 8.22A. Determine a value for the maximum safe pressure that may be exerted by the tip onto the soil.

Solution

The average undrained cohesion of the stiff clay is about 165 kN/m^2. Using this value with Terzaghi's formula:

$$q_u = cN_c = 165 \times 5.7 = 940 \text{ kN/m}^2$$

Make safe bearing capacity $= 430$ kN/m^2 $F = \dfrac{940}{430} = 2.19$

Various vertical sections through the soil must now be selected (A, B, C, D and E in Fig. 8.22A). Using a contact pressure value·of 430 kN/m², the induced shear stresses are obtained from Fig. 7.8B and for each section the variation in soil strength with depth is plotted along with the corresponding values of shear stress increments (Fig. 8.22B). From these plots the areas of overstressing (shown hatched) are apparent and it is possible to plot this area on a cross-section (Fig. 8.22C).

A considerable portion of the silt is overstressed and if this were applied to the design of a raft foundation carrying a normal structure it would not be acceptable. With a coal spoil heap, however, the amount of settlement induced would hardly be detrimental. Also, as the load will be applied gradually there will be a chance for the silt to partially consolidate and obtain some increase in strength before the full load is applied.

Due to the thickness of boulder clay there is little chance of a heave of the ground surface around the tip. For interest the overstressed zone corresponding to a contact pressure of 320 kN/m² is also shown on Fig. 8.22C.

If the contact pressure had been determined by considering the strength of the silt (average $c = 67$ kN/m²):

$$q_u = 5.7 \times 67 \text{ kN/m}^2 = 382 \text{ kN/m}^2$$

Safe bearing capacity (F = 2) = 191 kN/m²

Example 8.5

A sample of clay failed in an unconfined compression machine at a stress of 200 kN/m². Determine a safe value for the bearing capacity of the clay.

Solution

Failure stress = 200 kN/m², therefore cohesion $\doteq 100$ kN/m² $q_u = c_u$
$\frac{}{2}$

Using Terzaghi's formula and adopting a safety factor of 3:

$$\text{Safe bearing capacity} = 5.7 \frac{c}{3}$$

$$= \frac{5.7 \times 100}{3}$$

$$= 190 \text{ kN/m}^2$$

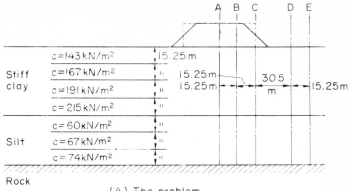

(A) The problem

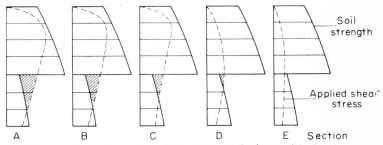

(B) Plot of strength and applied stress variations with depth

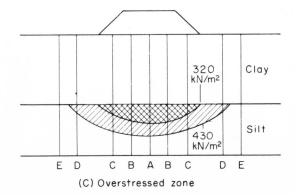

(C) Overstressed zone

Fig. 8.22 Example 8.4

Example 8.6

A soil layer has the following properties:

$$\phi = 0°, c = 12.5 \text{ kN/m}^2, \gamma = 20 \text{ kN/m}^3$$

A strip footing 2 m wide is to be founded at a depth of 5 m below the surface of the soil. Determine the ultimate bearing capacity of the soil.

Solution

The soil is purely cohesive and we therefore have a choice of either Terzaghi's or Skempton's solution.

$$\frac{z}{B} = \frac{5}{2} = 2.5;$$ this is greater than 1, so use the solution by Skempton.   *refer pg. 240.*

From Fig. 8.7, $N_c = 7.2$

$$q = cN_c + \gamma z = 12.5 \times 7.2 + 20 \times 5$$

$$= 1000 \text{ kN/m}^2$$

Example 8.7

A soil layer has the following properties:

$$\phi = 15°; c = 72 \text{ kN/m}^2; \gamma = 20 \text{ kN/m}^3$$

A footing, of dimensions 7.60×2.45 m, is to be founded at a depth of 1.52 m into this layer. Assuming a safety factor of 3, determine the safe bearing capacity value.

Solution

With a c-ϕ soil Terzaghi's formula is applicable.

For $\phi = 15°: N_c = 13, N_q = 5, N_\gamma = 2$

If the foundation were a strip footing the nett ultimate bearing capacity would be:

$$q = cN_c + \gamma z(N_q - 1) + 0.5\gamma BN\gamma$$

$$= 72 \times 13 + 20 \times 1.52 \times 4 + 0.5 \times 20 \times 2.45 \times 2$$

$$= 1155 \text{ kN/m}^2$$

Terzaghi & Peck (1948) state that the ultimate bearing capacity of a rectangular footing, with length L and width B, is given roughly by the expression:

$$q_{rect.} = q_{strip} \left[1 + 0.3 \frac{B}{L}\right]$$

Using this relationship the nett ultimate bearing capacity for the footing is:

$$1155 \times \left[1 + 0.3 \times \frac{2.45}{7.6}\right]$$

$$= 1265 \text{ kN/m}^2$$

Therefore safe bearing capacity $= \dfrac{1265}{3} + 1.52 \times 20$

$$= 452 \text{ kN/m}^2$$

Example 8.8

A purely cohesive soil has a unit weight of 23 kN/m³ and a cohesion of 150 kN/m². Determine the safe bearing capacity for a rectangular footing 10 m long and 2 m wide founded at a depth of 4 m into the clay.
Solution
The soil is purely cohesive. Skempton (1951) gives the following relationship for cohesive soils:

$$N_c \text{ (rectangle)} = \left[1 + 0.2 \frac{B}{L}\right] N_c \text{ (strip)}$$

N_c (strip) from Fig. 8.7 = 7.0 for $\dfrac{z}{B} = 2.0$

$$\therefore N_c \text{ (rectangle)} = \left(1 + 0.2 \times \frac{2}{10}\right) \times 7.0 = 7.3$$

$$q = cN_c = 150 \times 7.3 = 1095 \text{ kN/m}^2$$

Safe bearing capacity

$$\frac{1095}{3} + 23 \times 4$$

$$365 + 92 = 457 \text{ kN/m}^2$$

Example 8.9

A cylindrical precast concrete pile has a diameter of 250 mm and is to be driven through a 10 m thick layer of fine sand into a dense gravel layer. Ground water level occurs at a depth of 2 m below the top of the sand and a standard penetration test carried out at a depth of 5 m gave N = 15. The saturated density of the sand = 16 kN/m^3. A standard penetration test carried out at the surface of the gravel gave N = 40. If the pile is allowed to penetrate 1 m into the gravel, determine a value for the ultimate bearing capacity of the pile.

Solution

(A) Sand

Only frictional effects will occur.

$$N' = 15 + \tfrac{1}{2}(N - 15) = 15$$

Effective overburden at test level = $16 \times 5 - 9.81 \times 3 = 50.6$ kN/m^2

From Fig. 8.10   R.D. = 70% and N' = 34

From Fig. 8.12 $\phi = 37°$ *Too much.* ($0.5\phi - 0.75\phi$).

Assume $\delta/\phi = 0.8$ ∴ $\delta = 0.8 \times 37 = 30°$

Uncorrected N value indicates a medium sand, ∴ $K_s = 0.75$ approx.

$$Q_s = K_s p_0' \tan \delta \, A_s$$

$$= 0.75 \,(\, 10 \times 16 - 8 \times 9.81) \times 0.5774 \times \pi \times 0.25 \times 10$$

$$= 278 \text{ kN}$$

(B) Gravel

Effective overburden at surface = 81.5 kN/m^2 = $16 \times 5 - 9.81 \times 8$

From Fig. 8.10   R.D. = 100%   ∴ N' = 60

From Fig. 8.12 $\phi = 42°$ and, from Fig. 8.6, $N_q = 35$

$$Q_u = Q_b + Q_s$$

Assume that submerged unit weight of gravel = 10 kN/m^3

Then p_0' at base of pile = 81.5 + 10 = 91.5 kN/m^2

$$Q_b = 91.5 \,(35 - 1)\, \frac{\pi \times 0.25^2}{4} = 153 \text{ kN}$$

$$Q_s = 0.75 \times 91.5 \times \tan 42° \times \pi \times 0.25 \times 1$$

$$= 48.6 \text{ kN}$$

Ultimate bearing capacity of pile = 278 + 153 + 49 = 480 kN

EXERCISES ON CHAPTER 8

NOTE – Where applicable the answers quoted incorporate a factor of safety equal to 3.0.

8.1 A fine sand deposit is saturated throughout with a unit weight of 20 kN/m³. Ground water level is at a depth of 1 m below the surface. A standard penetration test, carried out at a depth of 2 m, gave an N value of 18. If the settlement is to be limited to not more than 25 mm, determine an allowable bearing pressure value for a 2 m square foundation founded at a depth of 2 m.
  Answer   180 kN/m² (N' ≑ 32)

8.2 A strip footing of width 1.83 m is to be founded in a saturated soil of unit weight 22.5 kN/m³ at a depth of 4.59 m. Ground water level occurs at a depth of 1.52 m below the surface of the soil, which is frictionless with a cohesive value of 143 kN/m²
  Determine a value for the safe bearing capacity of the foundation.
  Answer   445 kN/m²

8.3 A strip footing, 3 m wide, is to be founded at a depth of 2 m in a saturated soil of unit weight 19 kN/m³. The soil has an angle of internal friction of 28° and a cohesion of 5 kN/m². Ground water level is at a depth of 4 m.
  Determine a value for the safe bearing capacity of the foundation.
  Answer   380 kN/m²

8.4 A 2.44 m wide strip footing is to be founded in a coarse sand at a depth of 3.05 m. The unit weight of the sand is 19.3 kN/m³ and standard penetration tests at the 3.05 m depth gave an N value of 12.
  (i) Determine the safe bearing capacity of the foundation if settlement is of no account.
  (ii) Determine the allowable bearing pressure if settlement of the foundation is not to exceed 25 mm.
  Answers   (i) 1288 kN/m²
                (ii) 300 kN/m²

8.5 A single test pile, 300 mm diameter, is to be driven to a depth of 10 m in clay which has an undrained cohesive strength of 48.7 kN/m².
  Find the safe load that the pile can carry:

  (i) assuming a factor of safety of 2.5
  (ii) assuming factors of safety of 3.0 for the base and 1.5 for the shaft.

Answers (i) 150 kN   (ii) 148 kN

REFERENCES

Coffman, B. S.
    Estimating the relative density of sands. *Civ. Engng,* New York (1960).
Fellenius, W.
    Erdstatische Berechnungen (Ernst, Berlin, 1927).
Gibbs, H. J., & Holtz, W. G.
    Research on determining the density of sands by spoon penetration test. *Proc. 4th Int. Conf. Soil Mechanics and Foundation Engineering* (1957).
    ʾnstitution of Civil Engineers (London), Civil Engineering Code of Practice no. 4 (1954).
Meigh, A. C., & Nixon, I. K.
    Comparison of *in situ* tests for granular soils. *Proc. 5th Int. Conf. Soil Mechanics and Foundation Engineering* (1961).
Meyerhof, G.. G.
    The ultimate bearing capacity of foundations. *Géotechnique,* (1951).
    Recherche sur la force portante des pieux. *Annls Inst. tech. Bâtim.* **6,** (1953).
    Penetration tests and bearing capacity of cohesionless soils. *Proc. Am. Soc. civ. Engrs* (1956).
Palmer, D. J., & Stuart, J. G.
    Some observations on the standard penetration test and a correlation of the test with a new penetrometer. *Proc. 5th Int. Conf. Soil Mechanics and Foundation Engineering* (1957)
Peck, R. B., Hanson, W. E., & Thorburn, T. H.
    Foundation engineering (John Wiley, 1953).
Prandtl, L.
    Uber die Eindringungsfestigkeit (Harte) plastischer Baustoffe und die Festigkeit von Schneiden. *Z. angew. Math. Mech.* (1921)
Skempton, A. W.
    The bearing capacity of clays (Building Research Congress, 1951).
Sutherland, H. B.
    The use of *in situ* tests to estimate the allowable bearing pressures of cohesionless soils. *Struct. Engr* (1963)
Terzaghi, K.
    Theoretical soil mechanics (John Wiley, 1943).
Terzaghi, K. & Peck, R. B.
    Soil mechanics in engineering practice (John Wiley, 1948).
Whitaker, T.
    Experiments with model piles in groups. *Géotechnique* (1957).
Wilson, G.
    The calculation of the bearing capacity of footings on clay. *J. Instn civ. Engrs.* (1941).

9. Foundation Settlement, Soil Compression

Probably the most difficult of the problems that a Soils engineer is asked to solve is the accurate prediction of the settlement of a loaded foundation.

The problem is in two distinct parts: (i) the value of the total settlement that will occur, and (ii) the rate at which this value will be achieved.

When a soil is subjected to an increase in compressive stress due to a foundation load the resulting soil compression consists of elastic compression, primary compression and secondary compression.

Elastic compression. This compression is usually taken as occurring immediately after the application of the foundation load. Its vertical component causes a vertical movement of the foundation (immediate settlement) that in the case of a partially saturated soil is mainly due to the expulsion of gases and to the elastic bending and reorientation of the soil particles. With saturated soils immediate settlement effects are assumed to be the result of vertical soil compression before there is any change in volume.

Primary compression. The sudden application of a foundation load, besides causing elastic compression, creates a state of excess hydrostatic pressure in saturated soil. These excess pore water pressure values can only be dissipated by the gradual expulsion of water through the voids of the soil which results in a volume change that is time dependent. A soil experiencing such a volume change is said to be consolidating and the vertical component of the change is called the consolidation settlement.

Secondary compression. Volume changes that are more or less independent of the excess pore water pressure values cause secondary compression. The nature of these changes is not fully understood but it is apparently due to a form of plastic flow resulting in a displacement of the soil particles. Secondary compression effects can continue over long periods of time and, in the consolidation test, become apparent towards the end of the primary compression stage: due to the thinness of the sample, the excess pore water pressures are soon dissipated and it may appear that the main part of secondary compression occurs after primary compression is completed. This effect is absent in the case of an in situ clay layer because the large dimensions involved mean that a considerable time is required before the excess pore pressures drain away. During this time the effects of secondary

269

compression are also taking place so that, when primary compression is complete, little, if any, secondary effect is noticeable.

The terms 'primary' and 'secondary' are therefore seen to be rather arbitrary divisions of the single, continuous consolidation process. The time relationships of these two factors will be entirely different if they are obtained from two test samples of different thicknesses.

IMMEDIATE SETTLEMENT

Cohesive soils

If a saturated clay is loaded rapidly, the soil will be deformed during the load application and excess hydrostatic pore pressures are set up. This deformation occurs with virtually no volume change, and due to the low permeability of the clay little water is squeezed out of the voids. Vertical deformation due to the change in shape is the immediate settlement. -

This change in shape is illustrated in Fig. 9.1A, where an element of soil

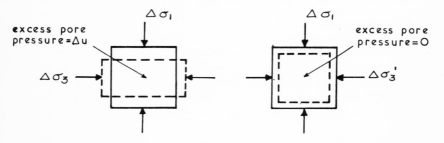

(A) Immediate settlement (B) Consolidation settlement

Fig. 9.1 Compressive deformations

is subjected to a vertical major principal stress increase $\Delta\sigma_1$, which induces an excess pore water pressure, Δu. The lateral expansion causes an increase in the minor principal stress, $\Delta\sigma_3$.

The formula for immediate settlement of a flexible foundation was provided by Terzaghi (1943) and is

$$\rho_i = \frac{pB(1 - \nu^2)Np}{E}$$

which gives the immediate settlement at the corners of a rectangular footing, length L and width B. In the case of a uniformly loaded, perfectly flexible square footing, the immediate settlement under its centre is twice that at its corners.

Various values for N_p are given in table 9.1.

Table 9.1

$\dfrac{L}{B}$	N_p
1.0	0.56
2.0	0.76
3.0	0.88
4.0	0.96
5.0	1.00

By the principle of superposition it is possible to determine the immediate settlement under any point of the base of a foundation (example 9.2).
A spoil heap or earth embankment can be taken as flexible and to determine the immediate settlement of deposits below such a construction the coefficients of table 9.1 should be used.

Foundations are generally more rigid than flexible and tend to impose a uniform settlement which is roughly the same value as the mean value of settlement under a flexible foundation. The mean value of settlement for a rectangular foundation on the surface of a semi-elastic medium is given by the expression:

$$\rho_i = \frac{pB\,(1 - \nu^2)\,Ip}{E}$$

where B = width of foundation
p = uniform contact pressure
E = Young's modulus of elasticity for the soil
ν = Poisson's ratio for the soil (= 0.5 in saturated soil)
I_p = an influence factor depending upon the dimensions of the foundation.
Skempton (1951) suggests the values for I_p given in table 9.2:

Table 9.2

$\dfrac{L}{B}$	I_p
circle	0.73
1	0.82
2	1.00
5	1.22
10	1.26

Immediate settlement of a thin clay layer

The coefficients of tables 9.1 and 9.2 only apply to foundations on deep
soil layers. Vertical stresses extend to about 4B below a strip footing and
the formulae, strictly speaking, are not applicable to layers thinner than
this, although little error is incurred if the coefficients are used for layers
of thicknesses greater than 2.0B. A drawback of the method is that it can
only be applied to a layer immediately below the foundation.

For cases when the thickness of the layer is less than 4.0B a solution is
possible with the use of coefficients prepared by Steinbrenner (1934),
whose procedure was to determine the immediate settlement at the top
of the layer (assuming infinite depth) and to calculate the settlement at
the bottom of the layer (again assuming infinite depth) below it. The
difference between the two values is the actual settlement of the layer.

Total immediate settlement at the corner of a rectangular foundation on
an infinite layer

$$= \rho_i = \frac{pB\,(1 - \nu^2)\,Ip}{E}$$

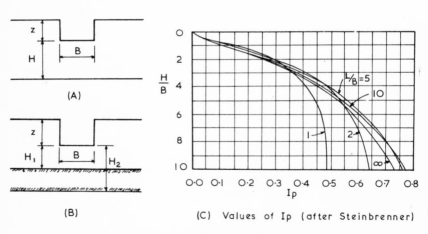

Fig. 9.2 Immediate settlement of a thin clay layer

The values of the coefficient I_p (when $\nu = 0.5$) are given in Fig. 9.2C. To
determine the settlement of a point beneath the foundation the area is
divided into rectangles that meet over the point (the same procedure used
when determining vertical stress increments by Steinbrenner's method).
The summation of the settlements of the corners of the rectangles gives
the total settlement of the point considered.

This method can be extended to determine the immediate settlement of a clay layer which is at some depth below the foundation. In Fig. 9.2B the settlement of the lower layer (of thickness $H_2 - H_1$) is obtained by first determining the settlement of a layer extending from below the foundation that is of thickness H_2 (using E_2); from this value is subtracted the imaginary settlement of the layer H_1 (again using E_2).

It should be noted that the settlement values obtained by this method are for a perfectly flexible foundation. Usually the value of settlement at the centre of the foundation is evaluated and reduced by a rigidity factor (generally taken as 0.8) to give a mean value of settlement that applies over the whole foundation.

The effect of depth

Fox (1948) showed that for deep foundations ($z > B$) the calculated immediate settlements are more than the actual ones, and a reduction may be applied. If $z = B$ the reduction is approximately 25 per cent, increasing to about 50 per cent for infinitely deep foundations.

Most foundations are shallow, however, and although this reduction can be allowed for when a layer of soil is some depth below a foundation the settlement effects in this case are small so it is not customary practice to reduce them further.

Determination of E

The modulus of elasticity, E, is usually obtained from the results of a consolidated undrained triaxial test carried out on a representative sample of the soil that is consolidated under a cell pressure approximating to the effective overburden pressure at the level from which the sample was taken. The soil is then sheared undrained to obtain the plot of total deviator stress against strain; this is never a straight line and to determine E a line must be drawn from the origin up to the value of deviator stress that will be experienced in the field when the foundation load is applied. In deep layers there is the problem of assessing which depth represents the average, and ideally the layer should be split into thinner layers with a value of E determined for each.

A certain amount of analysis work is necessary in order to carry out the above procedure. The increments of principal stress $\Delta\sigma_1$ and $\Delta\sigma_3$ must be obtained so that the value of $\Delta\sigma_1 - \Delta\sigma_3$ is known, and a safety factor of 3.0 is generally applied against bearing capacity failure. Skempton (1951) points out that when the factor of safety is 3.0 the maximum shear stress induced in the soil is not greater than 65 per cent of the ultimate shear strength, so that a value for E can be obtained directly from the triaxial test results by simply determining the strain corresponding to 65 per cent of the maximum deviator stress and dividing this value into its corresponding stress. The method produces results that are well within the range of accuracy possible with other techniques.

Cohesionless soils

Due to the high permeabilities of cohesionless soils, both the elastic and the primary effects occur more or less together. The resulting settlement from these factors is termed the immediate settlement.

The chance of bearing capacity failure in a foundation supported on a cohesionless soil is remote, as exercise 4 at the end of chapter 8 illustrates numerically. For cohesionless soils it has become standard practice to use settlement as the design criteria, and the allowable bearing pressure, p, is generally defined as the pressure that will cause an average settlement of 25 mm in the foundation.

The determination of p from the results of the standard penetration test has been discussed in chapter 8. If the actual bearing pressure is greater or less than the value of p the value of settlement is not known, and since it is difficult to obtain this value from laboratory tests resort must be made to in situ test results. The methods available for predicting this settlement are far from perfect, but recourse may be had to either the standard penetration test or the use of charts.

The standard penetration test

The results from this test can be used to evaluate immediate settlement in a cohesionless soil by means of the method proposed by De Beer & Martens (1957). The method is intended for use with the Dutch cone apparatus but can be adapted for the standard penetration test.

$$\text{Constant of compressibility, } C_s = 1.5 \frac{C_r}{p_{o1}}$$

where C_r = static cone resistance (kN/m^2)

p_{o1} = effective overburden pressure at the point tested.

$$\text{Total immediate settlement, } \rho_i = \frac{H}{C_s} \log_e \frac{p_{o2} + \Delta\sigma_z}{p_{o2}}$$

where $\Delta\sigma_z$ = vertical stress increase at the centre of the consolidating layer of thickness H

p_{o2} = effective overburden pressure at the centre of the layer before any excavation or load application.

Obviously the value of C_r obtained from the Dutch cone penetration test must be related to the recorded number of blows, N, obtained from the standard penetration test. Various workers have attempted to find this relationship, but so far the results have not been encouraging. Meigh & Nixon (1961) showed that over a number of sites C_r varied from 430 N to 1930 N (kN/m^2).

The relationship most commonly in use at the present time is that
proposed by Meyerhof (1956), which is:

$$C_r = 400\ N\ (kN/m^2)$$

where N is the actual number of blows recorded in the standard penetration
test. It will be appreciated that this relationship is, at best, approximate,
but an illustration of immediate settlement prediction by this method is
given in example 9.6.

The use of charts

Thorburn (1963) prepared a set of curves from which it is possible to predict N' from N. His curves are more elegant to use than those of Coffman and
give N' values similar to Gibbs & Holtz. In his paper Thorburn reproduced a
figure by Terzaghi & Peck which shows the relationship between the settlement of a 305 mm square plate under a given pressure and the N' value of
the soil immediately beneath it, and included extra information that he had
obtained from further plate loading tests. Thorburn's diagram is reproduced
in Fig. 9.3 and gives a means for determining the settlement of a square

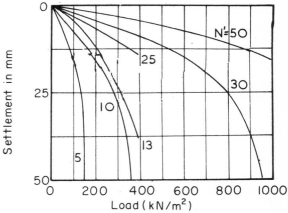

Fig. 9.3 Relationship between the settlement of a 305 mm square plate and the
corrected N value, N', in cohesionless soils (after Thorburn)

foundation sitting on a deep layer of cohesionless soil. The settlement, S_1, is
obtained from the charts and the settlement of the foundation, S, is
calculated from Terzaghi & Peck's formula:

$$S = S_1\left(\frac{2B}{B + 0.3}\right)^2$$

The curves are applicable to deep layers only, which can be taken to mean
a layer of thickness not less than 4.0B below the foundation. For
rectangular foundations a shape factor should presumably be used
(see table 9.3, based on Terzaghi's and Skempton's values, tables 9.1 and 9.2).

Table 9.3

L/B	shape factor (flexible)	shape factor (rigid)
1.0	1.0	1.0
2.0	1.35	1.22
3.0	1.57	1.31
4.0	1.71	1.41
5.0	1.78	1.49

NOTE: In table 9.3 the settlement of a rectangular foundation of width B = settlement of a square foundation of dimension B × shape factor (see example 9.6).

CONSOLIDATION SETTLEMENT

This effect occurs in clays where the value of permeability prevents the initial excess pore water pressures from draining away immediately. The design loading used to calculate consolidation settlement must be consistent with this effect.

A large wheel load rolling along a roadway resting on a clay will cause an immediate settlement that is in theory completely recoverable once the wheel has passed, but if the same load is applied permanently there will in addition be consolidation. Judgement is necessary in deciding what portion of the superimposed loading carried by a structure will be sustained long enough to cause consolidation, and this involves a quite different procedure to that used in a bearing capacity analysis which must allow for total dead and superimposed loadings.

One-dimensional consolidation

The pore water in a saturated clay will commence to drain away soon after immediate settlement has taken place, the removal of this water leading to the volume change known as consolidation (Fig. 9.1B). The element contracts both horizontally and vertically under the actions of $\Delta\sigma_3'$ and $\Delta\sigma_1'$, which gradually increase in magnitude as the excess pore water pressure, Δu, decreases. Eventually, when $\Delta u = 0$, then $\Delta\sigma_3' = \Delta\sigma_3$ and $\Delta\sigma_1' = \Delta\sigma_1$, and at this stage consolidation ceases, although secondary consolidation may still be apparent.

If it can be arranged (a) for the lateral expansion due to the change in shape to equal the lateral compression consequent upon the change in volume and (b) for these changes to occur together, then there will be no immediate settlement and the resulting compression will be one dimensional with all the strain occurring in the vertical direction. Settlement by one dimensional strain is by no means uncommon in practice, and most natural soil deposits have experienced one dimensional settlement during the process of deposition and consolidation.

The consolidation of a clay layer supporting a foundation whose dimensions are much greater than the layer's thickness is essentially one dimensional as lateral strain effects are negligible save at the edges.

The consolidation test

The apparatus generally used in the laboratory to determine the primary compression characteristics of a soil is known as the consolidation test apparatus (or oedometer) and is illustrated in Fig. 9.4A

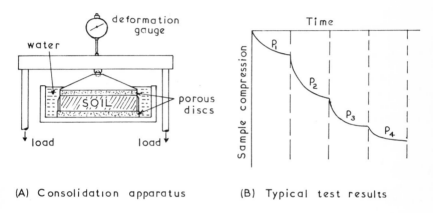

(A) Consolidation apparatus   (B) Typical test results

Fig. 9.4 The consolidation test

The soil sample (75 mm diameter and either 10 or 20 mm thick) is encased in a steel cutting ring. Porous discs, saturated with air-free water, are placed on top of and below the sample which is then inserted in the oedometer.

A vertical load is then applied and the procedure repeated, until by means of a dial gauge at intervals of time, readings being taken until the sample has achieved full consolidation (usually after a period of 24 hours). Further load increments are then applied and the procedure repeated, until the full stress range expected in situ has been covered by the test (Fig. 9.4B).

The test sample is generally flooded with water soon after the application of the first load increment in order to prevent evaporation from it.

After the sample has consolidated under its final load increment the pressure is released in stages at 24 hour intervals and the sample allowed to expand. In this way an expansion to time curve can also be obtained.

After the loading has been completely removed the final thickness of the sample can be obtained, from which it is possible to calculate the void ratio of the soil for each stage of consolidation under the load increments. The graph of void ratio to consolidation pressure can then be drawn, such a curve generally being referred to as an e-p curve (Fig. 9.5A).

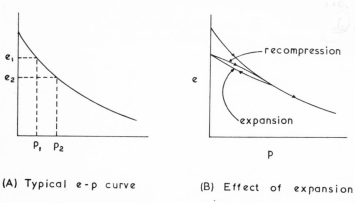

(A) Typical e-p curve   (B) Effect of expansion

Fig. 9.5 Void ratio to effective pressure curves

It should be noted that the values of p refer to effective stress, for after consolidation the excess pore pressures become zero and the applied stress increment is equal to the effective stress increment.

If the sample is recompressed after the initial cycle of compression and expansion, the e-p curve for the whole operation is similar to the curves shown in Fig. 9.5; the recompression curve is flatter than the original compression curve, primary compression being made up of (i) a reversible part and (ii) an irreversible part. Once the consolidation pressure is extended beyond the original consolidation pressure value (the preconsolidation pressure), the e-p curve follows the trend of the original compression curve.

All types of soil, whether sand. silt or clay, have the form of compression curve illustrated in Fig. 9.5. The curve shown can be produced quite quickly in the laboratory for teaching purposes, using a dry sand sample, but consolidation problems are mainly concerned with clays and the oedometer is therefore only used to test these types of soil.

Volumetric change. The volume change per unit of original volume constitutes the volumetric change. If a mass of soil of volume V_1 is compressed to a volume V_2, the assumption is made that the change in volume has been caused by a reduction in the volume of the voids.

Volumetric change

$$= \frac{V_1 - V_2}{V_1} = \frac{(1 + e_1) - (1 + e_2)}{1 + e_1} = \frac{e_1 - e_2}{1 + e_1}$$

The slope of the e-p curve is given the symbol 'a'.

$$e_1 = \text{void ratio at } p_1$$
$$e_2 = \text{void ratio at } p_2$$

Then

$$a = \frac{e_1 - e_2}{p_1 - p_2} \; m^2/kN$$

i.e.

$$a = \frac{de}{dp}$$

The slope of the e-p curve is seen to decrease with increase in pressure; in other words, a is not a constant but will vary depending upon the pressure. Settlement problems are usually only concerned with a range of pressure (that between the initial pressure and the final pressure), and over this range a is taken as constant by assuming that the e-p curve between these two pressure values is a straight line.

Coefficient of volume compressibility m_v. This value, which is sometimes called the coefficient of volume decrease, represents the compression of a soil, per unit of original thickness, due to a unit increase in pressure, i.e.

$$m_v = \text{Volumetric change/unit of pressure increase.}$$

If H_1 = original thickness and H_2 = final thickness,

volumetric change $= \dfrac{V_1 - V_2}{V_1} = \dfrac{H_1 - H_2}{H_1}$ (as area is constant)

$$= \frac{e_1 - e_2}{1 + e_1}$$

Now $\quad a = \dfrac{e_1 - e_2}{dp}$

$\therefore$ Volumetric change $\quad = \dfrac{a\ dp}{1 + e_1}$

$$\therefore m_v = \dfrac{a\ dp}{1 + e_1}\dfrac{1}{dp} = \dfrac{a}{1 + e_1}\ \ m^2/kN$$

Once the coefficient of volume decrease has been obtained we know the compression/unit thickness/unit pressure increase. It is therefore an easy matter to predict the total consolidation settlement of a clay layer of thickness H:

$$\text{Total settlement} = \rho_c = m_v\ dp\ H$$

Typical values of m_v are given in table 9.4.

Table 9.4

Soil	$m_v\ (m^2/kN)$
Peat	$1.0\ \times\ 10^{-2} - 2.0\ \times\ 10^{-3}$
Plastic clay (normally consolidated alluvial clays)	$2.0\ \times\ 10^{-3} - 2.5\ \times\ 10^{-4}$
Stiff clay	$2.5\ \times\ 10^{-4} - 1.25 \times\ 10^{-4}$
Hard clay (boulder clays)	$1.25 \times\ 10^{-4} - 6.25 \times\ 10^{-5}$

In the laboratory consolidation test the compression of the sample is one dimensional as there is lateral confinement, the initial excess pore water pressure induced in a saturated clay on loading being equal to the magnitude of the applied major principal stress (due to the fact that there is no lateral yield). This applies no matter what type of soil is tested, provided it is saturated.

One dimensional consolidation can be produced in a triaxial test specimen by means of a special procedure known as the K_0 test (see Bishop & Henkel, 1962).

The virgin consolidation curve

Clay is generally formed by the process of sedimentation from a liquid in which the soil particles were gradually deposited and compressed as more material was placed above them. The e-p curve corresponding to this natural process of consolidation is known as the virgin consolidation curve (Fig. 9.6A).

This curve is approximately logarithmic. If the values are plotted to a semi-log scale (e to a natural scale, p to a logarithmic scale), the result is a

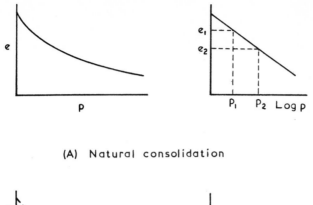

(A)   Natural consolidation

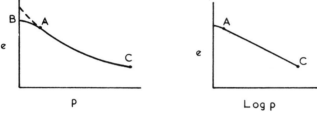

(B)   Normally consolidated clay

Fig. 9.6 e–p and e-log p curves for natural consolidation and for a normally consolidated clay

straight line of equation:

$$e = e_0 - C_C \log_{10} \frac{p_0 + dp}{p_0}$$

Hence e_2 can be expressed in terms of e_1:

$$e_2 = e_1 - C_C \log_{10} \frac{p_2}{p_1}$$

C_C is known as the compression index of the clay.

Compression curve for a normally consolidated clay. A normally consolidated clay is one that has never experienced a consolidation pressure greater than that corresponding to its present overburden. The compression curve of such a soil is shown in Fig. 9.6B.

The clay was originally compressed, by the weight of material above, along the virgin consolidation curve to some point A. Due to the removal of pressure during sampling the soil has expanded to point B. Hence from B to A the soil is being recompressed whereas from A to C the virgin consolidation curve is followed.

The semi-log plot is shown in Fig. 9.6B. As before on the straight line part:

$$e_2 = e_1 - C_C \log_{10} \frac{p_2}{p_1}$$

Compression curve for an overconsolidated clay. An overconsolidated clay is one which has been subjected to a preconsolidation pressure in excess of its existing overburden (Fig. 9.7A), the resulting compression

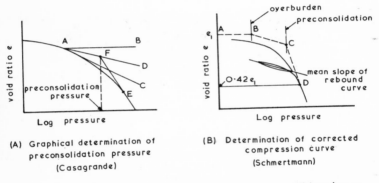

(A) Graphical determination of
preconsolidation pressure
(Casagrande)

(B) Determination of corrected
compression curve
(Schmertmann)

Fig. 9.7 Compression curves for an overconsolidated clay

being much less than for a normally consolidated clay. The semi-log plot is no longer a straight line and a compression index value for an overconsolidated clay is no longer a constant.

From the e-p curve it is possible to determine an approximate value for the preconsolidated pressure with the use of a graphical method proposed by Casagrande (1936). First estimate the point of greatest curvature, A, then draw a horizontal line through A (AB) and the tangent to the curve at A (AC). Bisect the angle BAC to give the line AD, and locate the straight part of the compression curve (in Fig. 9.7A the straight part commences at point E). Finally project the straight part of the curve upwards to cut AD in F. The point F then gives the value of the preconsolidation pressure.

Evaluation of consolidation settlement from the compression index

$$\frac{dH}{H_1} = \frac{e_1 - e_2}{1 + e_1}$$

$$\therefore dH = \frac{e_1 - e_2}{1 + e_1} H_1$$

$$e_1 - e_2 = C_C \log_{10} \frac{p_2}{p_1}$$

$$\therefore \rho_C = dH = \frac{C_C}{1 + e_1} \log_{10} \frac{p_2}{p_1} . H_1$$

This equation is only relevant when a clay is being compressed for the first time and therefore cannot be used for an overconsolidated clay.

Determination of compression index C_C. Terzaghi & Peck (1949) have shown that there is an approximate relationship between the liquid limit of a normally consolidated clay and its compression index. This relationship has been established experimentally and is:

$$C_C \doteqdot 0.009 \text{ (L.L.} - 10 \text{ per cent)}$$

Application of consolidation test results

The range of pressure generally considered in a settlement analysis is the increase from p_1 (the existing vertical effective overburden pressure) to p_2 (the vertical effective pressure that will operate once the foundation load has been applied and consolidation has taken place), so that in the previous discussion e_1 represents the void ratio corresponding to the effective overburden pressure and e_2 represents the final void ratio after consolidation. In some text books and papers the initial void ratio, e_1, is given the symbol e_0.

Obtaining a test sample entails removing all of the stresses which are applied to it, this reduction in effective stress causing the sample to either swell or develop negative pore water pressures within itself. Due to the restraining effect of the sampling tube most soil samples tend to have a negative pore pressure.

In the consolidation test the sample is submerged in water to prevent evaporation losses, with the result that the negative pore pressures will tend to draw in water and the sample consequently swells. To obviate this effect the normal procedure is to start the test by applying the first load increment and then to add the water, but if the sample still tends to swell an increased load increment must be added and the test readings started again. The point e_1 is taken to be the position on the test e-p curve that corresponds to the effective overburden pressure at the depth from which the sample was taken; in the case of a uniform deposit various values of e_1 can be obtained for selected points throughout the layer by reading off the test values of void ratio corresponding to the relevant effective overburden pressures. Generally the test e-p curve lies a little below the actual in situ e-p curve, the amount of departure depending upon the degree of disturbance in the test sample. Bearing in mind the inaccuracies involved in any analysis, this departure from the consolidation curve will generally be of small significance unless the sample is severely disturbed and most settlement analyses are based on the actual test results.

An alternative method, mainly applicable to overconsolidated clays, has been proposed by Schmertmann (1953), who points out that e_1 (he uses the symbol e_0) must be equal to mG, where m is the in situ moisture content at the point considered, and that in a consolidation test on an ideal soil with no disturbance the void ratio of the sample should remain constant at e_1 throughout the pressure range from zero to the effective overburden pressure value. Schmertmann found that the test e-p curve tends to cut the in situ virgin consolidation curve at a void ratio value somewhere between 37 and 42 per cent of e_1 and concluded that a reasonable figure for this intersection is $e = 0.42e_1$.

In order to obtain the corrected curve, with disturbance effects removed, the test sample is either loaded through a pressure range that eventually reduces the void ratio of the sample to $0.42e_1$ or else the test is extended far enough for extrapolated values to be obtained, at least one cycle of expansion and recompression being carried out during the test. The approximate value of the preconsolidation pressure is obtained and the test results are put in the form of a semi-log plot of void ratio to log p (Fig. 9.7B). The value of e_1 is obtained from mG, m being found from a separate test sample (usually cuttings obtained during the preparation of the consolidation test sample). It is now possible to plot on the test curve (point A) and a horizontal line (AB) is drawn to cut the ordinate of the existing overburden pressure at point B; a line BC is next drawn parallel to the mean slope of the laboratory rebound curve to cut the preconsolidation pressure ordinate at point C, and the value of void ratio equal to $0.42e_1$ is obtained and established on the test curve (point D). Finally points C and D are joined. The corrected curve therefore consits of the three straight lines: AB (parallel to the pressure axis with a constant void ratio value e_1), BC (representing the recompression of the soil up to the preconsolidation pressure), and CD (representing initial compression along the virgin consolidation line).

Apart from the elimination of disturbance effects the method is useful because it permits the use of a formula similar to the compression index of a normally consolidated clay:

$$\rho_c = \frac{C}{1 + e_1} \log_{10} \frac{p_2}{p_1} H$$

where C is the slope of the corrected curve (generally recompression). If the pressure range extends into initial compression the calculation must be carried out in two parts using the two different C values.

General consolidation

In the case of a foundation of finite dimensions, such as a footing sitting on a thick bed of clay, lateral strains will occur and the consolidation is no longer one dimensional. If two saturated clays of equal compressibility and thickness are subjected to the same size of foundation and loading, the resulting settlements may be quite different even though the consolidation tests on the clays would give identical results. This is because lateral strain effects in the field may induce unequal pore pressures whereas in the consolidation test the induced pore pressure is always equal to the increment of applied stress.

$$\text{For a saturated soil } \Delta u = \Delta \sigma_3 + A (\Delta \sigma_1 - \Delta \sigma_3)$$

Let p_1' = initial effective major principal stress

$\Delta \sigma_1$ = increment of total major principal stress due to the foundation loading

Δu = excess pore water pressure induced by the load.

The effective major principal stress on load application will be:

$$p_1' + \Delta \sigma_1 - \Delta u$$

The effective major principal stress after consolidation will be:

$$p_1' + \Delta \sigma_1$$

Let p_3' = initial effective minor principal stress.

$\Delta \sigma_3$ = increment of total minor principal stress due to the foundation loading.

The horizontal effective stress on load application will be:

$$p_3' + \Delta \sigma_3 - \Delta u$$

If the expression for Δu is examined it will be seen that Δu is greater than $\Delta\sigma_3$. The horizontal effective stress therefore reduces when the load is applied and there will be a lateral expansion of the soil. Hence in the early stages of consolidation the clay will undergo a recompression in the horizontal direction for an effective stress increase of $\Delta u - \Delta\sigma_3$; the strain from this recompression will be small but as consolidation continues the effective stress increases beyond the original value of $p_3{}'$ and the strain effects will become larger until consolidation ceases.

Settlement analysis
The method of settlement analysis most commonly in use is that proposed by Skempton & Bjerrum (1957). In this procedure the lateral expansion and compression effects are ignored, since the authors maintain that such a simplification cannot introduce a maximum error of more than 20 per cent and when they compared the actual settlements of several structures with predicted values using their method the greatest difference was in fact only 15 per cent.

Ignoring secondary consolidation, the total settlement of a foundation is given by the expression:

$$\rho = \rho i + \rho_c$$

where ρi = immediate settlement
ρ_c = consolidation settlement

In the consolidation test:

$$\rho_{oed} = m_V \Delta\sigma_1 h \qquad \ldots (A)$$

where h = sample thickness
Since there is no lateral strain in the consolidation, $\Delta\sigma_1 = \Delta u$.

Hence $\qquad\qquad\qquad \rho_{oed} = m_V \Delta u h$

Or

$$\rho_c = \int_O^H m_V \Delta u \, dH \qquad \ldots (B)$$

where H = thickness of consolidating layer.
In a saturated soil $\Delta u = \Delta\sigma_3 + A(\Delta\sigma_1 - \Delta\sigma_3)$
This may be expressed as:

$$\Delta u = \Delta\sigma_1 \left[A + \frac{\Delta\sigma_3}{\Delta\sigma_1}(1 - A) \right]$$

and, substituting in (B):

$$\rho_c = \int_0^H m_v \Delta\sigma_1 \left[A + \frac{\Delta\sigma_3}{\Delta\sigma_1}(1 - A) \right] dH \qquad \ldots (C)$$

Equation (C) can be expressed in terms of equation (A):

$$\rho_c = \mu \rho_{oed}$$

where $\mu =$

$$\frac{\int_0^H m_v \Delta\sigma_1 \left[A + \frac{\Delta\sigma_3}{\Delta\sigma_1}(1 - A) \right] dH}{\int_0^H m_v \Delta\sigma_1 dH}$$

If m_v and A are assumed constant with depth the equation for μ reduces to:

$$\mu = A + (1 - A)\alpha \qquad \ldots (D)$$

where

$$\alpha = \frac{\int_0^H \Delta\sigma_3 dH}{\int_0^H \Delta\sigma_1 dH}$$

Poisson's ratio for a saturated soil is generally taken as 0.5 at the stage when the load is applied so α is a geometrical parameter which can be determined, various values for α that were obtained by Skempton & Bjerrum being given in table 9.5.

Table 9.5

$\frac{H}{B}$	Circular footing	Strip footing
0	1.00	1.00
0.25	0.67	0.74
0.50	0.50	0.53
1.0	0.38	0.37
2.0	0.30	0.26
4.0	0.28	0.20
10.0	0.26	0.14
∞	0.25	0

The value of the pore pressure coefficient A can now be substituted in equation (D) and a value for μ obtained, typical results being:

Soft sensitive clays . . . possibly greater than 1.0

Normally consolidated clays . . . generally less than 1.0

Average overconsolidated clays . . . approximately 0.5

Heavily overconsolidated clays . . . perhaps as little as 0.25

STRESS PATHS

The use of stress paths in the analysis of consolidation problems was evolved by Lambe (1964, 1967), one advantage being that the design engineer can develop a 'feel' of the problem instead of blindly applying formulae. A stress path can be used in place of the more familiar Mohr circle and has the advantage of showing the continuous stress change throughout the stress range to which the soil is subjected. If a typical Mohr circle is examined (Fig. 9.8) the point of maximum shear stress has

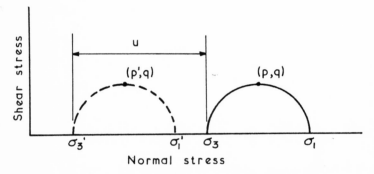

Fig. 9.8 Points of maximum shear stress

the co-ordinates p and q where:

$$p = \frac{\sigma_1 + \sigma_3}{2} \text{ and } q = \frac{\sigma_1 - \sigma_3}{2},$$

σ_1 and σ_3 being the total principal stresses.

In terms of effective stresses, $\sigma_1{'}$ and $\sigma_3{'}$, the point of maximum shear has the co-ordinates $p{'}$ and q where

$$p{'} = \frac{\sigma_1{'} + \sigma_3{'}}{2}$$

If a soil is subjected to a range of values of σ_1 and σ_3 the point of maximum shear stress can be obtained for each stress circle; the line joining these points, in the order that they occurred, is termed the stress path or stress vector of maximum shear. Any other point instead of maximum shear can be used to determine a stress path, e.g. the point of maximum obliquity, but Lambe maintains that the stress paths of maximum shear are not only simple to use but also more applicable to consolidation work.

Typical effective stress paths obtained from a series of consolidated undrained triaxial tests on samples of normally consolidated clay together with the effective stress circles at failure are shown in Fig 9.9.

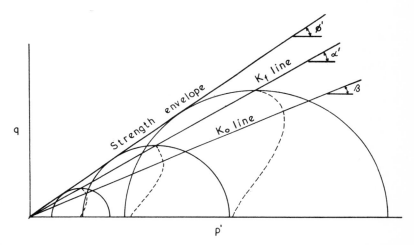

Fig. 9.9 Typical undrained effective stress paths obtained from consolidated undrained triaxial tests on a normally consolidated clay

Ratios of σ_3'/σ_1'
If the results of a drained shear test on a soil are considered, the Mohr circle diagram is as shown in Fig. 9.9. The line tangential to the stress circles is the strength envelope, inclined at ϕ' to the normal stress axis. If each Mohr circle is considered it is seen that the ratio σ_3'/σ_1' is a constant, to which the symbol K_f is applied.

The K_f line. If the points of maximum shear for each effective stress circle p_f' and q_f are joined together the stress path of maximum shear stress at failure is obtained. This line is called the K_f line and is inclined at angle α' to the normal stress axis; obviously $\tan \alpha' = \sin \phi'$.

The K_o line. For a soil undergoing one-dimensional consolidation the ratio σ_3'/σ_1' is again constant and its value is given the symbol K_o. Plotting the maximum shear stress points of these stress circles enables the stress path for one-dimensional consolidation, the K_o line, to be determined; this line is inclined at angle β to the normal stress axis.

K_o is the coefficient of earth pressure at rest. For consolidation work K_o may be defined for a soil with a history of one-dimensional strain as the ratio:

$$K_o = \frac{\text{Lateral effective stress}}{\text{Vertical effective stress}}$$

Stress paths in the consolidation test
Figure 9.10 shows the stress conditions that arise during and after the

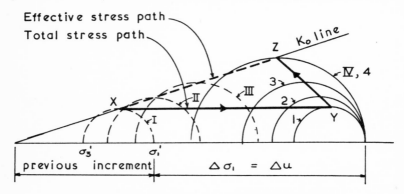

Fig. 9.10 Stress paths in the consolidation test

application of a pressure increment in the consolidation test. Initially the sample has been consolidated under a previous load and the pore pressure is zero; the Mohr circle is represented by (p,q) the point X, circle I. As soon as the vertical pressure increase, $\Delta\sigma_1$, is applied, the total stresses move from X to Y (circle 1). As the soil is saturated $\Delta u = \Delta\sigma_1$ and the effective stress circle is still represented by point X. As consolidation commences the pore water pressure, Δu, begins to decrease and $\Delta\sigma_1'$ begins to increase. The consolidation is one-dimensional and therefore an increase in the major principal effective stress, $\Delta\sigma_1'$, will induce an increase in the minor principal effective stress $\Delta\sigma_3' = K_o\Delta\sigma_1'$. Hence the effective stress circles move steadily towards point Z (circles II, III and IV), where Z represents full consolidation.

The total stress circles can be determined from a study of the effective stress circles. For example the difference between $\Delta\sigma_1$ and $\Delta\sigma_1'$ for circle III represents the pore water pressure within the sample at that time; hence $\Delta\sigma_3$ at this stage in the consolidation is $\Delta\sigma_3'$ for circle II plus the value of the pore water pressure. It can be seen therefore that Δu

decreases with consolidation and the size of the Mohr circle for total stress increases until the point Z is reached (circles 2, 3 and 4). Obviously circles 4 and IV are coincident.

Stress path for general consolidation

The effective stress plot of Fig. 9.11 represents a typical case of general consolidation. The soil is normally consolidated and point A represents

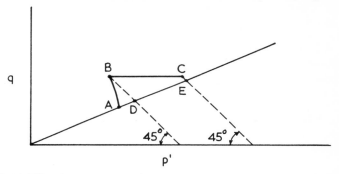

Fig. 9.11 Effective stress path for the general consolidation of a normally consolidated clay

the initial K_o consolidation; AB is the effective stress path on the application of the foundation load and BC is the effective stress path during consolidation.

Skempton & Bjeerum's assumption that lateral strain effects during consolidation can be ignored presupposes that the strain due to the stress path BC is the same as that produced by the stress path DE. The fact that the method proposed by Skempton & Bjeerum gives reasonable results indicates that the effective stress path during the consolidation of soil in a typical foundation problem is indeed fairly close to the effective stress path DE of Fig. 9.11. There are occasions when this will not be so, however, and the stress path method of analysis can give a more reasonable prediction of settlement values (see Lambe 1964, 1967). The calculation of settlement in a soft soil layer under an embankment by this procedure has been discussed by Smith (1968), and the method is also applicable to coal spoil heaps.

ALLOWABLE BEARING PRESSURE

From the discussions in both this chapter and chapter 8 it will be seen that two criteria must be taken account of in foundation design: (i) the bearing pressure must not cause detrimental settlements, and (ii) the factor of safety against bearing capacity failure must be adequate. These two rules usually give different values of bearing pressure and the lower value (called the allowable bearing pressure) is the one used in design.

Allowable settlement

It is not easy to decide what value of settlement will have a detrimental effect on a structure, because uniform settlement of the entire structure will have little adverse effect whereas differential settlement will induce stresses not usually allowed for in the design.

There are two principal effects from differential settlement: (i) the architectural effect (plaster cracking etc), and (ii) the structural effect (redistribution of moments and shears).

Terzaghi & Peck (1948) maintain that most ordinary structures can withstand differential settlements of 20 mm between adjacent columns and if foundations on sand are designed for 25 mm maximum settlement the differential settlements will be satisfactory. Skempton & MacDonald (1956) specified that the angular rotation between adjacent columns for foundations on clay should not exceed 1/300, with the proviso that slow settlements may permit a greater value, whilst Bozozuk (1962) examined the settlement effects on various old two-storey brick houses in Ottawa and summarized his findings as:

Damage	Angular rotation
none	1/180
slight	1/120
moderate	1/90
heavy to severe	1/50

These empirical rules are intended to limit damage to the architectural effect, but statically determinate structures (such as simply supported bridge decks, etc.) can withstand greater settlements than those quoted. Opinions on this important subject vary considerably and were discussed by Rutledge (1964) at the closing of the American Society of Civil Engineers' conference on settlement.

EXAMPLES ON CHAPTER 9

Example 9.1

A reinforced concrete foundation, of dimensions 20 m X 40 m exerts a uniform pressure of 200 kN/m^2 on a semi-infinite soil layer (E = 50 MN/m^2).

Determine the value of immediate settlement under the foundation using table 9.2.

Solution

$$\frac{L}{B} = \frac{40}{20} = 2.0 \quad \text{From table 9.2 } I_p = 1.0$$

$$\rho_i = \frac{pB(1 - \nu^2)}{E} I_p = \frac{200 \times 20}{50\,000} \times 0.75 = 0.06 \text{ m} = 60 \text{ mm}$$

Example 9.2

The plan of a proposed spoil heap is shown in Fig. 9.12A. The tip will be about 23 m high and will sit on a thick, soft alluvial deposit ($E = 15$ MN/m²). It is estimated that the eventual uniform bearing pressure on the soil will be

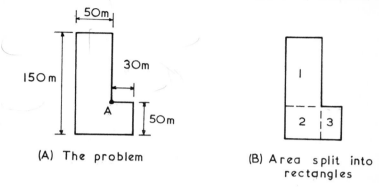

(A) The problem

(B) Area split into rectangles

Fig. 9.12 Example 9.2

about 300 kN/m². Estimate the immediate settlement under the point A at the surface of the soil.

Solution

The procedure is to divide the plan area into a number of rectangles, the corners of which must meet at the point A; in Fig. 9.12B it is seen that three rectangles are required. As the structure is flexible and the soil deposit is thick, the coefficients of table 9.1 should be used:

$$\text{Rectangle (1): } 100 \text{ m} \times 50 \text{ m } \frac{L}{B} = 2.0, \quad N_p = 0.76$$

$$\text{Rectangle (2): } 50 \text{ m} \times 50 \text{ m } \frac{L}{B} = 1.0, \quad N_p = 0.56$$

$$\text{Rectangle (3): } 50 \text{ m} \times 30 \text{ m } \frac{L}{B} = 1.67, \quad N_p = 0.64$$

$$\rho_i = \frac{p}{E} (1 - v^2) (N_{p1}B_1 + N_{p2}B_2 + N_{p3}B_3)$$

$$= \frac{300 \times 0.75}{15\,000} (0.76 \times 50 + 0.56 \times 50 + 0.64 \times 30)$$

$$= 1.27 \text{ m}$$

Example 9.3

The following results were obtained from a consolidation test on a sample of saturated clay, each pressure increment having been maintained for 24 hours.

Pressure (kN/m^2)	Thickness of sample after consolidation (mm)
0	20.0 *original thickness*
50	19.65
100	19.52
200	19.35
400	19.15
800	18.95
0	19.25

After it had expanded for 24 hours the sample was removed from the apparatus and found to have a moisture content of 25 per cent. The particle specific gravity of the soil was 2.65.

Plot the void-ratio to effective pressure curve and determine the value of the coefficient of volume change for a pressure range of 250–350 kN/m². *Solution*

$$m = 0.25; G = 2.65$$

Now e = mG (as soil is saturated) = 0.25 × 2.65 = 0.662. This is the void ratio corresponding to a sample thickness of 19.25 mm.

$$\frac{dH}{H_1} = \frac{de}{1 + e_1} \therefore de = \frac{(1 + e_1)}{H_1} dH = \frac{1.662}{19.25} dH = 0.0865 \, dH$$

The values of e at the end of each consolidation can be calculated from this expression.

Pressure	H	dH	de	$e = mG + $
0.0	20.0	+0.75	+0.065	0.727
0.5	19.65	+0.40	+0.035	0.697
1.0	19.52	+0.27	+0.023	0.685
2.0	19.35	+0.10	+0.009	0.671
4.0	19.15	−0.10	−0.009	0.653
8.0	18.95	−0.30	−0.026	0.636
0.0	19.25	0	0	0.662

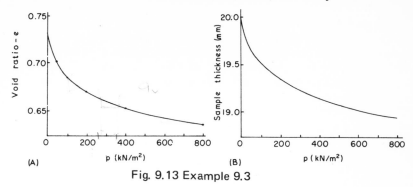

Fig. 9.13 Example 9.3

From the e-p curve in Fig. 9.13A:

$$e \text{ at } 250 \text{ kN/m}^2 = 0.666$$
$$e \text{ at } 350 \text{ kN/m}^2 = 0.658$$

$$a = \frac{de}{dp} = \frac{0.666 - 0.658}{100} = 0.000\,08 \text{ m}^2/\text{kN}$$

$$\therefore m_v = \frac{a}{1 + e_1} = \frac{0.000\,08}{1.666} = 4.8 \times 10^{-5} \text{ m}^2/\text{kN}$$

Alternative method for determining m_v. m_v can be expressed in terms of thicknesses:

$$m_v = \frac{dH}{H_1} \frac{1}{dp} = \frac{1}{H_1} \frac{dH}{dp}$$

dH/dp is the slope of the curve of thickness of sample against pressure. Hence m_v can be obtained by finding the slope of the curve at the required pressure and dividing by the original thickness. The thickness/pressure curve is shown in Fig. 9.13B; from it:

$$H \text{ at } 250 \text{ kN/m}^2 = 19.28$$
$$H \text{ at } 350 \text{ kN/m}^2 = 19.19$$

$$m_v = \frac{19.28 - 19.19}{19.28 \times 100} = \frac{0.09}{19.28 \times 100} = 4.7 \times 10^{-5} \text{ m}^2/\text{kN}$$

If a layer of this clay, 20 m thick, had been subjected to this pressure increase then the consolidation settlement would have been:

$$\rho_c = m_v H dp = 0.000\,047 \times 20 \times 100 \times 1000 = 96 \text{ mm}$$

Example 9.4

A soft, normally consolidated clay layer is 15 m thick with a natural moisture content of 45 per cent. The clay has a saturated unit weight of 17.2 kN/m^3, a particle specific gravity of 2.68 and a liquid limit of 65 per cent. A foundation load will subject the centre of the layer to a vertical stress increase of 10.0 kN/m^2. Determine an approximate value for the settlement of the foundation if ground water level is at the surface of the clay.

Solution

Initial vertical effective stress
at centre of layer

$$= (17.2 - 9.81) \frac{15}{2}$$

$$= 55.4 \text{ kN/m}^2$$

Final effective vertical stress = 55.4 + 10 = 65.4 kN/m^2
Initial void ratio, $e_1 = mG = 0.45 \times 2.68 = 1.21$

$$C_c = 0.009 (65 - 10) = 0.009 \times 55 = 0.495$$

$$\rho_c = \frac{0.495}{2.21} \times \log_{10} \frac{65.4}{55.4} \times 15$$

$$= 0.024 \text{ m} = 240 \text{ mm}$$

This method can be used for a rough settlement analysis of a relatively unimportant small structure on a soft clay layer. For large structures, consolidation tests would be carried out.

Example 9.5

A sample of the clay of example 9.3 was subjected to a consolidated undrained triaxial test with the results shown in Fig. 9.14B. The sample was taken from a layer 20 m thick and has a saturated unit weight of 18.5 kN/m^3.

It is proposed to construct a reinforced concrete foundation, length 30 m and width 10 m, on the top of the layer. The uniform bearing pressure will be 200 kN/m^2; determine the total settlement of the foundation under its centre if the ground water level occurs at a depth of 5 m below the top of the layer.

Solution

The vertical pressure increment at the centre of the layer can be obtained by splitting the plan area into four rectangles (Fig. 9.14A) and using Fig. 7.2

$$\Delta\sigma_1 = 110 \text{ kN/m}^2$$

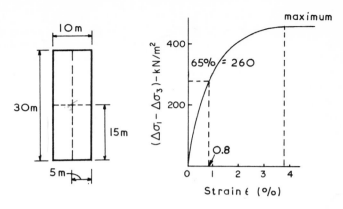

(A) Foundation plan   (B)   Triaxial results

Fig. 9.14 Example 9.5

In order to obtain the E value for the soil, $\Delta\sigma_3$ should now be evaluated so that the deviator stress $(\Delta\sigma_1 - \Delta\sigma_3)$ can be obtained.

Alternatively the approximate method can be used:

65 per cent of maximum deviator stress = $0.65 \times 400 = 260$ kN/m².

Strain at this value (from Fig. 9.14B) = 0.8 per cent

$$\text{Hence } E = \frac{260 \times 100}{0.8} = 32\,500 \text{ kN/m}^2 = 32.5 \text{ MN/m}^2$$

Immediate settlement. Using the rectangles of Fig. 9.14B and Fig. 9.2:

$$\frac{L}{B} = \frac{15}{5} = 3.0 \quad \frac{H}{B} = \frac{20}{5} = 4.0$$

Hence $I_p = 0.48 \times 4.0 = 1.92$ for rectangle

$$\rho_i = \frac{pB}{E}(1 - \nu^2)\,Ip$$

$$= \frac{200}{32\,500} \times 5 \times 0.75 \times 1.92 \times 0.8 \qquad (0.8 = \text{rigidity factor})$$

$$= 0.036 \text{ m} = 36 \text{ mm}$$

Consolidation settlement. Initial effective overburden pressure

$$= 18.5 \times 10 - 9.81 \times 5$$
$$= 136 \text{ kN/m}^2$$

Hence the range of pressure involved is from 136 to 246 kN/m².
Using the e-p curve of Fig. 9.13A:

$$e_1 = 0.680; e_2 = 0.666$$

$$a = \frac{de}{dp} = \frac{0.680 - 0.666}{110} = \frac{0.014}{110} = 0.000\,127$$

$$m_v = \frac{a}{1 + e_1} = \frac{0.000\,127}{1.680} = 7.6 \times 10^{-5}$$

$$\rho_c = m_v \, dp \, H = 7.6 \times 110 \times 20 \times 10^{-5} = 0.167 \text{ m} = 167 \text{ mm}$$

Total settlement = 36 + 167 = 203 mm

Some reduction could possibly be applied to the value of ρ_c if the value
of μ was known.

Alternative method for determining ρ_c. In one-dimensional consolidation
the volumetric strain must be equal to the axial strain.

i.e. $$\frac{dH}{H} = \frac{\rho_c}{H} = \frac{de}{1 + e_1}$$

Hence $$\rho_c = \frac{de}{1 + e_1} H$$

In the example

$$\rho_c = \frac{0.680 - 0.666}{1.680} \times 20$$

$$= 0.008\,34 \times 20 = 0.167 \text{ m} = 167 \text{ mm}$$

Example 9.6·

A standard penetration test carried out in a deep cohesionless soil at a
depth of 1.5 m gave N = 10. The unit weight of the soil was 19.2 kN/m³.
Determine the immediate settlement of (i) a 1.5 m square foundation and
(ii) a 1.5 m wide 7.5 m long strip foundation if both foundations are loaded
uniformly to 460 kN/m² pressure and are founded at a depth of 1.5 m into
the soil.

Solution by Fig. 9.3

$$19.2 \times 1.5 = 28.8 \text{ kN/m}^2$$

From Fig. 8.10: R.D = 64 per cent and $N' = 30$
Net increase in loading $= 460 - 28.8 = 430 \text{ kN/m}^2$
From Fig. 9.3: settlement of a 305 mm square plate = 9 mm

$$\therefore \text{Settlement of a 1.5 m square base} = 9 \times \left(\frac{2 \times 1.5}{1.8}\right)^2$$

$$= 25 \text{ mm}$$

Settlement of a 1.5 m strip base $\quad = 25 \text{ shape factor}$

$$= 25 \times 1.49 \text{ (table 9.3)}$$

$$= 37 \text{ mm}$$

The Dutch cone method
$C_r = 400 N (\text{kN/m}^2)$ (Note that the uncorrected value of N is used)
$p_{o1} = 28.8 \text{ kN/m}^2$

$$C_s = 1.5 \times \frac{400}{28.8} = 208$$

The soil layer is deep but as significant stresses only extend down about 4.0 B below the foundation a finite thickness of layer equal to 4.0B (6 m) can be taken.

The layer must be divided into strips and the settlement established for each one, the summation of these effects giving the total settlement. Four layers, each 1.5 m thick, are selected, and the calculations are set out in tabular form:

1.5 m square footing

Depth below foundation (m)	$B = \frac{L}{z} = \frac{z}{z}$	$I\sigma$	$4I\sigma$	$\Delta\sigma_z (\text{kN/m}^2)$	$\rho_o (\text{kN/m}^2)$	$\frac{\rho_o + \Delta\sigma_z}{\rho_o}$	$\log_e \frac{\rho_o + \Delta\sigma_z}{\rho_o}$
0.75	1.0	0.18	0.72	309.6	43.20	8.17	2.1005
2.25	0.33	0.045	0.18	77.4	72.00	2.07	0.7275
3.75	0.20	0.02	0.08	34.4	100.8	1.69	0.5247
5.25	0.14	0.01	0.04	13.6	129.60	1.10	0.0953
							$\Sigma 3.4480$

$$\rho_i = \frac{1.5}{208} \times 3.448 = 0.0249 \text{ m} = 25 \text{ mm}$$

1.5 m strip footing

Depth below foundation (m)	$\dfrac{B}{z}$	$\dfrac{L}{z}$	$I\sigma$	$4I\sigma$	$\Delta\sigma_z$ (kN/m²)	ρ_o (kN/m²)	$\dfrac{\rho_o + \Delta\sigma_z}{\rho_o}$	$\log_e \dfrac{\rho_o + \Delta\sigma_z}{\rho_o}$
0.75	1.0	5.0	0.205	0.82	352.6	43.2	9.16	2.2148
2.25	0.33	1.67	0.095	0.380	163.4	72.38	3.26	1.1817
3.75	0.20	1.0	0.055	0.220	94.6	100.8	1.94	0.6627
5.25	0.14	0.71	0.033	0.132	56.8	129.6	1.51	0.4121
								$\overline{\Sigma 4.4713}$

$$\rho_i = \frac{1.5}{208} \times 4.4713 = 0.032 = 32\text{mm}$$

Example 9.7

The plan of a proposed raft foundation is shown in Fig. 9.15A. The uniform bearing pressure from the foundation will be 322 kN/m² and a site investigation has shown that the upper 7.62 m of the subsoil is a saturated coarse sand of unit weight 19.2 kN/m³ with ground water level occurring at a depth of 3.05 m below the top of the sand. The result from a standard penetration test taken at a depth of 4.57 m below the top of the sand gave N = 20. Below the sand there is a 30.5 m thick layer of clay (A = 0.75; E = 16.1 MN/m² ; $E_{swelling}$ = 64.4 MN/m²). The clay rests on hard sandstone (fig. 9.15B).

Determine the total settlement under the centre of the foundation.
Solution

Vertical pressure increments. Gross pressure = 322 kN/m². Relief due to excavation of 1.52 m sand = 1.52 × 19.2 = 29 kN/m².

$$\therefore \text{Nett foundation pressure} = 293 \text{ kN/m}^2$$

The foundation is split into four rectangles as shown in Fig. 9.15A, and Fig. 7.2 is then used.

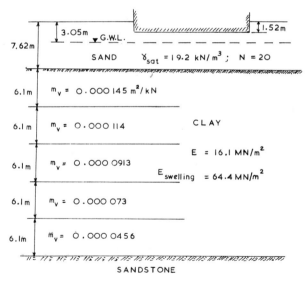

with overburden
1 N-find - relative density then
→ modified N'

Using modified N' and relative density
find settlement of a
plate 305 mm square
(s₁)

then find S of
relation as

$$S = S_1 \left(\frac{2B}{B+0.3} \right)^2$$

for any other type
of foundation just
apply appropriate
modification
fator to S.

(A)   Plan of foundation

54.88 m

18.30m

9.15 m

27.44m

7.62m

3.05m   G.W.L.

1.52m

SAND γ_{sat} = 19.2 kN/m³ ; N = 20

6.1m m_v = 0.000 145 m²/kN

6.1m m_v = 0.000 114   CLAY

6.1m m_v = 0.000 0913   E = 16.1 MN/m²

                         $E_{swelling}$ = 64.4 MN/m²

6.1m m_v = 0.000 073

6.1m m_v = 0.000 0456

SANDSTONE

(B)   Subsoil conditions

Fig. 9.15 Example 9.7

Depth below foundation (m)	$\dfrac{B}{z}$	$\dfrac{L}{z}$	$I\sigma$	$4I\sigma$	$\Delta\sigma_z$ (kN/m^2)
3.05	3.0	9.0	0.247	0.988	318
9.15	1.0	3.0	0.203	0.812	262
15.25	0.6	1.8	0.152	0.608	196
21.35	0.43	1.29	0.113	0.452	146
27.45	0.33	1.00	0.086	0.344	111
33.55	0.27	0.82	0.067	0.268	86

Immediate settlement. Sand: test value for $N = 20$

$$p_o' = 4.57 \times 19.2 - 1.52 \times 9.81 = 73 \ kN/m^2$$

$C_r - 400 N$.

$C_s = \dfrac{1.5 \, C_r}{P_o'}$

$$C_r = 400 \times 20 = 8000 \ kN/m^2$$

$$C_s = \frac{1.5 \times 8000}{72.83} = 164.8$$

$\rho_i = \dfrac{H}{C_s} \log_e \dfrac{P_{o2} + \Delta\sigma_z}{P_{o2}}$

$$\rho_i = \frac{6.1}{165} \log_e \frac{73 + 318}{73}$$

$$= 0.059 = 59 \ mm$$

The majority of the sand below the footing is submerged and it is customarily assumed that the settlement will be doubled (see page 246).

Hence ρ_i in the sand $= 118$ mm

Clay: in Fig. 9.2, $H_1 = 6.1$ m and $H_2 = 36.6$ m

For H_2: $\dfrac{L}{B} = \dfrac{27.44}{9.15} = 3.0; \dfrac{H}{B} = \dfrac{36.6}{9.15} = 4.0$ Hence $I_p = 0.475$

For H_1: $\dfrac{L}{B} = 3.0; \dfrac{H}{B} = \dfrac{6.1}{9.15} = 0.67$ Hence $I_p = 0.18$

Settlement under centre of foundation

$$\rho_i = \frac{pB}{E}(1 - v^2)\, 4I_p \times \text{rigidity factor}$$

$$= \frac{293}{16\,100} \times 9.15 \times 0.75 \times 4\,(0.475 - 0.18) \times 0.8$$

$$= 0.118\ \text{m} = 118\ \text{mm}$$

Heave effects: relief of pressure due to sand excavation $= 29\ \text{kN/m}^2$

$$\therefore \text{Heave} = \frac{29}{64\,400} \times 9.15 \times 0.75 \times 4\,(0.475 - 0.18) \times 0.8$$

$$= 0.0029\ \text{m} = 3\ \text{mm}$$

Hence ρ_i in clay $= 115$ mm

As can be seen from this example the effects of heave are usually only significant when a great depth of material is excavated.

Consolidation settlement. The clay layer has been divided into 5 layers of thickness, H, equal to 6.1 m

m_v	$\Delta\sigma_z$	$m_v\Delta\sigma_z H$
0.000 145	262	0.231
0.000 114	196	0.136
0.000 041 3	146	0.081
0.000 073	111	0.049
0.000 045 6	86	0.024
		0.521 m = 521 mm

This value of settlement can be reduced by the factor

$$\mu = A + (1 - A)\,\alpha$$

An approximate value for α can be obtained from table 9.4:

$$\alpha = 0.26$$

Hence $\mu = 0.75 + 0.25 \times 0.26 = 0.82$

$$\rho_c = 521 \times 0.82 = 448\ \text{mm}$$

Total settlement $= 118 + 115 + 448 = 671$ mm.

Example 9.8

A layer of soft, normally consolidated clay is 9.25 m thick and has an existing effective overburden pressure at its centre of 85 kN/m².

It is proposed to construct a flexible foundation on the surface of the clay and the increases in stresses at the centre of the clay, beneath the centre of the foundation, are estimated to be $\Delta\sigma_1 = 28.8$ kN/m² and $\Delta\sigma_3 = 19.2$ kN/m².

Consolidated undrained triaxial tests carried out on representative undisturbed samples of the clay gave the following results:

Cell pressure = 35 kN/m²

Strain (%)	Deviator stress (kN/m²)	Pore water pressure (kN/m²)	
0	0	0	
1	10.4	0.4	
2	20.7	4.8	
3	29.0	9.7	
4	33.2	13.8	
5	35.8	16.6	
6	37.3	17.9	
6.8	37.8	19.3	(failure)

Cell pressure = 70 kN/m²

0	0	0	
1	20.7	4.1	
2	42.7	12.8	
3	54.4	22.1	
4	63.4	30.4	
5	66.1	34.8	
6	71.7	37.9	
7	75.8	40.7	(failure)

By considering a point at the centre of the clay layer and below the centre of the foundation, draw the effective stress paths for undrained shear obtained from the tests and indicate the effective stress paths for the immediate and consolidation settlements that the foundation will experience.

Assume that $K_0 = 1 - \sin\phi$ and determine an approximate value for the immediate settlement of the foundation.

Solution

The first step is to plot out the two effective stress paths. The calculations are best set out in tabular form:

Cell pressure = 35 kN/m²

Strain	$\sigma_1 - \sigma_3$	u	$q = \dfrac{\sigma_1 - \sigma_2}{2}$	$p' = \dfrac{\sigma_1' + \sigma_3'}{2}$
0	0	0	0	35
1	10.4	0.4	5.2	39.8
2	20.7	4.8	10.3	40.5
3	29.7	9.7	14.5	39.8
4	33.2	13.2	16.6	38.4
5	35.8	16.6	17.9	36.3
6	37.3	17.9	18.6	35.7
6.8	37.8	19.3	18.9	34.6

Cell pressure = 70 kN/m²

0	0	0	0	70
1	20.7	4.1	10.3	76.2
2	42.7	12.8	21.3	78.5
3	54.4	22.1	27.2	75.1
4	63.4	30.4	31.7	71.3
5	66.1	34.8	33.0	68.2
6	71.7	37.9	35.8	67.9
7	75.8	40.7	37.9	67.2

The stress paths are shown in Fig. 9.16. From the K_f line tan α (= sin ϕ) = tan 28.5° = 0.543

$$\therefore K_0 = 1 - 0.543 = 0.457$$

Effective stresses at centre of layer before application of foundation load

$$\sigma_1'_I = 85 \text{ kN/m}^2$$

Clay is normally consolidated, therefore

$$\sigma_3'_I = 0.457 \times 85 = 38.8 \text{ kN/m}^2$$

$$\therefore \quad p' = \frac{85 + 38.8}{2} = 61.9; q = \frac{85 - 38.8}{2} = 23.1$$

The coordinates p' and q are plotted on Fig. 9.16 to give the point A, the initial state of stress in the soil.

Effective stress at centre of clay layer after application and consolidation of foundation load

$$\sigma_1'_F = \sigma_1'_I + \Delta\sigma_1 = 85 + 28.8 = 113.8 \text{ kN/m}^2$$

$$\sigma_3'_F = \sigma_3'_I + \Delta\sigma_3 = 38.8 + 19.2 = 58.0 \text{ kN/m}^2$$

$$\therefore p' = \frac{113.8 + 58}{2} = 85.9; \qquad q = \frac{113.8 - 58}{2} = 27.9$$

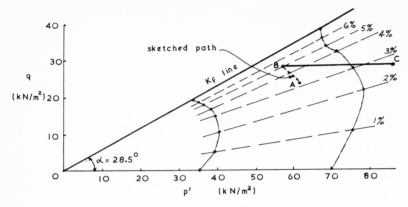

Fig. 9.16 Example 9.8

The coordinates p' and q are plotted in Fig. 9.16 to give the point C, the state of the effective stresses in the soil after consolidation. As illustrated in Fig. 9.11 the stress path from A to B represents the effect of the immediate settlement, whereas the stress path from B to C represents the effects of the consolidation settlement. The problem is to establish the point B, the point that represents the effective stress state in the soil immediately after the application of the foundation load.

During consolidation, at all times, $q = \frac{1}{2}(\sigma_1 - \sigma_3) = \frac{1}{2}(\sigma_1' - \sigma_3')$. Hence, no matter how the individual values of effective stress vary during consolidation, the value of q remains constant. The line BC must be parallel to the horizontal axis. Hence the point B must lie somewhere along the horizontal line through C.

From A to B the effective undrained stress path is unknown but it is possible to sketch in an approximate, but sufficiently accurate path, by comparing the two test stress paths on either side of it. This has been done in the figure. The immediate settlement can now be found. On the diagram the strain contours (lines joining equal strain values on the two test paths) are drawn. It is seen that the point A lies a little above the 3 per cent strain contour (3.2%). Point B lies on the 5 per cent strain contour. Hence the strain suffered with immediate settlement = 5 − 3.2 = 1.8%

$$\therefore \rho_i = \frac{1.8}{100} \times 9.25 = 0.167 \text{ m}$$

EXERCISES ON CHAPTER 9

1. Using the test results from example 4.9, determine an approximate value for E of the soil and calculate the average settlement of a foundation,

5 m X 1 m, founded on a thick layer of the same soil with a uniform
pressure of 600 kN/m²
  Answer: 58 mm

2. A rectangular, flexible foundation has dimensions L = 4 m, B = 2 m and
is loaded with a uniform pressure of 400 kN/m². The foundation sits
on a layer of deep clay, E = 10 MN/m². Determine the immediate
settlement values at its centre and at the central points of its edges.
  Answer At centre = 92 mm
       At centre of long edge = 67 mm
       At centre of short edge = 58 mm

3. A standard penetration test carried out at a depth of 5 m in a thick layer
of dry sand, unit weight 16 kN/m³, gave N = 10. Determine (i) from Fig. 9.3
and (ii) by the Dutch cone method the immediate settlement of a foundation,
10 m X 2 m, loaded with a nett uniform pressure of 400 kN/m² and placed
at a depth of 5 m into the sand.
  Answer: 89 mm approx.

4. A saturated sample of a normally consolidated clay gave the following
results when tested in a consolidation apparatus (each loading increment
was applied for 24 hours).

Consolidation pressure (kN/m²)	Thickness of sample (mm)
0	17.32
53.65	16.84
107.3	16.48
214.6	16.18
429.2	15.85
0	16.51

After the sample had been allowed to expand for 24 hours it was found
to have a moisture content of 30.2 per cent. The particle specific gravity
of the soil was 2.65.
(i) Plot the void ratio to effective pressure.
(ii) Plot the void ratio to log effective pressure and hence determine a
value for the compression index of the soil.
(iii) A 6.1 m layer of the soil is subjected to an existing effective overburden
pressure at its centre of 107.3 kN/m², and a foundation load will increase
the pressure at the centre of the layer by 80.5 kN/m². Determine the
probable total consolidation settlement of the layer (a) by the coefficient
of volume compressibility and (b) by the compression index. Explain why
the two methods give slightly different answers.

Answer: (a) Settlement by coefficient of volume compressibility = 85 mm
(b) Settlement by compression index = 98 mm

The compression index method is not so accurate as it represents the average of conditions throughout the entire pressure range whereas the coefficient of volume compressibility applies to the actual pressure range considered.

REFERENCES

Bishop, A. W., & Henkel, D. J.
 The measurements of soil properties in the triaxial test (Edward Arnold, 1962).

Bozozuk, M.
 Soil shrinkage damages shallow foundations at Ottawa. *Engng J. Can. Soc. civ. Engrs,* **45** (1962).

Casagrande, A.
 The determination of the preconsolidation load and its practical significance. *Proc. 1st Int. Conf. Soil Mechanics and Foundation Engineering* (1936).

De Beer, E., & Martens, A.
 Method of computation of an upper limit for the influence of the heterogeneity of sand layers in the settlement of bridges. *Proc. 4th Int. Conf. Soil Mechanics and Foundation Engineering* (1957).

Fox, E. N.
 The mean elastic settlement of a uniformly loaded area at a depth below the ground surface. *Proc. 2nd Int. Conf. Soil Mechanics and Foundation Engineering* (1948).

Lambe, T. W.
 Methods of estimating settlement. *Proc. Am. Soc. civ. Engrs Settlement Conf.* (1964).
 Stress path method. *Proc. Am. Soc. civ. Engrs* (1967)

Meigh, A. C., & Nixon, I. K.
 Comparison of *in situ* tests for granular soils. *Proc. 5th Int. Conf. Soil Mechanics and Foundation Engineering* (1961).

Meyerhof, G. G.
 Penetration tests and bearing capacity of cohesionless soils. *Proc. Am. Soc. civ. Engrs* (1956).

Rutledge, P. C.
 Summary and closing address. *Proc. Am. Soc. civ. Engrs Settlement Conf.* (1964).

Schmertann, J. H.
 Estimating the true consolidation behaviour of clay from laboratory test results. *Proc. Am. Soc. civ. Engrs* (1953).

Skempton, A. W.
 The bearing capacity of clays (Building Research Congress, 1951).

Skempton, A. W., & Bjerrum, L.
A contribution to settlement analysis of foundations on clay. *Géotechnique* (1957).
Skempton, A. W., & MacDonald, D. H.
The allowable settlement of buildings. *Proc. Instn civ. Engrs* (1956).
Smith, G. N.
Determining the settlements of embankments on soft clay. *Highways and Public Works* (1968).
Steinbrenner, W.
Tafeln zur Setzungsberechnung. *Strasse* (1934).
Terzaghi, K.
Theoretical soil mechanics (John Wiley, 1943).
Thorburn, S.
Tentative correction chart for the standard penetration test in non-cohesive soils. *Civ. Engng publ. Wks Rev.* (1963).

10. The Rate of Foundation Settlement

The settlement of a foundation in cohesionless soil and the elastic settlement of a foundation in clay can be assumed to occur as soon as the load is applied. The consolidation settlement of a foundation on clay will only take place as water seeps from the soil at a rate which will depend upon the permeability of the clay.

ANALOGY OF CONSOLIDATION SETTLEMENT

The model shown in Fig. 10.1 helps to give an understanding of the con-

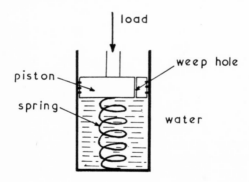

Fig. 10.1 Analogy of consolidation settlement

solidation process. When load is applied to the piston it will be carried initially by the water pressure created, but due to the weep hole there will be a slow bleeding of water from the cylinder accompanied by a progressive settlement of the piston until the spring is compressed to its corresponding load. In the analogy, the spring represents the compressible soil skeleton and the water represents the water in the voids of the soil; the size of the weep hole is analogous to the permeability of the soil.

The degree of consolidation, U, = $\dfrac{\text{Consolidation attained at time t}}{\text{Total consolidation}}$

DISTRIBUTION OF THE INITIAL EXCESS PORE PRESSURE, u_i

If we consider points below the centre of a foundation it is seen that there are three main forms of possible u_i distribution.

Uniform distribution can occur in thin layers (Fig. 10.2A), so that for all practical purposes u_i is constant and equals $\Delta\sigma_1$ at the centre of the layer.

Triangular distribution is found in a deep layer under a foundation, where u_i varies from a maximum value at the top to a negligible value (taken as zero) at some depth below the foundation (Fig. 10.2B[i]). The depth of this variation depends upon the dimensions of the footing. Figure 10.2B[ii] shows how a triangular distribution may vary from $u_i = 0$ at the top of a layer to u_i = a maximum value at the bottom; this condition can arise with a newly placed layer of soil, the applied pressure being the soil's weight.

Trapezoidal distribution results from the quite common situation of a clay layer located at some depth below the foundation (Fig. 10.2C[i]). In the case of a new embankment carrying a superimposed load, a reversed form of trapezoidal distribution is possible (Fig. 10.2C [ii]).

TERZAGHI'S THEORY OF CONSOLIDATION

Terzaghi's first presented this theory in 1925 and most practical work on the prediction of settlement rates is now based upon the differential equation he evolved. The main assumptions in the theory are:

(i) Soil is saturated and homogeneous.
(ii) The coefficient of permeability is constant.
(iii) Darcy's law of saturated flow applies.
(iv) The resulting compression is one dimensional.
(v) Water flows in one direction.
(vi) Volume changes are due solely to changes in void ratio, which are caused by corresponding changes in effective stress.

The expression for flow in a saturated soil has been established in chapter 3. The rate of volume change in a cube of volume dx.dy.dz is:

$$\left(k_x\frac{\partial^2 h}{\partial x^2} + k_y\frac{\partial^2 h}{\partial y^2} + k_z\frac{\partial^2 h}{\partial z^2}\right) dx.dy.dz$$

For one dimensional flow (assumption v) there is no component of hydraulic gradient in the x and y directions, and putting $k_z = k$ the expression becomes:

$$\text{Rate of change of volume} = k\frac{\partial^2 h}{\partial z^2} dx.dy.dz$$

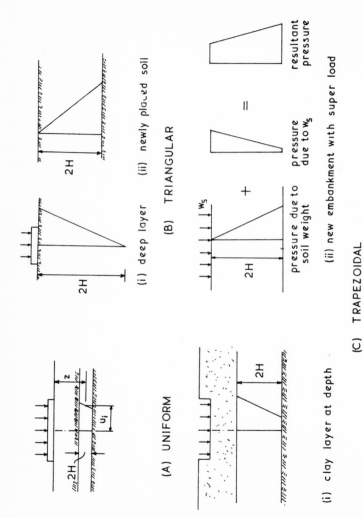

(A) UNIFORM

(i) deep layer

(ii) newly placed soil

(B) TRIANGULAR

pressure due to soil weight + pressure due to w_s = resultant pressure

(ii) new embankment with super load

(i) clay layer at depth

(C) TRAPEZOIDAL

Fig. 10.2 Forms of initial excess pore pressure distribution

The volume changes during consolidation are assumed to be caused by changes in void ratio.

$$\text{Porosity } n = \frac{V_v}{V} = \frac{e}{1 + e}$$

$$\text{Hence} \quad V_v = dx.dy.dz \, \frac{e}{1 + e}$$

Another expression for the rate of change of volume is therefore:

$$\frac{\partial}{\partial t} \left(dx.dy.dz \, \frac{e}{1 + e} \right)$$

Equating these two expressions:

$$k \, \frac{\partial^2 h}{\partial z^2} = \frac{1}{1 + e} \, \frac{\partial e}{\partial t}$$

The head, h, causing flow is the excess hydrostatic head caused by the excess pore water pressure, u.

$$h = \frac{u}{\gamma_w}$$

$$\therefore \quad \frac{k}{\gamma_w} \, \frac{\delta^2 u}{\delta_z^2} = \frac{1}{1 + e} \, \frac{\partial e}{\partial t}$$

With one dimensional consolidation there are no lateral strain effects and the increment of applied pressure is therefore numerically equal (but of opposite sign) to the increment of induced pore pressure. Hence an increment of applied pressure, dp, will cause an excess pore water pressure of du (= −dp).

$$\text{Now} \quad a = - \frac{de}{dp} \quad \text{Hence } a = \frac{de}{du}$$

$$\text{Or} \quad de = a \, du$$

Substituting for de:

$$\frac{k}{\gamma_w}(1+e)\frac{\partial^2 u}{\partial z^2} = a\frac{\partial u}{\partial t}$$

$$\therefore C_v\frac{\partial^2 u}{\partial z^2} = \frac{\partial u}{\partial t}$$

where C_v = the coefficient of consolidation and equals

$$\frac{k}{\gamma_w a}(1+e) = \frac{k}{\gamma_w m_v}$$

In the foregoing theory z is measured from the top of the clay and complete drainage is assumed at both the upper and lower surfaces, the thickness of the layer being taken as 2H. The initial excess pore pressure, u_i, = $-dp$.
The boundary conditions can be expressed mathematically:

When $z = 0$, $u = 0$
When $z = 2H$, $u = 0$
When $t = 0$, $u = u_i$

A solution for

$$C_v\frac{\partial^2 u}{\partial z^2} = \frac{\partial u}{\partial t}$$

that satisfies these conditions can be obtained and gives the value of the excess pore pressure at depth z at time t, u_z:

$$u_z = \sum_{m=0}^{m=\infty}\frac{2u_i}{M}\left(\sin\frac{Mz}{H}\right)e^{-M^2 T}$$

where u_i = the initial excess pore pressure, uniform over the whole depth

$M = \frac{1}{2}\pi(2m+1)$ where m is a positive integer varying from 0 to ∞

$T = \dfrac{C_v t}{H^2}$, known as the time factor

Due to the drainage at the top and bottom of the layer the value of u_i will immediately fall to zero at these points. With the mathematical solution it is possible to determine u at time t for any point within the layer. If these values of pore pressures are plotted, a curve (known as an isochrone) can be drawn through the points (Fig. 10.3B). The maximum excess pore

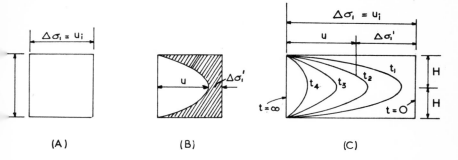

Fig. 10.3 Variation of excess pore pressures with depth and time

pressure is seen to be at the centre of the layer and, for any point, the applied pressure increment, $\Delta\sigma_1 = u + \Delta\sigma'_1$. After a considerable time u will become equal to zero and $\Delta\sigma_1$ will equal $\Delta\sigma'_1$.

The plot of isochrones for different time intervals is shown in Fig. 10.3C. For a particular point the degree of consolidation, U_z, will be equal to

$$\frac{u_i - u_z}{u_i}$$

The mathematical expression for U_z is:

$$U_z = 1 - \sum_{m=0}^{m=\infty} \frac{2}{M} \left(\sin \frac{Mz}{H} \right) e^{-M^2T}$$

Average degree of consolidation

Instead of thinking in terms of U_z, the degree of consolidation of a particular point at depth z, we think in terms of U, the average state of consolidation throughout the whole layer. The amount of consolidation still to be undergone at a certain time is represented by the area enclosed under the particular isochrone, and the total consolidation is represented by the area of the initial excess pore pressure distribution diagram (Fig. 10.3A). The consolidation achieved at this isochrone is therefore the total consolidation less the area under the curve (shown hatched in Fig. 10.3B).

Average degree of consolidation,

$$U = \frac{2Hu_i - \text{area under isochrone}}{2Hu_i}$$

The mathematical expression for U is:

$$U = 1 - \sum_{m=0}^{m=\infty} \frac{2}{M^2} e^{-M^2 T}$$

A theoretical relationship between U and T can therefore be established and is shown in Fig. 10.4, which also gives the relationship for u_i distributions that are not uniform.

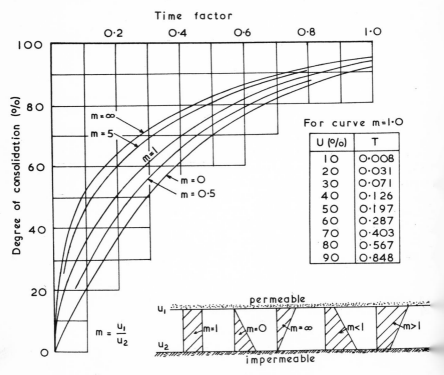

Fig. 10.4 Theoretical consolidation curves

For curve m=1·0

U (%)	T
10	0·008
20	0·031
30	0·071
40	0·126
50	0·197
60	0·287
70	0·403
80	0·567
90	0·848

Drainage path length

A consolidating soil layer is usually enclosed having at its top either the foundation or another layer of soil and beneath it either another soil layer or rock. If the materials above and below the layer are pervious, the water under pressure in the layer will travel either upwards or downwards (a concrete foundation is taken as being pervious compared to a clay layer). This case is known as two-way drainage and the drainage path length, i.e.

the maximum length that a water particle can travel, (Fig. 10.5A)

$$= \frac{\text{thickness of layer}}{2} = H$$

If one of the materials is impermeable, water will only travel in one direction — the one-way drainage case — and the length of the drainage path = thickness of layer = 2H (Fig. 10.5B).

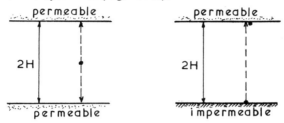

(A) Two way drainage   (B) One way drainage

Fig. 10.5 Drainage path lengths

The curves of Fig. 10.4 refer to cases of one-way drainage (drainage path length = 2H). Due to the approximations involved the curve for m = 1 is often taken for the other cases with the assumption that u_i is the initial excess pore pressure at the centre of the layer. For cases of two-way drainage the curve for m = 1 should be used and the drainage path length, for the determination of T, is taken as H.

Determination of the coefficient of consolidation, C_v, from the consolidation test

If for a particular pressure increment applied during a consolidation test the compression of the test sample is plotted against the square root of time, the result shown in Fig. 10.6 will be obtained.

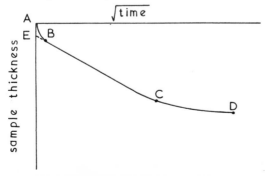

Fig. 10.6 Typical consolidation test results

The curve is seen to consist of three distinct parts: AB, BC and CD.

AB (initial compression or frictional lag). A small but rapid compression sometimes occurs at the commencement of the increment and is probably due to the compression of any air present or to the reorientation of some of the larger particles in the sample. In the majority of tests this effect is absent and points A and B are coincident. Initial compression is not considered to be due to any loss of water from the soil and should be treated as a zero error for which a correction is made.

BC (primary compression). All the compression in this part of the curve is taken as being due to the expulsion of water from the sample, although some secondary compression will also occur. When the pore pressure has been reduced to a negligible amount it is assumed that 100 per cent consolidation has been attained.

CD (secondary compression). The amount by which this effect is evident is a function of the test conditions and can hardly be related to an in situ value.

The square root of time 'fitting' method

It will be appreciated that the curve described above is an actual consolidation curve and would not be obtainable from one of the theoretical curves of Fig. 10.4 , which can only be used to plot the primary compression range. To evaluate the coefficient of consolidation it is necessary to establish the point C, representing 100 per cent primary consolidation, but it is difficult from a study of the test curve to fix C with accuracy and a procedure in which which the test curve is 'fitted' to the theoretical curve becomes necessary.

A method was described by Taylor (1948). If the theoretical curve of U against $\sqrt{T}$ is plotted for the case of a uniform initial excess pore pressure distribution, the curve will be like that shown in Fig. 10.7A. Up to values

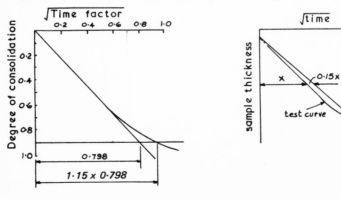

(A) Theoretical curve   (B) Establishment of t_{90}

Fig. 10.7 The square root of time 'fitting' method

of U equal to about 60 per cent, the curve is a straight line of equation $U = 1.13\sqrt{T}$, but if this straight line is extended to cut the ordinate $U = 90$ per cent the abscissa of the curve is seen to be 1.15 times the abscissa of the straight line. This fact is used to fit the test and theoretical curves.

With the test curve a corrected zero must first be established by projecting the straight line part of the primary compression back to cut the vertical axis at E (Fig. 10.6). A second line, starting through E, is now drawn such that all absicissas on it are 1.15 times the corresponding values on the laboratory curve, and the point at which this second line cuts the laboratory curve is taken to be the point representing 90 per cent primary consolidation (Fig. 10.7B).

To establish C_v, T_{90} is first found from the theoretical curve that fits the drainage conditions (the curve m = 1); t_{90} is determined from the test curve.

$$T_{90} = \frac{C_v t_{90}}{H^2}$$

i.e. $$C_v = \frac{T_{90} H^2}{t_{90}}$$

It is seen that the point of 90 per cent consolidation rather than the point for 100 per cent consolidation is used to establish C_v. This is simply a matter of suitability. A consolidation test sample is always drained on both surfaces and in the formula H is taken as half the mean thickness of the sample for the pressure range considered. At first glance it would seem that C_v could not possibly be constant, even for a fairly small pressure range, because as the effective stress is increased the void ratio decreases and both k and m_v decrease rapidly. However, the ratio of k/m_v remains sensibly constant over a large range of pressure so it is justifiable to assume that C_v is in fact constant.

One drawback of the consolidation theory is the assumption that both Poisson's ratio and the elastic modulus of the soil remain constant whereas in reality they both vary as consolidation proceeds. Due to this continuous variation there is a continuous change in the stress distribution within the soil which, in turn, causes a continuous change in the values of excess pore water pressures. Theories that allow for this effect of the change in applied stress with time have been prepared by Biot (1941) and extended by others, but the approximations involved (together with the sophistication of the mathematics) usually force the user back to the original Terzaghi equation.

Determination of the permeability coefficient from the consolidation test
Having established C_v, k can be obtained from the formula $k = C_v m_v \gamma_w$. It should be noted that since the mean thickness of the sample is used to

determine C_v, m_v should be taken as $a/(1 + \bar{e})$ where $\bar{e}$ is the mean void ratio over the appropriate pressure range.

Determination of the consolidation coefficient from the triaxial test

It is possible to determine the C_v value of a soil from the consolidation part of the consolidated undrained triaxial test. In this case the consolidation is three-dimensional and the value of C_v obtained is greater than would be the case if the soil were tested in the oedometer. Filter paper drains are usually placed around the sample to create radial drainage so that the time for consolidation is reduced. The effect of three-dimensional drainage is allowed for in the calculation for C_v, but the value obtained is not usually dependable as it is related to the relative permeabilities of the soil and the filter paper (Rowe, 1959).

The time taken for consolidation to occur in the triaxial test generally gives a good indication of the necessary rate of strain for the undrained shear part of the test, but it is not advisable to use this time to determine C_v unless there are no filter drains.

The consolidation characteristics of a partially saturated soil are best obtained from the triaxial test, which can give the initial pore water pressures and the volume change under undrained conditions. Having applied the cell pressure and noted these readings, the pore pressures within the sample are allowed to dissipate while further pore pressure measurements are taken; the accuracy of the results obtained is much greater than with the consolidation test as the difficulty of fitting the theoretical and test curves when air is present is largely removed. The dissipation test is described by Bishop & Henkel (1962).

The model law of consolidation

If two layers of the same clay with different drainage path lengths H_1 and H_2 are acted upon by the same pressure increase and reach the same degree of consolidation in times t_1 and t_2 respectively, then theoretically their coefficients of consolidation must be equal as must their time factors, T_1 and T_2.

$$T_1 = \frac{C_{v1} t_1}{H_1^2} \qquad T_2 = \frac{C_{v2} t_2}{H_2^2}$$

Equating: $$\frac{t_1}{H_1^2} = \frac{t_2}{H_2^2}$$

This gives a simple method for determining the degree of consolidation in a layer if the simplifying assumption is made that the compression recorded in the consolidation test is solely due to primary compression (see example 10.1).

Consolidation during construction

A sufficiently accurate solution is generally achieved by assuming that the entire foundation load is applied halfway through the construction period. For large constructions, spread over some years, it is sometimes useful to know the amount of consolidation that will have taken place by the end of construction, the problem being that whilst consolidating the clay is subjected to an increasing load.

Figure 10.8 illustrates the loading diagram during and after construction. While excavation is proceeding swelling may occur (see example 9.7) such as that which took place in the course of excavation for the piers of Chelsea Bridge, which involved the removal of about 9 m of London Clay and resulted in a heave of 6 mm (Skempton, Peck & McDonald, 1953). If the coefficient of swelling, C_{vs}, is known it would be fairly straightforward to obtain a solution, firstly as the pore pressures increase (swelling) and then as they decrease (consolidation), but the assumption is usually made that once the construction weight equals the weight of soil excavated (time t_1 in Fig. 10.8) heave is eliminated and consolidation commences. The

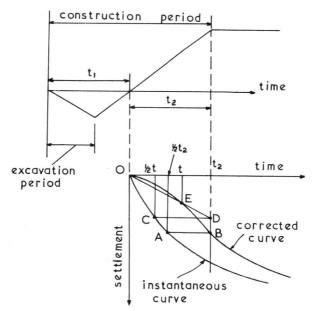

Fig. 10.8 Consolidation during construction

treatment of the problem has been discussed by Taylor (1948), who gave a graphical solution, and Lumb (1963), who prepared a theoretical solution for the case of a thin consolidating layer.

By plotting the load-time relationship the time t_1 can be found (Fig. 10.8), the time t_2 being taken as the time in which the nett foundation load is applied. The settlement curve, assuming instantaneous application of the load at time t_1, is now plotted and a correction is made to the curve by assuming that the actual consolidation settlement at the end of time t_2 has the same value as the settlement on the instantaneous curve at time $\frac{1}{2}t_2$ Point A, corresponding to $\frac{1}{2}t_2$, is obtained on the instantaneous curve, and point B is established on the corrected curve by drawing a horizontal from A to meet the ordinate of time t_2 at point B. To establish other points on the corrected curve the procedure is to (i) select a time, t, (ii) determine the settlement on the instantaneous curve for $\frac{1}{2}t$ (point C), (iii) draw a horizontal from C to meet the ordinate for t_2 at D, and (iv) join OD. Where OD cuts the ordinate for time t gives the point E on the corrected curve, the procedure being repeated with different values of t until sufficient points are established for the curve to be drawn. Points beyond B on the corrected curve are displaced horizontally by the distance AB from the corresponding points on the instantaneous curve (see example 10.4).

Consolidation by drainage in two and three dimensions

The majority of settlement analyses are based on the frequently incorrect assumption that the flow of water in the soil is one-dimensional, partly for ease of calculation and partly because in most cases knowledge of soil compression values in three dimensions is limited. There are occasions when this assumption can lead to significant errors (as in the case of an anisotropic soil with a horizontal permeability so much greater than its vertical value that the time-settlement relationship is considerably altered) and when dealing with a foundation which is relatively small compared to the thickness of the consolidating layer some form of analysis allowing for lateral drainage becomes necessary. For an isotropic, homogeneous soil the differential equation for three-dimensional consolidation is:

$$C_v \left(\frac{\partial^2 u}{\partial x^2} + \frac{\partial^2 u}{\partial y^2} + \frac{\partial^2 u}{\partial z^2} \right) = \frac{\partial u}{\partial t}$$

For two dimensions one of the terms in the bracket is dropped.

NUMERICAL DETERMINATION OF CONSOLIDATION RATES

When a consolidating layer of clay is subjected to an irregular distribution of initial excess pore water pressure, the theoretical solutions are not usually applicable unless the distribution can be approximated to one of the cases considered. In such circumstances the use of a numerical method is fairly common.

Gibson & Lumb (1953) illustrated how the numerical solution of consolidation problems can be obtained by using the explicit finite difference equation. The differential equation for one-dimensional consolidation has been established:

$$C_v \frac{\partial^2 u}{\partial z^2} = \frac{\partial u}{\partial t}$$

Consider part of a grid drawn on to a consolidating layer (Fig. 10.9A).

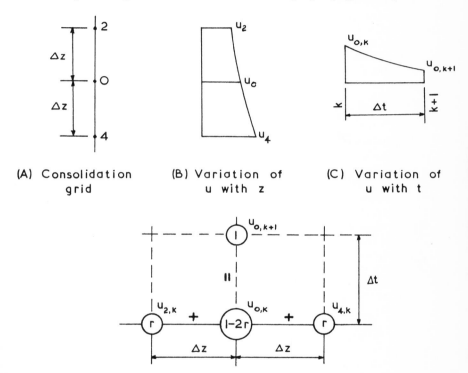

(A) Consolidation grid

(B) Variation of u with z

(C) Variation of u with t

(D) Schematic form of equation

Fig. 10.9 Explicit recurrence formula (general)

The variation of the excess pore pressure, u, with the depth, z, at a certain time, k, is shown in Fig. 10.9B, and the variation of u at the point 0 during a time increment from k to k + 1 is illustrated by Fig. 10.9C.

In Fig. 10.9B: from Taylor's theorem:

$$u_{2, k} = u_{0, k} - \Delta z\, u'_{0, k} + \frac{\Delta z^2}{2!}\, u''_{0, k} - \frac{\Delta z^3}{3!}\, u'''_{0, k} + \ldots$$

$$u_{4, k} = u_{0, k} + \Delta z\, u'_{0, k} + \frac{\Delta z^2}{2!}\, u''_{0, k} + \frac{\Delta z^3}{3!}\, u'''_{0, k} + \ldots$$

Adding and ignoring terms greater than 2nd order:

$$u_{2, k} + u_{4, k} = 2u_{0, k} + \Delta z^2 u''_{0, k}$$

$$\therefore \quad \frac{\partial^2 u}{\partial z^2} = u''_{0, k} = \frac{u_{2, k} + u_{4, k} - 2u_{0, k}}{\Delta z^2}$$

In Fig. 10.8C: $\dfrac{\partial u}{\partial t}$ is a function $u = f(t)$

By Taylor's theorem: $u_{0, k+1} = u_{0, k} + \Delta t\, u'_{0, k} + \dfrac{\Delta t^2}{2!}\, u''_{0, k} + \ldots$

Ignoring second derivatives and above:

$$\frac{\partial u}{\partial t} = u'_{0, k} = \frac{u_{0, k+1} - u_{0, k}}{\Delta t}$$

$$\therefore \quad C_v \left(\frac{u_{2, k} + u_{4, k} - 2u_{0, k}}{\Delta z^2} \right) = \frac{u_{0, k+1} - u_{0, k}}{\Delta t}$$

$$\therefore \quad u_{0, k+1} = r(u_{2, k} + u_{4, k} - 2u_{0, k}) + u_{0, k}$$

$$\text{where} \quad r = \frac{C_v \Delta t}{\Delta z^2}$$

The schematic form of this expression is shown in Fig. 10.9D. Hence if a series of points in a consolidating layer are established, Δz apart, it is possible by numerical iteration to work out the values of u at any time interval after consolidation has commenced if the initial excess values, u_i, are known.

Impermeable boundary conditions. Figure 10.10A illustrates this case in which conditions at the boundary are represented by $\dfrac{\partial u}{\partial z} = 0$

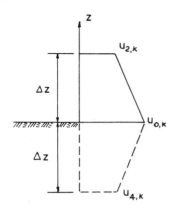
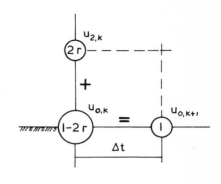

(A) Variation of u with z   (B) Schematic form of equation

Fig. 10.10 Explicit recurrence formula: treatment for an impermeable
boundary

Hence between the points 2_k and 4_k:

$$\frac{\partial u}{\partial z} = \frac{u_{2,k} - u_{4,k}}{2\Delta z} = 0$$

i.e. $u_{2,k} = u_{4,k}$

The equation therefore becomes: $u_{0,k+1} = 2r(u_{2,k} - u_{0,k}) + u_{0,k}$

and is shown in schematic form in Fig. 10.10B.

The boundary equation can also be used at the centre of a double drained
layer with a symmetrical initial pore pressure distribution, values for only
half the layer needing to be evaluated.

Errors associated with the explicit equation. A full discussion of this
subject was given by Crandall (1956), but briefly errors fall into two main
groups: truncation errors (due to ignoring the higher derivatives) and round-
ing-off errors (due to working to only a certain number of decimal places).
The size of the space increment, Δz, affects both these errors but in different
ways: the smaller Δz is, the less the truncation error that arises but the
greater the round-off error tends to become.

The value of r is also important. For stability r must not be greater than 0.5 and, for minimum truncation errors, should be 1/6; the usual practice is to take r as near as possible to 0.5. This restriction means that the time interval must be short and a considerable number of iterations become necessary to obtain the solution for a large time interval. For these cases use can be made of either the implicit finite difference equation (Crank & Nicolson, 1947) or the relaxation method (Leibmann 1955).

Construction pore pressures in an earth dam

A knowledge of the induced pore pressures occurring during the construction of an earth dam or embankment is necessary so that stability analyses can be carried out and a suitable construction rate determined. Such a problem is best solved by numerical methods. During the construction of an earth dam (or an embankment) the placing of material above that already in position increases the pore water pressure whilst consolidation has the effect of decreasing it: the problem is one of a layer of soil that is consolidating as it is increased in thickness. Gibson (1958) examined this condition. If it is assumed that the water in the soil will experience vertical drainage only, the finite difference equation becomes:

$$u_{0,\,k+1} = r(u_{2,\,k} + u_{4,\,k} - 2u_{0,\,k}) + u_{0,\,k} + \bar{B}\gamma\Delta z$$

where Δz = the grid spacing, and also the increment of dam thickness placed in time Δt.

γ = density of dam material

$\bar{B}$ = pore pressure coefficient

$$r = \frac{C_v\Delta t}{\Delta z^2}$$

In order that Δz is constant throughout the full height of the dam, all construction periods must be approximated to the same linear relationship and then transformed into a series of steps. The formula can only be applied to a layer that has some finite thickness, and as the layer does not exist initially it is necessary to obtain a solution by some other method for the early stages of construction when the dam is insufficiently thick for the formula to be applicable. Smith (1968) has shown how the relaxation procedure can be used for this initial stage.

Numerical solutions for two- and three-dimensional consolidation

Two-dimensional consolidation

The differential equation for two-dimensional consolidation has already been given:

$$C_v\left(\frac{\partial^2 u}{\partial x^2} + \frac{\partial^2 u}{\partial y^2}\right) = \frac{\partial u}{\partial t}$$

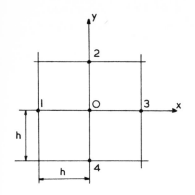

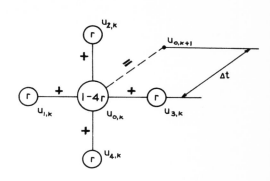

(A) Consolidation grid   (B) Schematic form of equation

Fig. 10.11 Schematic form of the finite difference equation (two-dimensional)

Part of a consolidation grid is shown in Fig. 10.11A; from the previous discussion of the finite difference equation we can write down:

$$\frac{\partial u}{\delta t} = \frac{u_{0,\,k+1} - u_{0,\,k}}{\Delta t}$$

$$\frac{\partial^2 u}{\partial y^2} = \frac{C_v}{h^2}\,(u_{2,\,k} + u_{4,\,k} - 2u_{0,\,k})$$

$$\frac{\partial^2 u}{\partial x^2} = \frac{C_v}{h^2}\,(u_{1,\,k} + u_{3,\,k} - 2u_{0,\,k})$$

Hence the explicit finite difference equation is:

$$u_{0,\,k+1} = r(u_{1,\,k} + u_{2,\,k} + u_{3,\,k} + u_{4,\,k} + u_{0,\,k}\,(1 - 4r)$$

$$\text{where } r = \frac{C_v \Delta t}{h^2}$$

The schematic form of this equation is illustrated in Fig. 10.11B.

Impermeable boundary condition. Impermeable boundaries are treated as for the one-dimensional case.

Three-dimensional consolidation

For instances of radial symmetry the differential equation can be expressed in polar co-ordinates:

$$C_v\left(\frac{\partial^2 u}{\partial R^2} + \frac{1}{R}\frac{\partial u}{\partial R} + \frac{\partial^2 u}{\partial z^2}\right) = \frac{\partial u}{\partial t}$$

Then
$$\frac{\partial u}{\partial t} = \frac{u_{0,\,k+1} - u_{0,\,k}}{\Delta t}$$

$$\frac{\partial^2 u}{\partial z^2} = \frac{u_{2,\,k} + u_{4,\,k} - 2u_{0,\,k}}{\Delta z^2}$$

$$\frac{\partial^2 u}{\partial R^2} = \frac{u_{1,\,k} + u_{3,\,k} - 2u_{0,\,k}}{\Delta R^2}$$

$$\frac{1}{r}\frac{\partial u}{\partial R} = \frac{1}{R}\left(\frac{u_{3,\,k} - u_{1,\,k}}{2\Delta R}\right)$$

If we put $\Delta z = \Delta R = h$ the finite difference equation becomes:

$$u_{0,\,k+1} = r(u_{2,\,k} + u_{4,\,k}) + u_{0,\,k}(1 - 4r) + ru_{1,\,k}\left(1 - \frac{h}{2R}\right) +$$

$$+ ru_{3,\,k}\left(1 + \frac{h}{2R}\right) \text{ where } r = \frac{C_v \Delta t}{h^2}$$

At the origin, where $R = 0$

$$\frac{1}{R}\frac{\partial u}{\partial R} \longrightarrow \frac{\partial^2 u}{\partial R^2}$$

and the equation becomes:

$$u_{0,\,k+1} = ru_{2,\,k} + 4r_{3,\,k} + ru_{4,\,k} + u_{0,\,k}(1 - 6r)$$

Using the convention $R = mh$, the schematic form for the explicit equation is shown in Fig. 10.12A (for a point at the origin) and Fig. 10.12B (for other interior points).

For drainage in the vertical direction the procedure is the same, but for radial drainage the expression for $u_{0,\,k+1}$ at a boundary point, where

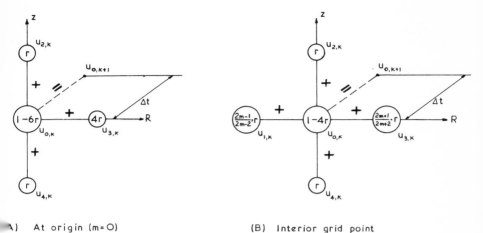

(A) At origin (m = O)   (B) Interior grid point

Fig. 10.12 Schematic form of the finite difference equation (three-dimensional)

$\partial u / \partial R = 0$, is given by

$$u_{0,\,k+1} = r(u_{2,\,k} + u_{4,\,k}) + 2ru_{1,\,k} + u_{0,\,k}\,(1 - 4r)$$

Value of r. Scott (1963) pointed out that in three-dimensional work the explicit recurrence formula is stable if r is either equal to or less than 1/6. This is not so severe a restriction as it would at first appear, since with three-dimensional drainage the time required to reach a high degree of consolidation is much less than for one-dimensional drainage. For two-dimensional work r should not exceed 0.25.

Determination of initial excess pore water pressure values

For one-dimensional consolidation problems, u_i can at any point be taken as equal to the increment of the total major principal stress at that point. For two- and three-dimensional problems u_i must be obtained from the formula:

$$u_i = B[\Delta\sigma_3 + A(\Delta\sigma_1 - \Delta\sigma_3)]$$

As the clay is assumed saturated, $B = 1.0$

Sand Drains

Sometimes the natural rate of consolidation of a particular soil is too slow, particularly when the layer overlies an impermeable material and, in order that the structure may carry out its intended purpose, the rate of consolidation must be increased. An example of where this type of problem can occur is an embankment designed to carry road traffic. It is essential that most of the settlement has taken place before the pavement is constructed if excessive cracking is to be avoided.

From the Model Law of Consolidation it is known that the rate of consolidation is proportional to the square of the drainage path length. Obviously the consolidation rate is increased if horizontal, as well as vertical, drainage paths are made available to the pore water. This can be achieved by the installation of a system of sand drains, which is essentially a set of vertical boreholes put down through the layer, ideally to a firmer material, and then backfilled with porous material, such as a suitably graded sand. The method was first used across a marsh in California and is described by Porter (1936).

A typical arrangement is shown in Fig. 10.13A. There are occasions when the sand drains are made to puncture through an impermeable layer when there is a pervious layer beneath it. This creates two-way vertical drainage, as well as lateral, and results in a considerable speeding up of construction.

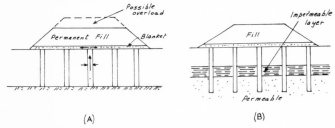

(A)   (B)

Fig. 10.13 Typical sand drain arrangements

Diameter of drains: vary from 300 to 600 mm. Diameters less than 300 mm are generally difficult to install unless the surrounding soil is considerably remoulded.

Spacing of drains: depends upon the type of soil in which they are placed. Spacings vary between 1.5 and 4.5 m. Sand drains are effective if the spacing, a, is less than the thickness of the consolidating layer, 2H.

Arrangement of grid

Sand drains are laid out in either square (Fig. 10.14A) or triangular (Fig. 10.14B) patterns. For triangular arrangements the grid forms a series of

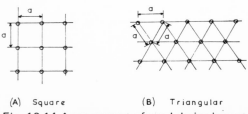

(A) Square   (B)   Triangular

Fig. 10.14 Arrangement of sand drains layout

equilateral triangles the sides of which are equal to the drain spacing.
Barron (1948) maintains that triangular spacing is more economical. In his
paper he solved the consolidation theory for sand drains.

Depth of sand drains: dictated by subsoil conditions. Sand drains have been
installed to depths of up to 45 m.

Type of sand used: should be clean and able to carry away water yet not
permit the fine particles of soil to be washed in.

Drainage blanket: after drains are installed a blanket of gravel and sand,
from 0.33 to 1.0 m thick, is spread over the entire area to provide lateral
drainage at the base of the fill.

Overfill or overload fill: often used in conjunction with sand drains. It
consists of extra fill material placed above the permanent fill to accelerate
consolidation. Once piezometer measurements indicate that consolidation
has become very slow this overload is removed. Usual period of application
of an overload is about one month.

Strain effects: although there is lateral drainage, lateral strain effects are
assumed to be negligible. Hence the consolidation of a soil layer in which
sand drains are placed is still obtained from the expression:

$$\rho_c = m_v \, d_p \, 2H$$

Consolidation Theory
The three-dimensional consolidation equation is:

$$C_h \left[\frac{\partial^2 u}{\partial r^2} + \frac{1}{r} \frac{\partial u}{\partial r} \right] + C_v \frac{\partial^2 u}{\partial z^2}$$

where C_h = coefficient of consolidation for horizontal drainage (when it
    can be measured: otherwise use C_v).

The various coordinate directions of the equation are shown in Fig. 10.15.
The equation can be solved by finite differences.

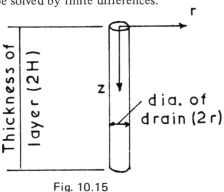

Fig. 10.15

Equivalent radius
The effect of each sand drain extends to the end of its equivalent radius,
which differs for square and triangular arrangements.

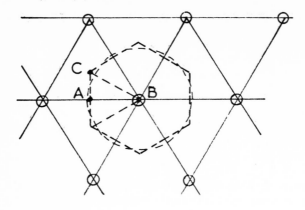

Fig. 10.16

For a square system:
Area of square enclosed by grid = a^2
Area of equivalent circle of radius R = a^2
i.e. $\pi R^2 = a^2$
or R = 0.564a
For a triangular system:
A hexagon is formed by bisecting the various grid lines joining adjacent drains (Fig. 10.16). A typical hexagon is shown in the figure from which it is seen that the base of triangle ABC, i.e. the line AB, = a/2.

Now $\qquad$ AC = AB tan $\angle$ CBA = $\frac{a}{2}$ tan 30° = $\frac{a}{2\sqrt{3}}$

Hence, area of triangle ABC = $\frac{1}{2} \times \frac{a}{2} \times \frac{a}{2\sqrt{3}} = \frac{a^2}{8\sqrt{3}}$

So that the total area of the hexagon = $12 \times \frac{a^2}{8\sqrt{3}} = 0.865\,a^2$

and the radius of the equivalent circle, R = 0.525a
Determination of consolidation rates from curves
Barron has produced curves which give the relationship between the degree of consolidation due to radial flow only, U_r, and the corresponding radial time factor, T_r.

$$T_r = \frac{C_h t}{4R^2}$$

where t = time considered.

These curves are reproduced in Fig. 10.17 and it can be seen that they involve the use of factor n. This factor is simply the ratio of the equivalent radius to the sand drain radius.

$$n = \frac{R}{r} \text{ and should lie between 5 to 100.}$$

To determine U (for both radial and vertical drainage) for a particular time, t, the procedure becomes:

(i) Determine U_z from the normal consolidation curves of U_z against T_z (Fig. 10.4).

$$T_z = \frac{C_v t}{H^2} \text{ where H = vertical drainage path.}$$

(ii) Determine U_r from Barron's curves of U_r against T_r.
(iii) Determine resultant percentage consolidation, U, from:

$$U = 100 - \frac{1}{100}(100 - U_z)(100 - U_r)$$

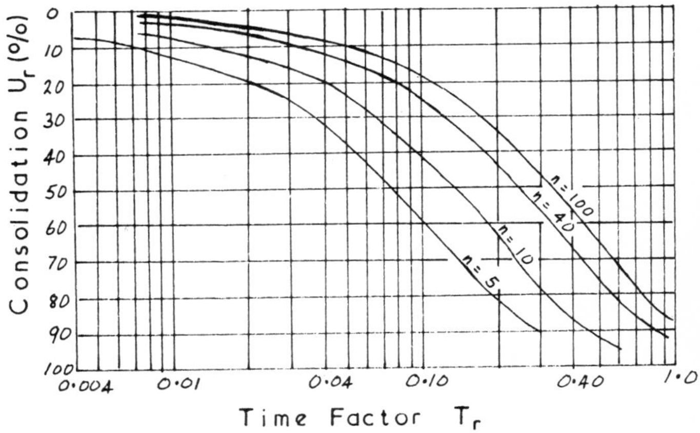

Fig. 10.17 Radial consolidation rates. (After Barron, 1948)

Smear effects

The curves in Fig. 10.17 are for idealized drains, perfectly installed, clean and working correctly. Wells are often installed by driving cased holes and then backfilling as the casing is withdrawn, a procedure that causes distortion and remoulding in the adjacent soil. In varved clays (clays with sandwich type layers of silt and sand within them) the finer and more impervious layers are dragged down and smear over the more pervious layers to create a zone of reduced permeability around the perimeter of the drain. This smeared zone reduces the rate of consolidation, and in situ measurements to check on the estimated settlement rate are necessary on all but the smallest of jobs.

Effectiveness of sand drains

Sand drains are particularly suitable for soft clays but have little effect on soils with small primary but large secondary effects, such as peat. See Lake (1963).

EXAMPLES ON CHAPTER 10 .

Example 10.1

During a pressure increment a consolidation test sample attained 25 per cent primary consolidation in 5 minutes with a mean thickness of 18 mm. How long would it take a 20 m thick layer of the same soil to reach the same degree of consolidation if (i) the layer was drained on both surfaces and (ii) it was drained on the top surface only?

Solution

In the consolidation test the sample is drained top and bottom

$$\therefore H_1 \frac{18}{2} = 9.0 \text{ mm}$$

(i) With layer drained on both surfaces $H_2 = 10 \text{ m} = 10\,000 \text{ mm}$

$$t_2 = \frac{t_1}{H_1^2} H_2^2 = \frac{5 \times 10\,000^2}{9^2} \times \frac{1}{60} \times \frac{1}{24} \times \frac{1}{365} = 11.7 \text{ years}$$

(ii) With layer drained on top surface only $H_2 = 20 \text{ m}$

$$\therefore t_2 = 4 \times 11.7 = 47 \text{ years}$$

Example 10.2

A 19.1 mm thick clay sample, drained top and bottom, reached 30 per cent consolidation in 10 minutes. How long would it take the same sample to reach 50 per cent consolidation?

Solution

As U is known (30 per cent) we can obtain T, either from Fig. 10.4 or by using the relationship that $U = 1.13\sqrt{T}$ (up to U = 60 per cent).

$$T_{30} = \left(\frac{0.3}{1.13}\right)^2 = 0.07$$

$$T = \frac{C_v t}{H^2}, \text{ so } C_v = \frac{0.07 \times 9.55^2}{10} = 0.6384 \text{ mm}^2/\text{min}$$

$$T_{50} = \left(\frac{0.5}{1.13}\right)^2 = 0.197 \text{ (or obtain from Fig. 10.5)}$$

$$t_{50} = \frac{T_{50} H^2}{C_v} = \frac{0.197 \times 9.55^2}{0.6384} = 28.1 \text{ min}$$

Example 10.3

Results obtained from a consolidation test on a clay sample for a pressure increment of 100–200 kN/m² were:

Thickness of sample (mm)	Time (min)
12.200	0
12.141	¼
12.108	1
12.075	2¼
12.046	4
11.985	9
11.922	16
11.865	25
11.827	36
11.809	49
11.800	64

(i) Determine the coefficient of consolidation of the soil.

(ii) How long would a layer of this clay, 10 m thick and drained on its top top surface only, take to reach 75 per cent primary consolidation?

(iii) If the void ratios at the beginning and end of the increment were 0.94 and 0.82 respectively, determine the value of the coefficient of permeability.

Solution

(i) The first step is to determine t_{90}. The thickness of the sample is plotted against the square root of time (Fig. 10.18) and if necessary the curve is

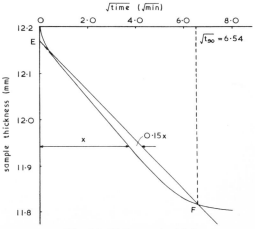

Fig. 10.18 Example 10.3

corrected for zero error to establish the point E. The 1.15 line is next drawn from E and where it cuts the test curve (point F) it gives $\sqrt{t_{90}} = 6.54$. Hence $t_{90} = 42.7$ min.

From the curve for m = 1 (Fig. 10.4), $T_{90} = 0.85$

$$T = \frac{C_v t}{H^2}$$

Mean thickness of sample during increment (corrected initial thickness 12.168)

$$= \frac{12.168 + 11.800}{2} = 11.984 \text{ mm}$$

$$\therefore \quad H = \frac{11.984}{2} = 5.992 \text{ mm}$$

$$C_v = \frac{0.85 \times 5.992^2}{42.7} = 0.715 \text{ mm}^2/\text{min}$$

(ii) For U = 75 per cent, T = 0.48 (from Fig. 10.4)

Drainage path length of layer = 10 m = 10 000 mm

Time to reach 75 per cent consolidation $= \dfrac{0.48 \times 10\,000^2}{0.715} \times \dfrac{1}{60} \times \dfrac{1}{24} \times \dfrac{1}{365}$

$$= 128 \text{ years}$$

(iii) $\qquad a = \dfrac{de}{dp} = \dfrac{0.94 - 0.82}{100} = 0.0012$

$$\bar{e} = \frac{0.94 + 0.82}{2} = 0.88$$

Average $m_v = \dfrac{a}{1 + \bar{e}} = \dfrac{0.0012}{1.88} = 0.000\,638 \text{ m}^2/\text{kN}$

$$k = C_v \gamma_w \, m_v \quad 0.715 \times 9.81 \times 0.000\,638 = 4.48 \times 10^{-3} \text{ mm/min}.$$

Example 10.4

If in example 9.7 the excavation will take 6 months and the structure will be completed in a further 18 months, determine the settlement to time relationship for the central point of the raft during the first 5 years. The clay has a C_v value of 1.86 m²/year and the sandstone may be considered permeable.

Solution
The initial excess pore water pressure distribution will be roughly trapezoidal. The first step is to determine the values of excess pore pressures at the top and bottom of the clay layer.

	Depth below foundation (m)	$\frac{B}{Z}$	$\frac{L}{Z}$	I_σ	$4I_\sigma$	$\Delta\sigma_1$ (kN/m²)
Top of clay	6.1	1.5	4.5	0.229	0.916	268
Bottom of clay	36.6	0.25	0.75	0.06	0.24	70

$m = \dfrac{268}{70} = 3.82$; values of T are obtained from Fig. 10.4.

Drainage path length = 15.25 m

t (years)	$T = \dfrac{C_v t}{H^2}$	U (%)	ρ_c (in)
1	0.008	10	44.8
2	0.016	15	67.2
3	0.024	18	80.6
4	0.032	22	98.6
5	0.040	24	107.5

Plotting the values of consolidation against time gives the settlement curve for instantaneous loading, which can be corrected to allow for the construction period (Fig. 10.19, which also shows the immediate settlement to time plot). The summation of these two plots gives the total settlement to time relationship.

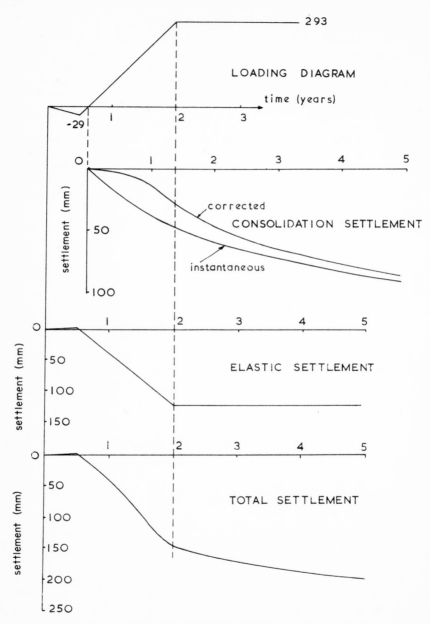

Fig. 10.19 Example 10.4

Example 10.5
A layer of clay 4 m thick is drained on its top surface and has a uniform initial excess pore pressure distribution. The consolidation coefficient of the clay is 0.1 m^2/month. Using a numerical method, determine the degree of consolidation that the layer will have undergone 24 months after the commencement of consolidation. Check your answer by the theoretical curves of Fig. 10.4.

Solution
In a numerical solution the grid must first be established: for this example the layer has been split into 4 layers each of $\Delta z = 1.0$ m (it is important to remember that since Simpson's rule is being applied to determine the degree of consolidation, the layer should be divided into an even number of strips). The initial excess pore pressure values have been taken everywhere throughout the layer as equal to 100 units.

In 24 months $$r = \frac{C_v t}{\Delta z^2} = \frac{0.1 \times 24}{1.0} = 2.4$$

For the finite difference equation r must not be greater than 0.5, so use 5 time increments, i.e. $\Delta t = 4.8$ months and

$$r = \frac{0.1 \times 4.8}{1.0} = 0.48$$

Due to the instantaneous dissipation at the drained surface the excess pore pressure distribution at time = 0 can be taken as that shown in Fig. 10.20

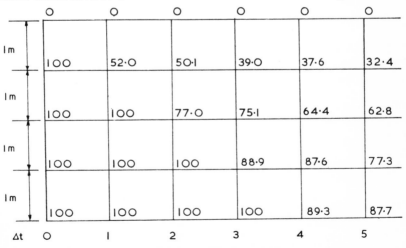

Fig. 10.20 Example 10.5

(the values obtained during the iteration process are also given). The finite difference formula is applied to each point of the grid, except at the drained surface:

$$u_{0,\,k+1} = r(u_{2,\,k} + u_{4,\,k} - 2u_{0,\,k}) + u_{0,\,k}$$

For example, with the first time increment the point next to the drained surface has $u = 0.48(0 + 100 - 2 \times 100) + 100 = 52.0$. Note that at the undrained surface the finite difference equation alters.

Degree of consolidation. Area of initial excess pore pressure distribution diagram = $4 \times 100 = 400$.

Area under final isochrone is obtained by Simpson's rule:

$$\frac{1.0}{3}(87.7 + 4(32.4 + 77.3) + 2 \times 62.8) = 217$$

Hence
$$U = \frac{400 - 217}{400} = 45.7 \text{ per cent}$$

Checking by the theoretical curve:
Total time = 24 months, H = 4 m

$$T = \frac{C_v t}{H^2} = \frac{0.1 \times 24}{16} = 0.15$$

From Fig. 10.4: U = 45 per cent
A problem such as this would not normally be solved by a numerical method.

Example 10.6

At a stage in its construction an earth embankment has attained a height of 9.12 m and has the excess pore water pressure distribution shown in Fig. 10.21A. A proposal has been made that further construction will be at the rate of 1.52 m thickness of material placed in one month, the unit weight of the placed material to be 19.2 kN/m^3 and its $\bar{B}$ value about 0.85. Determine approximate values for the excess pore pressures that will exist within the embankment 3 months after further construction is commenced. C_v for the soil = 0.558 m^2/month.

Solution
Check the r value with Δz taken as equal to 5.0 ft.
For $\Delta z = 5$ ft, t = 1.0 month

$$r = \frac{0.558 \times 1}{(1.52)^2} = 0.241$$

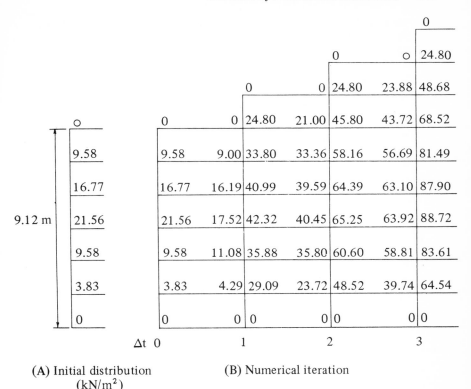

(A) Initial distribution
   (kN/m²)

(B) Numerical iteration

Fig. 10.21 Example 10.6

This value of r is satisfactory and has been used in the solution (if r had been greater than 0.5 then Δt and Δz would have had to be varied until r was less than 0.5.

A 1.52 m deposit of the soil will induce an excess pressure, throughout the whole embankment, of $1.52 \times 19.2 \times \bar{B} = 24.8 \text{ kN/m}^2$. This pressure value must be added to the value at each grid point for each time increment. The pore pressure increase is in fact applied gradually over a month, but for a numerical solution we must assume that it is applied in a series of steps, i.e. 24.8 kN/m^2 at t = 1 month, at t = 2 month, and at t = 3 months. From t = 0 to t = 1 no increment is assumed to be added and the initial pore pressures will have dissipated further before they are increased.

The numerical iteration is shown in Fig. 10.21B.

Example 10.7

A soft clay layer, $m_v = 2.5 \times 10^{-4}$ m^2/kN; $C_v = 0.187$ m^2/month, is 9.2 m thick and overlies impervious shale. An embankment, to be constructed in six months, will subject the centre of the layer to a pressure increase of 100 kN/m^2. It is expected that a roadway will be placed on top of the embankment one year after the start of construction and maximum allowable settlement after this is to be 25 mm.

Determine a suitable sand drain system to achieve the requirements.

Solution

$$\rho_c = m_v \text{ dp } 2H = \frac{2.5}{10\,000} \times 100 \times 9.2 \times 1000 = 230 \text{ mm}$$

$\therefore$ minimum settlement that must have occurred by the time the roadway is constructed = 230 − 25 = 205 mm.

i.e.
$$U = \frac{205}{230} = 90\%$$

Assume that settlement commences at $\frac{1}{2}$ the construction time for the embankment. Then time to reach

$$U = 90\% = 12 - \frac{6}{2} = 9 \text{ months.}$$

$$T_z = \frac{C_v t}{H^2} = \frac{0.187 \times 9}{9.2^2} = 0.020$$

Try 450 mm (0.45 m) diameter drains in a triangular pattern.

Select n = 10.

Then   R/r = 10 and R = 2.25 m

Hence $a = \dfrac{2.25}{0.525} = 4.3$ m

Select a grid spacing of 3 m.

R = 0.525 × 3 = 1.575 m

$$n = \frac{1.575}{0.225} = 0.7$$

$$T_r = \frac{C_v t}{4R^2} = \frac{0.187 \times 9}{4 \times 1.575^2} = 0.169 \quad \text{(Note that no value for } C_h \text{ was given so } C_v \text{ must be used)}$$

From Fig. 10.17, $U_r = 66\%$

$$U = \frac{1}{100}(100 - 16)(100 - 66)$$

$$= 71.4\%, \text{ which is not sufficient}$$

Try a = 2.25 m

R = 1.18 m

n = 5.25

$$T_r = \frac{0.187 \times 9}{4 \times 1.18^2} = 0.302$$

From graph, $U_r = 90\%$

Total consolidation percentage $= 100 - \frac{1}{100}(100 - 16)(100 - 90) = 91.6\%$

The arrangement is satisfactory.

Obviously no sand drain system could be designed as quickly as this. The object of the example is simply to illustrate the method. The question of installation costs must be considered and several schemes would have to be closely examined before a final arrangement could be decided upon.

EXERCISES ON CHAPTER 10

10.1 A soil sample in an oedometer test experienced 30 per cent primary consolidation after 10 minutes. How long would it take the sample to reach 80 per cent consolidation?

Answer: 80 min

10.2 A 5 m thick clay layer has an average C_v value of 5.0×10^{-2} mm²/min. If the layer is subjected to a uniform initial excess pore pressure distribution, determine the time it will take to reach 90 per cent consolidation (i) if drained on both surfaces and (ii) if drained on its upper surface only.

Answer: (i) 200 years ~~w·+bb~~ y/
              (ii) 800 years ~~ffb5.7+~~ y.

10.3 In a consolidation test the following readings were obtained for a pressure increment:

Sample thickness (mm)	Time (min)
16.97	0
16.84	¼
16.76	1
16.61	4
16.46	9
16.31	16
16.15	25
16.08	36
16.03	49
15.98	64
15.95	81

(i) Determine the coefficient of consolidation of the sample.
(ii) From the point for $U = 90$ per cent on the test curve, establish the

point for $U = 50$ per cent and hence obtain the test value for t_{50}. Check your value from the formula

$$t_{50} = \frac{T_{50}H^2}{C_v}$$

Answer: $C_v = 1.28$ mm^2/min
            $t_{50} = 1.02$ min

10.4 A sample in a consolidation test had a mean thickness of 18.1 mm during a pressure increment of 150 to 290 kN/m^2. The sample achieved 50 per cent consolidation in 12.5 min. If the initial and final void ratios for the increment were 1.03 and 0.97 respectively, determine a value for the coefficient of permeability of the soil.
    Answer: $k = 2.78 \times 10^{-6}$ mm/min
            2.66×10^{-6} mm/min

10.5 A 2 m thick layer of clay, drained at its upper surface only, is subjected to a triangular distribution of initial excess pore water pressure varying from 1000 kN/m^2 at the upper surface to 0.0 at the base. The C_v value of the clay is 1.8×10^{-3} m^2/month. By dividing the layer into 4 equal slices, determine, numerically, the degree of consolidation after 4 years.
NOTE: If the total time is split into 7 increments, $r = 0.494$.
    Answer: $U = 15$ per cent

REFERENCES

Barron, R. A.
    Consolidation of fine grained soils by drain wells. *Proc. Am. Soc. C.E.* (1948)
Biot, M. A.
    General theory of three dimensional consolidation. *J. appl. Phys.* (1941).
Bishop, A. W., & Henkel, D. J.
    The measurement of soil properties in the triaxial test (Edward Arnold, 2nd edn, 1962).
Crandall, S. H.
    Engineering analysis (Addison Wesley, 1956).
Crank, J., & Nicolson, P.
    A practical method for numerical evaluation of solutions of partial differential equations of the heat conduction type. *Proc. Camb. phil. Soc. math. phys. Sci.* (1947).
Gibson, R. E.
    The progress of consolidation in a clay layer increasing in thickness with time. *Géotechnique* (1958).

Gibson, R. E., & Lumb, P.
> Numerical solution of some problems in the consolidation of clay.
> *Proc. Instn. civ. Engrs* (1953).

Lake, J. R.
> A full-scale experiment to determine the effectiveness of vertical sand
> drains in peat under a road embankment in Dunbartonshire.
> Scotland. (European Conference on Soil Mechanics and Foundation
> Engineering, Weisbaden, Germany, 1963.)

Leibmann, G.
> The solution of transient heat flow and heat transfer problems by
> relaxation. *Br. J. appl. Phys.* (1955).

Lumb, P.
> Rate of settlement of a clay layer due to a gradually applied load.
> *Civ. Engng publ. Wks Rev.* (1963).

Porter, O. J.
> Studies of fill construction over mud flats including a description of
> experimental construction using vertical sand drains to hasten
> stabilization. *Proc. Int. Conf. Soil Mechs. and Foundation Engineering,*
> (1936).

Rowe, P. W.
> Measurements of the coefficient of consolidation of lacustrine clay.
> *Géotechnique* (1959).

Scott, R. F.
> *Principles of soil mechanics* (Addison Wesley, 1963).

Skempton, A. W., Peck, R. B., & MacDonald, D. H.
> Settlement analysis of six structures in Chicago and London. *Proc.
> Instn. civ. Engrs* (1955).

Smith, G. N.
> Construction pore pressures in an earth dam. *Civ. Engng publ. Wks
> Rev.* (1968).

Terzaghi, K.
> *Erdbaumechanik auf bodenphysikalischer grundlage* (Deuticke,
> Vienna, 1925).

Taylor, D. W.
> *Fundamentals of soil mechanics* (John Wiley, 1948).

11. Compaction and Soil Mechanics Aspects of Highway Design

The process of mechanically pressing together the particles of a soil to increase the density (compaction) is extensively employed in the construction of embankments and in strengthening the subgrades of roads and runways.

Many workers in the field talk about consolidating a soil when they really mean compacting it. Strictly speaking, consolidation is the gradual expulsion of water from the voids of a saturated cohesive soil with consequent reduction in volume, whereas compaction is the packing together of soil particles by the expulsion of air.

The densities achieved by compaction are invariably expressed as dry densities, generally in kg/m^3 although, occasionally, the units g/ml $(= Mg/m^3)$ are used. The moisture content at which maximum dry density is obtained for a given amount of compaction is known as the optimum moisture content.

LABORATORY COMPACTION TESTS

British Standard compaction test

The procedure which forms the basis of the British Standard compaction test (BS 1377) was introduced by Proctor in 1933 and used a compactive effort which roughly corresponded to that available in the field at the time.

The sample of soil to be tested (usually air dried) is passed through a ¾ in sieve and the amount of gravel retained may be noted; if the quantity is large a correction must be applied to the test results. Next 2½ kg of the soil passing the sieve is thoroughly mixed with water to give a fairly low moisture content (some 5 per cent less than the natural moisture content of the soil if this is known, otherwise a value of about 6 per cent will generally prove suitable). The soil is placed in an airtight container for 2 or 3 hours so that the water can migrate through it, and is then compacted in a 101.6 mm diameter mould by means of a 2.5 kg hammer with a 50.8 mm diameter head falling freely from 305 mm above the top of the soil. Compaction is effected in three layers, each being given 25 blows (Fig. 11.1).

The compaction can be considered satisfactory when the soil in the mould is not more than about 6 mm above the top, otherwise the test results should be discarded. The top of the soil is now trimmed level with the mould, the base is removed, and the mould and soil are weighed. Moisture content samples are taken from the top and base of the soil.

The test is now repeated using a further batch of soil mixed to a moisture

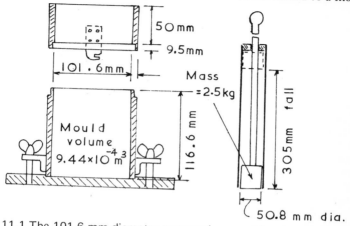

Fig. 11.1 The 101.6 mm diameter compaction mould and standard compaction hammer

content some 2 per cent higher, and the procedure is continued until the weight of wet soil in the mould passes a maximum value and begins to decrease. Once the moisture contents have been determined the graph of dry density variation with moisture content can be plotted (Fig. 11.2), the calculations for a particular compaction being:

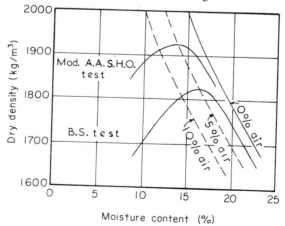

Fig. 11.2 Typical compaction test results

M_1 = Mass of mould (to the nearest gram)
M_2 = Mass of mould + soil (to the nearest gram)
m   = moisture content (as a decimal)
γ_b = 1.06 $(M_2 - M_1)$ kg/m^3

$$\gamma_d = 1.06 \frac{(M_2 - M_1)}{(1 + m)} \text{ kg/m}^3$$

When the values of dry density and moisture content are plotted the resulting curve has a peak value of dry density. The reason for this is that at low m values the soil is stiff and difficult to compact, resulting in a low dry density with a high void ratio; as m is increased the water lubricates the soil, increasing the workability and producing high dry density and low void ratio, but beyond o.m.c. the water tends to keep the soil particles apart and gives low dry densities and high void ratios.

With all soils an increase in the compactive effort results in an increase in the maximum dry density and a decrease in the optimum moisture content (Fig. 11.2).

Saturation line

Figure 11.2 illustrates the saturation line, or zero air voids line as it is often called. It represents the dry densities that would be obtained if all the air in the soil could be expelled, so that after compaction the sample became fully saturated; this state is impossible to achieve by compaction either in the laboratory or in the field, but with the compactive efforts now available it is quite common for a soil to have as little as 5 per cent air voids after compaction, i.e. it is 95 per cent saturated.

Correction for gravel content

The percentage of material retained on a 20 mm sieve, X, can be obtained either by weighing the amount on the sieve (if the soil is oven dried) or else from the particle size distribution curve. In the compacted sample this percentage of gravel has been replaced by an equal mass of soil of smaller size. Generally the particle specific gravity of the gravel, G, will be greater than that of the soil so that the volume of the gravel excluded would occupy a smaller volume that the soil which replaced it.

If ρ_d = maximum dry density obtained from the test, then the mass of gravel excluded

$$= \frac{X}{100} \rho_d$$

Considering unit volume, the volume of soil that replaced the gravel = X, so:

$$\text{volume of gravel omitted} = \frac{X}{100} \frac{\rho_d}{\rho_w}$$

(assuming the voids at maximum density to be completely filled). Hence maximum dry density,

$$\gamma_{d_{max}} = \frac{\rho_d}{1 + \dfrac{X}{100}\left(\dfrac{\rho_d}{\rho_w}G - 1\right)}$$

Similarly optimum moisture content, o.m.c.

$$= \frac{100 - X}{100}m$$

where m = the optimum moisture content obtained from the test.

Standard compaction in the 152.4 mm diameter mould

The main disadvantage of the standard compaction test is that, even with the correction applied, the results are not representative for a soil with a large percentage of particles whose size is greater than 20 mm. The test was therefore adapted for a 152.4 mm diameter mould using soil that had been passed through a 30 mm sieve: the procedure is similar to the original one and employs the same hammer, but the number of blows applied to each of the three layers is increased to 55 and the soil is compacted to a height of 127 mm (giving a volume of 2.32×10^{-3} m^3). Correction for particles over 30 mm in size can be carried out in the manner proposed for the 20 mm size. When only a small amount of soil is available the test can be repeated on the soil by breaking it out of the mould after each test and mixing in some 2 per cent more water, although with this method there is a slight risk that some of the larger particles will be ground down to give a small increase in the value of $\rho_{d\ max}$.

The hand hammer is still often used on site, but in most soils laboratories it has been replaced by automatic compaction machines.

The modified A.A.S.H.O. test

Since the introduction of the Proctor test much larger earth moving and compaction equipment have become available. To allow for this, a test proposed by the U.S. War Department in 1943 was adopted by the

American Association of State Highway Officials and has since been accepted for use in Britain.

The procedure is similar to that already described except that the hammer has a mass of 4.55 kg and has a free fall of 457 mm from above the top of the soil, compaction taking place in 5 layers. For samples sieved through a 20 mm sieve and compacted in the 101.6 mm mould the number of blows remains the same (25 per layer), but for samples sieved through a 30 mm sieve and compacted in the 152.4 mm mould the number of blows per layer is increased to 55. Typical results are shown in Fig. 11.2.

IN SITU COMPACTION TESTS

Laboratory tests are useful for the classification and selection of fill materials for earthworks, but it is not usually possible to apply results from these tests to work in the field due to the difference in the compactive efforts. For large earthworks full scale tests should be carried out, compacting a test section with the actual plant that will ultimately be employed on the project. In this way it is possible to determine the number of passes of the machine required to achieve the desired dry density.

Main types of compaction plant

The three main types of compaction equipment are (i) rollers, (ii) rammers and (iii) vibrators, rollers being by far the most common. In addition, the compactive effort from construction traffic is also useful, provided that the wheel tracks are spread out.

Smooth-wheeled roller

Probably the most commonly used roller in the world, certainly in Britain, is the 3-wheeled Tandem 8000 — 10 000 kg roller. It is self-propelled by diesel engine, is much more manoeuvrable than the old-fashioned steam roller due to the introduction of steering gears, and has a weight distribution that can be altered by the addition of ballast to the rolls. The 8000—10 000 kg version is the most common variant, but models ranging from 2000—20 000 kg are also available.

The smooth-wheeled vibratory roller is also self-propelled and has a dead mass varying from 2500 to 4000 kg. The compactive effort is raised by vibration, generally in the form of a rotating shaft (powered by the propulsion unit) that carries out-of-balance weights. Tests have shown that the best results on both heavy clays and granular soils are obtained when the frequency of vibration is in the range 2200—2400 cycles per minute. Vibration is obviously more effective in granular soil but tests carried out by the Road Research Laboratory (1952) showed that, in a cohesive silty clay, the effect of vibration on a 200 mm layer doubled the compactive effort.

The successful operation of smooth wheeled rollers is difficult (and often impossible) when site conditions are wet, and in these circumstances rollers that can be towed by either track-laying or wheeled tractors are used. Both dead weight and vibratory units are available commercially, and several contractors engaged on heavy earthworks have built 13 500 kg towed assemblies. These units have concrete wheels and can not only be used in conditions where a self-propelled smooth-wheeled roller would be unable to move, but may also be operated at higher speeds, thus partially offsetting the additional costs of the heavy towing unit required.

Pneumatic-tyred roller

In its usual form the pneumatic-tyred roller is a container or platform mounted between two axles, the rear axle generally having three wheels and the forward axle two (so arranged that they track in with the rear wheels), although some models have 5 wheels at the back and 4 at the front. The dead load is supplied by weights placed in the container to give a mass range from 12 000 to 45 000 kg. A certain amount of vertical movement of the wheels is provided for so that the roller can exert a steady pressure on uneven ground—a useful facility in the initial stages of a fill.

This type of roller originated as a towed unit but is now also produced in a self-propelled form; it is suitable for most types of soil and has particular advantages on wet cohesive materials.

Sheepsfoot roller

This roller consists of a hollow steel drum from which the feet project, dead weight being provided by placing water or wet sand inside the drum. It is generally used as a towed assembly (although self-propelled units are available), with the drums mounted either singly or in pairs.

The feet are usually either club-shaped (100 × 75 mm) or tapered (57 mm × 57 mm), the number on a 5000 kg roller varying between 64 and 88. Variations in the shape of the feet have been tried in America with a view to increasing the operating speed.

The sheepsfoot roller is only satisfactory on cohesive soils, but at low moisture contents the resulting compaction of such soils is probably better than can be obtained with other forms of plant. Their use in Britain is rather infrequent because of the generally wet conditions.

The grid roller

This is a towed unit consisting of rolls made up from 38 mm diameter steel bars at 130 mm centres, giving spaces of 90 mm square. The usual mass of the roller is about 5500 kg which can be increased to around 11 000 kg by the addition of dead weights; there are generally two rolls, but a thi.d can be added to give greater coverage. The grid roller is suitable for all soil types, including wet clays and silts.

Roller outputs and costs

A comparison of the outputs of various rollers is given in the following table, which has been compiled from Lewis (1966).

POSSIBLE OUTPUTS OF PLANT

Type of plant	Average output of plant						Remarks
	Width compacted (mm)	Speed of rolling (m/min)	No. of passes	Area compacted per hour (m²)	Depth of layer (mm)	Output per hour (m³)	
8000 kg smooth-wheeled roller	1800	70	4	1220	150	185	Suitable for all soil types, except wet clay and uniformly graded sand.
8000 kg vibratory roller	2000	37	4	870	300	265	Suitable for all soil types.
45 000 kg pneumatic-tyred roller	2400	66	3	4000	250	612	Suitable for all soils, but particularly good on wet, cohesive soils.
Sheepsfoot roller (towed and non-vibratory; clubfoot)	3700	270	6 14 32	8200 3500 1530	225	1875 804 350	A different number of passes required on clay, sandy clay, and gravel/sand.
13 500 kg grid roller (with 80 h.p. track layer)	1600	135	7	1500	200	300	Suitable for all types of soil over a wide range of moisture content.
13 500 kg grid roller (with 150 h.p. wheeled)	1600	270	8	2640	200	536	Not especially suitable for uniformly graded sand or in wet conditions.
Stothert & Pitt 72 000 kg towed vibrator roller (4000 k_3)	1700	40	7	485	225	111	Suitable for granular soils.

Rammers and vibrators

Rammers can be used for all soil types and are useful when rolling is impractical due to restricted site conditions. Vibrators will produce high dry densities at low moisture content in sands and gravels and are particularly useful when other plant cannot be used.

SPECIFICATION OF FIELD DRY DENSITY

The required dry density can be specified either by relative compaction or in terms of the final air void percentage obtained.

The ratio between the maximum dry densities obtained in situ and those derived from the standard compaction test is known as the relative compaction, typical values being as follows:

$\rho_{d\,max}$ from the standard test (kg/m^3)	Minimum relative compaction $(\%)$
1450 − 1600	100
1600 − 1750	95
1750 − 1900	95
1900 − 2050	90
over 2050	90

If dry density is expressed in terms of the final air void percentage, a value of 5 to 10 per cent is generally demanded, depending upon the maximum dry density achieved from the standard compaction test.

For most work a 5 per cent variation in the value specified by either method is allowed for a fine grained soil and about 10 per cent for a coarse grained soil, provided that the mean value achieved is equal to or greater than that specified. The Department of the Environment specifies that, in the construction of an embankment, the upper 0.6 m below formation level should have an air voids ratio of not more than 5 per cent, whilst for compacted material below this a figure of not more than 10 per cent is required.

Typical dry density values attained in situ

The maximum dry density depends upon the type of soil compacted. For a well graded gravel a dry density of about 2250 kg/m^3 is possible, but with a heavy clay the dry density may be as little as 1440 kg/m^3.

ADJUSTMENT OF MOISTURE CONTENT IN THE FIELD

Ideally a soil should be either wet or dried out to the o.m.c. corresponding to the compaction equipment used, although a variation of some 2 per cent from optimum makes little difference in the density values achieved. In arid climates the adjustment of moisture content is essential but varying the moisture content in Britain can hold up construction if inclement weather subsequently necessitates an interval of several days for the soil to dry out.

With the main types of compaction plant the optimum content of many soils is fairly near to the natural moisture content; in these cases compaction with the soil at its natural moisture content can be carried out. The Department of the Environment specifies that compaction of cohesive soils ma[·] may only be carried out when the moisture content is not more than 2 per cent above the plastic limit: if the natural moisture content is greater than this the soil must either be allowed to dry or must not be used. The Department states that a granular material can be compacted at its natural moisture content provided that the variation from this value is not more than − 2 to +1 per cent, with the additional proviso that if the results are not satisfactory the moisture content must be altered until it is within the range of optimum to − 3 per cent optimum (as obtained from the standard compaction test).

OVERCOMPACTION

Care should be taken to ensure that the compactive effort in the field does not take the soil into the range beyond optimum moisture content. In Fig. 11.3 the point A represents the maximum dry density corresponding

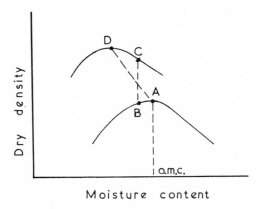

Fig. 11.3 Overcompaction

to the optimum moisture content. If the soil being compacted has a moisture content just below the optimum value the dry density attained will be point B, but if compaction is continued after this stage the optimum moisture content decreases (to point D) and the soil will reach the density shown by point C. Although the dry density is higher, point C is well past the optimum value and the soil will therefore be much softer than if compaction had been stopped once point B had been reached.

Tests for bulk density and moisture content must be carried out at regular intervals if proper control of the compaction is to be achieved. American practice, now widely used in Britain, is to take at least four density tests per 8 hour shift with a minimum of one test for each 400 m³ of earthwork compacted.

BULK DENSITY TESTS

Core-cutter method

Details of the core-cutter apparatus, which is suitable for cohesive soils, are given in Fig. 11.4. After the cutter has been first pressed into the soil and then dug out, the soil is trimmed to the size of the cutter and both cutter and soil are weighed; knowing the weight and dimensions of the cutter, the bulk density of the soil can be obtained.

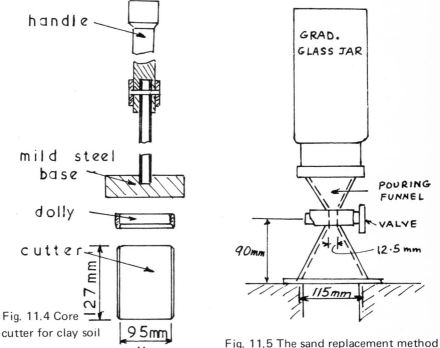

Fig. 11.4 Core cutter for clay soil

Fig. 11.5 The sand replacement method

Sand replacement method

For granular soils the apparatus shown in Fig. 11.5 is used. A small hole (about 0.001 m³) is dug and the mass of the excavated material is carefully determined. The volume of the hole thus formed is obtained by pouring into it sand from a special graduated container; knowing the weight of sand in the container before and after the test, the weight of sand in the hole and hence the volume of the hole can be determined.

The penetration needle

This apparatus (Fig. 11.6) can be used for spot checks on the bulk density of cohesive soils and consists basically of a needle attached to a

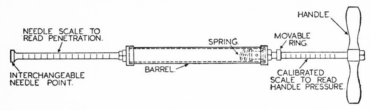

Fig. 11.6 The penetration needle

spring loaded plunger, an array of interchangeable needle tips being available ranging from 6.45 to 645 mm² according to the type of soil tested. A calibration of penetration against density is obtained by pushing the needle into specially prepared samples at different densities and noting the penetration.

MOISTURE CONTENT TESTS

Quick moisture content determinations are necessary in order to avoid halting the work until test results are available. In addition to the following tests, a set of moisture content samples are usually taken for an accurate evaluation in which the soil is oven dried.

Pycnometer

A sample of the wet soil is placed in the pycnometer and weighed, after which the pycnometer is topped up with water and weighed again. Knowing the weight of the pycnometer and the particle specific gravity of the soil, the moisture content can be determined.

Speedy moisture tester

A known mass of the wet soil is placed in a pressurised container and a quantity of calcium carbide is added, the chamber then being sealed and the two materials brought into contact by shaking. The reaction of the carbide on the water in the soil produces acetylene gas, the amount (and hence the pressure) of which depends upon the quantity of water in the soil. A pressure gauge, calibrated for moisture content, is fitted at the base of the cylinder and from this the moisture content can be read off as soon as the needle records a steady level. A characteristic of the apparatus that must be corrected for is that the value of moisture content obtained is in terms of the wet weight of soil.

Nuclear radiation

An aluminium probe, containing a neutron source, is pushed into the soil. The neutrons emitted from the source lose their energy by collision with the hydrogen atoms of the soil water and since the number of slow neutrons thus produced depends upon the amount of water present, a measure of the moisture content can be obtained. The apparatus may also be used to measure density (Meigh & Skipp, 1960).

SOIL MECHANICS ASPECTS OF HIGHWAY DESIGN AND COMPACTION

Highway design in the United Kingdom is based upon the recommendations of Road Research Laboratory Road Note 29, *A guide to the structural design of pavements*, of which the reader is advised to obtain a copy. Methods of design are constantly being revised and evidence of this continual research can be seen by comparing the 1970 third edition of R.R.L. Road Note 29 with the original 1960 edition.

Probably the most comprehensive road research programme was the road tests conducted by the American Association of State Highway Officials in Illinois. Six traffic loops (with a large number of different test strips), each dual carriageway and of average length three miles, were constructed. From November 1958 to November 1960 traffic ran continuously over five of these loops — each of the ten lanes carrying only vehicles of specified weights. After a year the vehicles had driven a total of five million miles. Some of the information obtained from these tests is now incorporated in R.R.L. Road Note 29.

Until recently, highway design loads were defined in terms of the number of commercial vehicles per day likely to be carried by the road 20 years after its construction (assuming a growth rate of 4 per cent per year). A commercial vehicle was defined as a goods or public service vehicle whose unloaded weight exceeded 1500 kg. Traffic is now defined in terms of the cumulative equivalent number of standard axle loads of 8200 kg mass that will be carried by the road during its lifetime.

Design of pavements

A road or runway consists of two parts, the pavement and the subgrade.

Pavement: distributes wheel loads over an area so that the bearing capacity of the subgrade is not exceeded. It usually consists of two or more layers of material: a top layer or wearing surface which is durable and waterproof, and a base material. For economical reasons the base material is sometimes split into two layers, a base and a sub-base (Fig. 11.7).

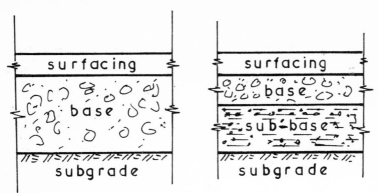

Fig. 11.7 Pavement construction

Subgrade: the natural soil upon which the pavement is laid. The subgrade is seldom strong enough to carry a wheel load directly. There are two possibilities:

(a) Improve the strength of the subgrade and thereby reduce the required pavement thickness.

(b) Design and construct a sufficiently thick pavement to suit the subgrade.

Types of pavement

Flexible: lean concrete bases, cement-bound granular bases, tar or bitumen-bound macadam, all overlaid with bituminous surfaces.

Rigid: reinforced concrete base and surface.

Choice of pavement depends largely upon the local economic considerations.

Estimation of traffic

Private cars have a negligible effect and for design work the number of commercial vehicles (now defined as of weight 1500 kg mass, i.e. 15 kN) is used. With this number the average number of axle loads to which the road will be subjected can be obtained by the relation:

(i) Motorways and trunk roads, i.e. roads designed to carry more than 1000 commercial vehicles, in each direction, per day: average number of axles = 2.7 per vehicle.

(ii) Roads designed to carry 250–1000 vehicles/day: 2.4 per vehicle.

(iii) Residential and other public roads: 2.25 per vehicle.

The design charts in R.R.L. Road Note 29 are for the design of two-lane single carriage roads or the slow lanes in other types of road. Normally the design thickness is carried right across the carriageway. Unless traffic growth rate has been established it should be taken as 4 per cent per year.

The load values of the commercial axles will not generally be known. Comprehensive studies of axle loads on typical roads have been undertaken and these observations, in conjunction with the equivalence factors derived from the A.A.S.H.O. road test, have been incorporated into Table 2 of the

Road Note, by which it becomes possible to convert commercial axle loads into the equivalent number of standard axle loads.

Table 2 of R.R.L. Road Note 29
Reproduced by permission of the Controller of Her Majesty's Stationery Office

Road type	No. of axles per commercial vehicle	No. of standard axles per commercial axle	No. of standard axles per commercial vehicle
Motorways, trunk roads	2.7	0.4	1.08
250–1000 commercial vehicles	2.4	0.3	0.72
Other public roads	2.25	0.2	0.45

Design life of pavements
It is the responsibility of the design engineer to decide upon the structural life that he requires from a pavement. The number of years chosen is influenced by the type of road and whether it is flexible or of a concrete form. With flexible pavements it is economical to design for a relatively short life and to resurface to increase the life and to improve riding qualities whenever necessary. Flexible pavements are therefore normally designed for a life of 20 years.

With a concrete road a major extension of life involves considerable problems and such roads are therefore usually designed for a life of not less than 40 years.

Cumulative standard axle loads
The cumulative number of axle loads is simply the estimated number of standard axle loads to which the road will be subjected during its life:
e.g. design life = 40 years, standard axles/day = 600

$$\text{Cumulative axle loads} = 365 \times 600 \times 40 = 8\,760\,000$$

Subgrade strength
The strength of the subgrade is the main factor in determining the thickness of the pavement, although its susceptibility to frost must also be considered. Subgrade strength is expressed in terms of its California Bearing Ratio (C.B.R.) value. The C.B.R. value is measured by an empirical test devised by the California State Highway Association and is simply the resistance to a penetration of 2.54 mm of a standard cylindrical plunger of 50 mm diameter, expressed as a percentage of the known resistance of the plunger

to 2.54 mm in penetration in crushed aggregate, (taken as 13.39 kN).
Laboratory C.B.R. test. The C.B.R. test is generally carried out in the
laboratory on remoulded samples of the subgrade, as described in BS 1377:
1967 *Methods of testing soils for civil engineering purposes.* The sample
must be compacted at the equilibrium moisture content to the dry density
likely to apply after the road has been constructed.

The determination of the equilibrium moisture content has been discussed
previously. The dry density value can only be truly determined from full-
sized field tests using the compaction equipment that will eventually be used
for the road construction. Where this is impracticable, the dry density can
be taken as that corresponding to 5 per cent air voids at a moisture content
corresponding to the o.m.c. of the standard compaction test. In some soils
this will not be satisfactory — it is impossible to give a general rule; for
example, in silts, a spongy condition may well be achieved if a compaction
to 5 per cent air voids is attempted. This state of the soil would not be
allowed to happen in situ and the laboratory tester must therefore increase
the air voids percentage until the condition disappears.

The mould into which the soil is placed has a diameter of 152 mm and a
depth of 177 mm. The final compacted sample has dimensions 152 mm
diameter and 127 mm height. The soil is broken down, passed through a 20 mm
sieve and adjusted to have the appropriate moisture content.
(i) Static compaction: sufficient wet soil to fill the mould when compacted
is weighed out and placed in the mould. The soil is now compressed into
the mould in a compression machine to the required height dimension. This
is the most satisfactory method.
(ii) Dynamic compaction: the weighed wet soil is compacted into the mould
in five layers using the modified A.A.S.H.O. hammer (4.5 kg mass falling
458 mm). The number of blows for each layer is determined by experience,
several trial runs being necessary before the amount of compactive effort
required to leave the soil less than 6 mm proud of the mould top is determined. The soil is now trimmed and the mould weighed so that the density
can be determined.

The rate of penetration of the plunger is kept constant at 1.27 mm/min.
The load is measured by means of the proving ring attached to the plunger
at each of the following penetrations: 0.635, 1.27, 1.91, 2.54, 3.81, 5.08,
7.62, 10.16 and 12.7 mm.

Test results are plotted in the form of a load/penetration diagram by
drawing a curve through the experimental points. Usually the curve will
be convex upwards (Curve Test 1 in Fig. 11.9), but sometimes the initial
part of the curve is concave upwards and, over this section, a correction
becomes necessary. The correction consists of drawing a tangent to the
curve at its steepest slope and producing it back to cut the penetration axis.
This point is regarded as the origin of the penetration scale for the corrected
curve.

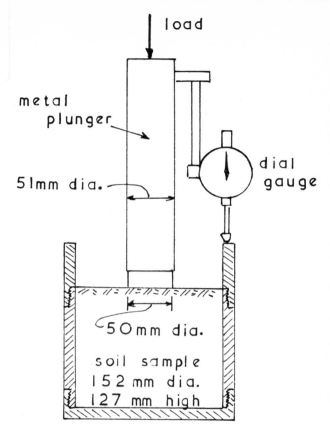

Fig. 11.8 The California bearing ratio test

In situ C.B.R. test. Where a subgrade will not be improved by compaction, i.e. a heavy clay, in situ C.B.R. values can be obtained as a guide in design work. It should be remembered that the moisture content of the soil must be at its equilibrium value and the test must therefore be carried out on freshly exposed soil at a depth of not less than one metre.

Comments on C.B.R. tests. Road Note 29 makes the point that unless there is specialist equipment and experience the results of C.B.R. tests can be suspect. In such cases use should be made of Table 3 of the Road Note which gives a rough relationship between most of the common soils of this country and their C.B.R. values.

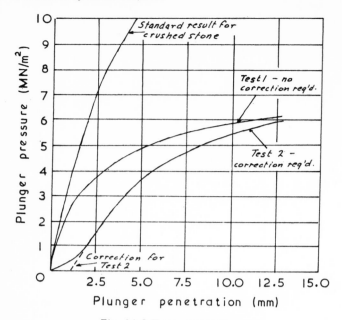

Fig. 11.9 Typical C.B.R. results

Although better than nothing, the figures of Table 3 should be treated with caution.

Frost susceptibility of subgrades and base materials

The road research laboratory has carried out considerable work in this field. A summary of their findings to date is contained in Appendix 1 of the Road Note.

Cohesive soils can be regarded as non-frost-susceptible when P.I. is greater than 15 per cent for well drained soils and 20 per cent for poorly drained soils (i.e. water-table within 600 mm of formation level).

Non-cohesive soils: except for limestone gravels, may be regarded as non-frost-susceptible if with less than 10 per cent fines.

Limestone gravels are likely to be frost-susceptible if the average saturation moisture content of the limestone aggregate exceeds 2 per cent.

Chalks: all crushed chalks are frost-susceptible. Magnitude of heave increases linearly with the saturation moisture content of the chalk aggregate.

Limestone: all oolitic and magnesian limestones with an average saturation moisture content of 3 per cent or more must be regarded as frost-susceptible.

All hard limestones with less than 2 per cent of average saturation moisture content within the aggregate and with 10 per cent or less fines can be regarded as non-frost-susceptible.

Table 3 of R.R.L. Road Note 29
Reproduced by permission of the Controller of Her Majesty's Stationery
Office

Soil type	P.I. (%)	C.B.R. (%)	
		Depth of water below formation	
		> 600 mm	600 mm or less
heavy clay	70	2	1
	60	2	1.5
	50	2.5	2
	40	3	2
silty clay	30	5	3
sandy clay	20	6	4
	10	7	5
silt	–	2	1
sand (poorly graded)	non-plastic	20	10
sand (well graded)	non-plastic	40	15
well graded sandy gravel	non-plastic	60	20

Granites: crushed granites with less than 10 per cent fines can be regarded as non-frost-susceptible.

Burnt colliery shales: very liable to frost heave. No relationship is known, so that tests on representative samples are regarded as essential before the material is used in the top 450 mm of the road structure.

Slags: crushed, graded slags are not liable to frost heave if they have less than 10 per cent fines.

Pulverised fuel ash: coarse fuel ashes with less than 40 per cent fines are unlikely to be frost-susceptible.

Fine ashes may be frost-susceptible and tests should be carried out before such materials are used in the top 450 mm.

Drainage and weather protection

Whenever practicable the water table should be prevented from rising to within 600 mm of the formation level. This may be done by subsoil drainage or by raising the formation level by means of an embankment. If neither of these measures is practicable the high water table condition, referred to in Table 3, should be used for design.

Flexible pavement design

Having determined the cumulative standard axle loads and the C.B.R. of the subgrade it is then possible to determine the thickness of the sub-base material from Fig. 6 of Road Note 29.

If the C.B.R. of the subgrade is in excess of the minimum requirement for the sub-base, no sub-base is required. If a sub-base is required then the minimum thickness to be placed is 150 mm (80 mm for traffic less than 0.5 million standard axles).

If the C.B.R. of the subgrade is less than 2 per cent then the thickness of the sub-base is determined by adding 150 mm to the thickness required with a subgrade C.B.R. of 2 per cent. This may not be sufficient for local soft spots that may require special treatment during construction.

The sub-base itself should have a C.B.R. of not less than 30 per cent (20 per cent for traffic less than 0.5 million standard axles).

For the selection and thickness of base material and surfacing, reference should be made to Road Note 29.

No material within 450 mm of the road surface should be frost-susceptible. (The exception is for a road with less than 0.5 million standard axles, where the thickness requirement may be relaxed if local experience justifies this.) With a frost-susceptible subgrade the total constructional thickness must not be less than 450 mm (regardless of C.B.R. values).

Concrete pavement design

For concrete pavement design, subgrades are split into three categories:
Weak: subgrade with C.B.R. equal to or less than 2 per cent: 150 mm
Normal: subgrades other than those defined by the other categories: 80 mm
Very stable: subgrades with C.B.R. values equal or greater than 15 per cent (includes foundations of old roads)

Minimum thickness of sub-base for each subgrade type is given above. If heavy construction vehicles are to work over the prepared sub-base the minimum thickness can be doubled if the designer considers it necessary.

Thicknesses of concrete slabs placed on top of the sub-base are given in Road Note 29. The frost-susceptibility minimum thickness applies to concrete roads and the sub-base thickness must be adjusted accordingly.

Design examples

Several examples are given in Road Note 29.

EXAMPLES ON CHAPTER 11

Example 11.1

The following results were obtained from a standard compaction test:

Bulk density (kg/m^3)   1987   2083   2147   2208   2188   2147
Moisture content (%)   11.3   12.2   13.0   14.2   15.1   16.4

Plot the curve of dry density against moisture content and draw the saturation line on the diagram (G = 2.70).

Solution

m (%)	ρ_d (kg/m³)
11.3	$\dfrac{1987}{1.113} = 1785$
12.2	$\dfrac{2083}{1.122} = 1857$
13.0	$\dfrac{2147}{1.13} = 1900$
14.2	$\dfrac{2208}{1.142} = 1880$
15.1	$\dfrac{2188}{1.151} = 1901$
16.4	$\dfrac{2147}{1.164} = 1845$

The plot of dry density to moisture content is shown in Fig. 11.10.
Saturation line (zero air voids line). In this case the soil would be
saturated and e = mG. The procedure is to select values for the moisture

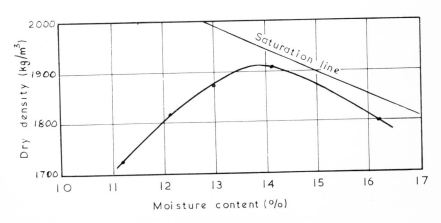

Fig. 11.10 Example 11.1

content and to determine the void ratio e; the dry density for this value of void ratio can then be evaluated.

At m = 14 per cent, e = 0.14 × 2.7 = 0.378

$$\rho_d = \rho_w \frac{G}{1 + e} = 1955 \text{ kg/m}^3$$

Similarly:

At m = 15 per cent, ρ_d = 1923 kg/m^3

m = 16 per cent, ρ_d = 1883 kg/m^3

Example 11.2

A standard compaction test on a soil sample that had been passed through a 20 mm sieve gave a maximum dry density of 1907 kg/m^3 and an optimum moisture content of 13.7 per cent. If the percentage mass of the soil retained on the sieve was 20, determine more correct values for $\rho_{d_{max}}$ and the o.m.c. The particle specific gravity of the retained particles was 2.78.

Solution

$$\rho_{d_{max}} = \frac{\rho_d}{1 + \dfrac{X}{100}\left(\dfrac{\rho_d}{\rho_w G} - 1\right)}$$

$$= \frac{1907}{1 + 0.2\left(\dfrac{1907}{62.4 \times 2.78} - 1\right)}$$

$$= 2035 \text{ kg/m}^3$$

$$\text{o.m.c.} = \frac{100 - Xm}{100} = \frac{80}{100} \times 0.137 = 11.0 \text{ per cent}$$

EXERCISES ON CHAPTER 11

11.1 The results of a compaction test on a soil are set out below.

Moisture content (%)	9.0	10.2	12.5	13.4	14.8	16.0
Bulk density (kg/m^3)	1923	2051	2220	2220	2179	2096

Plot the dry density to moisture content curve and determine the maximum dry density and the optimum moisture content.

If the particle specific gravity of the soil was 2.68, determine the air void percentage at maximum dry density.

Answer: $\rho_{d_{max}}$ = 1974 kg/m^3

o.m.c. = 12.6 per cent

percentage air voids = 5.0

11.2 A standard compaction test was carried out in a 101.6 mm diameter mould, of volume 9.44×10^{-4} m^3.

Test results were:

Moisture content per cent	10.0	11.0	12.0	13.0	14.0
Mass of wet soil and mould (g)	3168	3300	3334	3350	3320

Plot the curve of dry density against moisture content and determine the test values for $\rho_{d_{max}}$ and o.m.c.

On your diagram plot the zero and 5 per cent air voids lines (take G as 2.65). If the percentage of gravel omitted from the test (particle specific gravity = 2.73) was 10 per cent, determine more correct values for $\rho_{d_{max}}$ and the o.m.c.

Answer: From test, $\gamma \rho_{d_{max}}$ = 1962 kg/m^3; o.m.c. = 12.7 per cent

Corrected values: $\rho_{d_{max}}$ = 2035 kg/m^3; o.m.c. = 11.5 per cent

NOTE: To plot the 5 per cent air voids line, select a series of moisture content values and determine e for each case from e = mG/S. The values of dry density can now be determined from $\rho_d = \rho_w G/(1 + e)$. These points will lie on the 5 per cent air voids line.

REFERENCES

British Standards Institution

BS 1377:1967 *Methods of testing soils for civil engineering purposes.*
Lewis, W. A.

Full-scale studies of the performance of plant in the compaction of soils and granular base materials. *Proc. Instn mech. Engrs* (1967).
Meigh, A. C., & Skipp, B. O.

Gamma-ray and neutron methods of measuring soil density and moisture. *Géotechnique* (1960).
Proctor, R. R.

Fundamental principles of soil compaction. *Engng News Rec.* (1933).
H.M. Stationery Office

Soil Mechanics for road engineers (1952)
H.M. Stationery Office

Specification for roads and bridges (Ministry of Transport, 3rd edn, 1963).
H.M. Stationery Office.

Road Research Laboratory Road Note 29: *A guide to the structural design of pavements* (Dept of the Environment, 1970).
U.S. War Department

"Compaction tests and control; A, Methods of compaction tests," in *Design of runways, aprons and taxiways at Army Air Force stations,* part II (1943).

12. Soil Suction and Partial Saturation

The top metre of a natural soil deposit in this country is subjected to large seasonal variations in moisture content, particularly if the soil is supporting vegetation. Generally a soil loses strength as it becomes wetter, so that the thickness of pavement required for a proposed highway is much greater if designed for the winter strength of the subgrade as opposed to the summer strength.

One way around this problem is to place the proposed foundation at a depth of at least one metre below the ground surface. This is standard practice for most structures, but would be an extremely costly procedure if applied to a roadway.

Equilibrium moisture content

The placing of an impervious road surface isolates soil from rainfall, evaporation and plant transpiration. After the construction of such a surface the moisture content within the soil tends to settle down to a set of more or less steady values. For each depth there is a particular value and it is referred to as the equilibrium moisture content It has a value somewhere between the winter and summer values of moisture content at the same depth when the soil is unprotected. The Road Research Laboratory has carried out a considerable amount of investigation in this field. One of the tests carried out gave the results seen in Table 12.1.

It is obvious that, for economic reasons, a roadway should be designed to suit the subgrade when it has reached equilibrium moisture content conditions. For small works the equilibrium moisture content can be taken as being equal to the moisture content occurring in the natural soil at a depth

Table 12.1

	m (%) 0.3 m under grass verge	CBR	Required thickness (mm)	m (%) 0.3 m under road centre	CBR	Required thickness (mm)
Summer	10.5%	2	40	17.0%	6	38
Winter	20.5%	32	66	16.8%	6	38

of about 1 m, provided that this soil is the same as the soil that will be at the formation level. For important works, and where a distribution with depth is required, the equilibrium moisture content can be determined from laboratory and in situ tests.

Soil suction

As has been shown in chapter 2, capillary water in a soil is in a state of reduced pressure or suction. Throughout a soil the air and water interfaces consist of menisci, the curvature of which indicate the amount of suction. If the moisture content of a soil is reduced, the water interfaces recede into the smaller pores, their radii of curvature decrease and the suction increases. This increase in soil suction with decrease in moisture content applies over the full range of moisture content, from saturated to dry. Its value varies from zero, when saturated, to extremely high values of tension when approaching fully dry.

Due to the large variation in values it is neccessary to adopt some form of logarithmic scale if we are to show the relationship between suction and moisture content for a given soil. Schofield (1935) evolved the pF scale which is now generally used. With the pF scale, negative pressure values are expressed in terms of the height, in millimetres, of a suspended column of water. The logarithm of one tenth of this height, to the base ten, is known as the pF value.

Table 12.2

pF value	Equivalent suction	
	mm water	kN/m^2
0	10	0.1
1	100	0.98
2	1 000	9.81
3	10 000	98.1
4	100 000	981.0
5	1 000 000	9 810
6	10 000 000	98 100

Due to the logarithmic effect, pF = 0 does not quite correspond to suspended length = 0.

It is seen from Table 12.2 of pF values that the principle of soil suction depends upon the ability of the pore water to carry high tensile stresses. There is no proof that this is indeed what happens. Ordinary water can carry tensile stresses in the order of 100 kN/m^2. It may be that, within the very fine recesses of a soil, the contained water has different properties to ordinary water, enabling it to carry these high stress values. This concept of high tensile stresses in water may really be an analogy similar to that of surface tension.

Negative pore water pressures

In most soil mechanics work, pore water pressures are measured relative to atmospheric pressure. It is possible to have negative pore water pressures caused by the application of an external stress system, and it is also possible to have negative pore water pressures induced by capillary effects in unloaded soils.

The term 'negative pore water pressure' is taken here to mean any pressure deficiency which occurs in situ, or within a laboratory test sample, when subjected to some form of externally applied stress system. It is given the symbol $-u$.

The term 'suction', or 'soil suction', is taken here to be any pressure deficiency occurring within an unloaded soil. It is given the symbol s.

Measurement

There are several methods by which suction can be measured. Only three methods will be briefly discussed here. A more complete list has been given by Croney & Coleman (1960).

Suction plate method: for suctions from pF = 0 to pF = 3 the apparatus shown in Fig. 12.1 can be used.

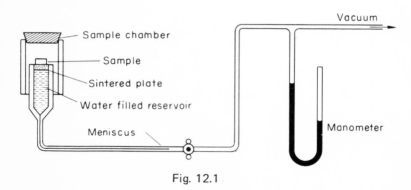

Fig. 12.1

The water-filled reservoir is sealed with a No. 5 sintered glass plate and connected to a horizontal tube. A small soil sample is placed on the plate. The suction in the soil causes water to flow from the water into the sample, thus moving the position of the meniscus. The meniscus can be returned to its original position by the application of a vacuum. This applied suction, which can be measured by the manometer, gives the value of the soil suction.

By testing several samples, allowing them to attain equilibrium under different applied suctions and then determining their moisture contents, a suction to moisture content relationship can be established.

High pressure membrane method: for suctions from pF = 0 to pF = 6.2. This apparatus is an extension of the suction plate method. The sample is placed on a sintered bronze disc and inserted into a high pressure cell. Compressed air, at a value close to the anticipated suction value, is inserted into the cell. The sample is then left to attain equilibrium by the applied pressure pushing water from the soil until it balances the suction. Several samples can be tested, with different applied pressures, to obtain a suction/ moisture content relationship.

The consolidation apparatus: as will be indicated later, the standard consolidation apparatus can be used to exert a known suction on a saturated clay sample.

Typical results

A typical soil suction to moisture content curve for a loam soil is shown in Fig. 12.2.

In practice, any element of soil below the surface is subjected to some form of overburden pressure, either from the self weight of the soil above it or some form of loading on the surface. The suction of the element, s, in the unloaded state, is modified by the effect of the overburden. This modified suction is, of course, the final pore water pressure, u, either positive or negative, that the element has reached.

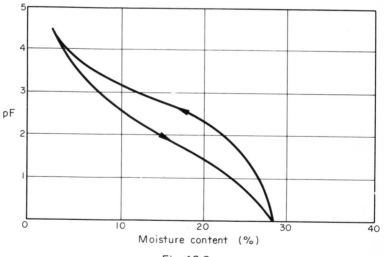

Fig. 12.2

Croney and Coleman (1953) evolved an expression relating the final pore water pressure, u, to the suction value and the total overburden pressure. A form of their expression is:

$$u = \alpha p - s$$

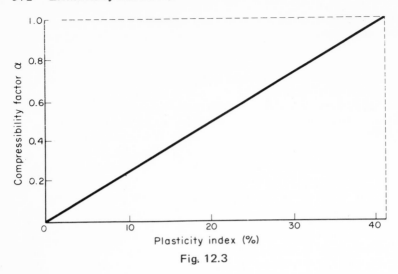

Fig. 12.3

where s = suction value for the unloaded soil at the same moisture content
as the in situ value
p = total normal pressure at the point considered
α = that fraction of p that is effective in changing the pressure of
the water in the element.

From the theory of consolidation we know that, for saturated soils, a
change in volume can only take place if there is a loss of water from the
soil, which necessitates a change in pore pressure values. This fact enables
us to fix the two extreme values of α. In the case of a rigid material, such
as chalk, or an incompressible soil, such as compact sand, no volume changes
occur if a load is applied. The applied load is carried entirely by the solid
skeleton and no portion of the load affects the pore water pressure, which
will remain at its original suction value. For these instance $\alpha = 0$ and $s = -u$.

For a compressible clay an applied load is initially carried entirely by the
water which is gradually expelled as consolidation occurs. For these instances
$\alpha = 1$ and $s = p - u$.

For a heavy clay the suction value is equal to the effective stress. During
consolidation the effective stress increases, as u decreases, i.e. water is
expelled from the soil until the suction value equals the applied pressure.
Many soils will have values of α lying somewhere between 0 and 1.0. A silt
will have an α value of approximately 0.5. For accurate work α can be
found from soil tests.

Compressibility factor value
The most direct method to determine the compressibility factor value is to
measure the in situ pore water pressure and the total overburden pressure at

the point considered. A sample is then removed and its suction value immediately determined. α is then obtained from the formula $u = \alpha p - s$. A further method does not require u to be known. The sample is collected and s determined. The sample is then subjected to an overall pressure by means of mercury and the resulting pore water pressure measured. Again α can be determined from $u = \alpha p - s$.

The Road Research Laboratory (1958) evolved an approximate relationship between the compressibility factor and the plasticity index. A simplified, and slightly extended, form of their curve is given in Fig. 12.3.

For a soil insulated from vegetation and rainfall by an impervious surface, such as a road or runway, the distribution of pore water pressure with depth is governed by the position of the water table. Once equilibrium has been achieved and vertical movement of water has ceased, then the pore water pressure at a point x m above the water table will be a negative pressure corresponding to a head of x m of water. Similarly, the pore water pressure at a point x m below the water table will be a positive pressure corresponding to a head of x m of water.

From the equation $u = \alpha p - s$ it is possible to determine s and, knowing the s to m relationship, it becomes possible to determine the equilibrium moisture content distribution with depth. The relationship between moisture content and suction is subjected to a hysteresis effect in that the value of suction for a given moisture content is different if the soil is drying out or is being wetted. The appropriate set of values should be used to correspond with the time of year that construction will take place. In the summer the soil will become wetter and in the winter it will become drier after construction of the roadway.

Position of water table
The most important part of any pavement design work is the determination of the highest level to which the water level will reach in the course of a year. This can only be determined by in situ observations. For cohesive soils there should be little difficulty. During the site investigation, boreholes should be prepared for water level observations which should then be carried out for several months and at least throughout the winter.

With sandy soils and podzols care should be taken to determine whether or not a layer of less permeable soil, formed by leached material from the soil layers above, does not occur at some depth within the soil. The presence of a hardpan layer could mean that, for some part of the year, a perched water table exists. Any water level investigations during boring will only locate the true water table level, which can be at quite a depth in granular soils with good drainage characteristics.

Obviously, if there is such a layer, the depth from formation to this level should be taken as the minimum depth to the water table in order to determine equilibrium moisture contents.

PARTIALLY SATURATED SOILS

When the voids of a soil contain both air and water the soil is said to be partially saturated.

Degree of saturation is defined by the ratio:

$$S = \frac{\text{volume of water}}{\text{volume of voids}}$$

Due to surface tension effects the pore water pressure, u_w, is always less than the pore air pressure, u_a. The value $(u_a - u_w)$ represents the difference in pressure, or the suction, between the two phases.

Consider a soil with a fairly low S value. There pore water will consist mainly of menisci around particle contacts, as illustrated in Fig. 12.4.

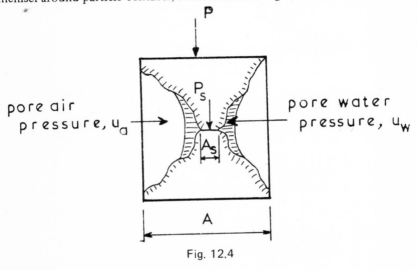

Fig. 12.4

Consider a plane passing through the point of contact of two soil particles. Let the respective areas be:

A — gross area
A_s — area of particle contact
A_a — area on which air pressure acts
A_w — area on which water pressure acts.

Let $\dfrac{A_s}{A} = a$ and let $\dfrac{A_w}{A} = \chi$

Then $\dfrac{A_s}{A} = (1 - a - \chi)$

Consider unit area by putting A = 1, then:

$$A_s = a; \quad A_w = \chi; \quad A_a = (1 - a - \chi)$$

For equilibrium $P = P_s + A_w u_w + A_a u_a$

Hence the force carried by the fluid and gas in the voids is:

$$A_w u_w + A_a u_a$$

Hence the equivalent pore pressure $= \chi u_w + (1 - a - \chi)u_a$

It is reasonable to assume that an equation of the form of Terzaghi's equation $(\sigma' = \sigma - u)$ must exist for partially saturated soils. Hence:

$$\sigma' = \sigma - [\chi u_w + (1 - a - \chi)u_a]$$

It has been shown that, for soils, the area ratio, a, is negligible. Hence:

$$\sigma' = \sigma - [\chi u_w + (1 - \chi)u_a]$$

leading to Bishop's equation:

$$\sigma' = \sigma - [u_a - \chi(u_a - u_w)]$$

Strictly speaking, χ is not an area, but the assumption, as shown, helps to create a simple model of the problem.

χ need not necessarily be the same for problems of shear strength and volume change, although in most practical problems any difference is very small.

There are two obvious limits for χ:

When S = 100% χ = 1.0 and $\sigma' = \sigma - u_w$

When S = 0% χ = 0.0 and $\sigma' = -u_a$

There is the special case when u_a = atmospheric pressure, which applies in most civil engineering problems. Pressures are then expressed relative to atmospheric pressure which is taken as zero.

For this case the equation becomes:

$$\sigma' = \sigma - \chi u_w$$

Determination of χ from triaxial tests

Bishop, Alpan, Blight & Donald (1960) suggested that the parameter χ can be estimated from shear tests if it is assumed that, for a given initial void ratio, the values c' and ϕ' are independent of the degree of saturation.

If a series of partially saturated soil samples, compacted to the same water content, are sheared under various values of $\sigma_3 - u_a$ it is possible to plot the average compressive stress values at failure, $\dfrac{\sigma_1 + \sigma_3}{2} - u_a$; $\dfrac{\sigma_1 + \sigma_3}{2} - u_w$

against maximum shear stress at failure $\dfrac{\sigma_1 - \sigma_3}{2}$ and, by joining these points, to obtain two stress lines. These lines are found to converge as the soil approaches saturation (Fig. 12.5).

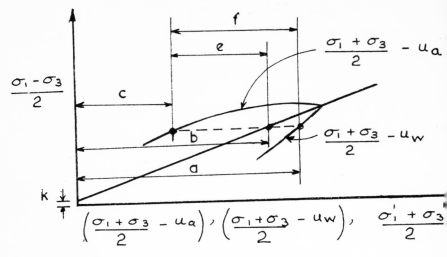

Fig. 12.5 (after Bishop, Alpan, Blight & Donald)

If consolidated undrained tests are carried out on the same soil saturated by back pressure it becomes possible to superimpose a p', q plot onto the diagram, $\frac{\sigma_1 + \sigma_3}{2}, \frac{\sigma_1 - \sigma_3}{2}$. This line is the K_f line and if its slope, α', and its intercept on the $\frac{\sigma_1 - \sigma_3}{2}$ axis, k, are known it is then possible to obtain the values of ϕ' and c':

$$\sin \phi' = \tan \alpha'$$

$$c' = k \frac{\tan \phi'}{\tan \alpha'}$$

The equation for effective stress in a partially saturated soil is:

$$\sigma' = \sigma - u_a + \chi (u_a - u_w)$$

The average principal effective stress $\frac{1}{2} (\sigma_1' + \sigma_3')$ is given by the expression:

$$\tfrac{1}{2} (\sigma_1' + \sigma_3') = \tfrac{1}{2} (\sigma_1 + \sigma_3) - u_a + \chi (u_a - u_w)$$

i.e.
$$\chi = \frac{\tfrac{1}{2} (\sigma_1' + \sigma_3') - \tfrac{1}{2} (\sigma_1 + \sigma_3) - u_a}{u_a - u_w}.$$

$$= \frac{b - c}{a - c} = \frac{e}{f}$$

The triaxial tests may be carried out either at constant $(\sigma_3 - u_a)$ obtained by controlling u_a throughout the test and measuring u_w, or by shearing the soil undrained and measuring both u_a and u_w.

The state of the air and the water phases in partially saturated soils

If a soil is completely dry then only air pressures will occur within its pores. If the soil is completely saturated, only water pressures can occur. Obviously the effects of the water and air phases in a soil depend upon the degree of saturation.

Barden (1965) has discussed how moisture affects clays and how the two phases exist in various states. As a guide for comparison Barden assumed that optimum moisture content gives a degree of saturation of 90 per cent but pointed out that, in reality, the value of S optimum varies with the type of soil.

Extremely dry S < 5 per cent

The air phase is continuous throughout the soil mass and the water is in the form of highly viscous adsorbed water firmly attached to the skeleton by capillary forces. As S is so small the parameter is also small and the effective stress equation becomes $\sigma' = \sigma - u_a$.

Water pressures cannot be measured and the suction term $(u_a - u_w)$ is very high.

Dry of optimum 5 per cent < S < 90 per cent

As more water is added to a soil there is a gradual transition from adsorbed to free water. The water tends to redistribute itself until the curvature of the air-water menisci are equal throughout the soil. At this stage both air and water pressures can be measured. The suction term $(u_a - u_w)$ can still be large and u_w will rarely exceed zero. Bishop's effective stress equation applies.

At optimum S = 90 per cent

This seems to be a changeover point from a continuous air to a discontinuous air system.

Wet of optimum S > 90 per cent

Air no longer exists in a free state and is said to be occluded. There is no way of measuring u_a and the air exists in the form of bubbles which can cause the pore fluid to be highly compressible but has little or no effect on the pressure of the pore fluid, which is now equal to u_w so that the effective stress equation has become $\sigma' = \sigma - u_w$.

A good example of occlusion was given by Gilbert (1959) who showed that in a Vicksburg silty clay the air was continuous at a moisture content 4 per cent below o.m.c. and occluded at a moisture content of 3 per cent above optimum.

Very wet S > 95 per cent

It can be assumed that the small amount of air still present in the soil is trapped by the skeleton. Although the pore fluid will still tend to be highly compressible, any fluid that flows from the soil will be fairly incompressible.

Conclusions

For sands and gravels above ground water level suction effects are fairly negligible and the term $(u_a - u_w)$ is of little significance.

For most soils when the degree of saturation is relatively high, from about S = 90 per cent the air is occluded and can be assumed to have little effect on the water pressure (which is the pressure measured if a piezometer is inserted into the soil). For most practical problems, then, the effective stress equation reduces to $\sigma' = \sigma - u_w$. The exception is fine grained soils near to but on the dry side of optimum, where the air may not be occluded and the full form of the effective stress equation must be used.

TESTING TECHNIQUES FOR PARTIALLY SATURATED SOILS

The techniques for testing partially saturated soils are (or shoud *should* be) considerably different from the techniques for saturated soils. The difference is due to the need to measure (and differentiate between) the pore air and the pore water pressures. There are various papers which describe these methods: a good summary is given by Bishop & Henkel (1962).

Briefly, pore water pressures are measured through saturated, fine-pored ceramic discs which, due to their high air entry values, act as filters and remain saturated at all times, so that the water in the pores of the disc is in pressure equilibrium with the pore water in the soil.

Pore air pressure values can be measured through coarse pored ceramic discs, or glass-fibre filters, with a moisture retention capacity so low that it is unable to draw water from the soil.(i.e. its suction value is less than the $u_a - u_w$ value operating within the soil and consequently it remains practically dry). The air contained in the pores of this coarse filter remains in pressure equilibrium with the pore air in the soil.

It is well known that the equalisation of the pore fluid pressure throughout a triaxial sample is important when pore pressure measurements are to be taken. It is this condition that governs the rate at which a sample of saturated soil may be sheared. Partially saturated soil is generally less permeable than saturated, and very slow shear rates are required for such a soil. In this connection it must be appreciated that a transference of air from the soil sample to the water within the triaxial cell can take place by diffusion through the rubber membrane. If an 'undrained' test is to last for more than a few hours a special type of triaxial cell, in which an inner perspex ring allows the membrane to be surrounded by mercury, should be used.

Common errors in testing partially saturated soils

In many soils laboratories consolidated undrained tests are carried out on compacted partially saturated samples to determine c' and ϕ'. The technique is to use one measurement for pore pressure, u, in the hope that this pressure will somehow be the equivalent pore pressure in the soil so that the expression $\sigma' = \sigma - u$ may be used.

This procedure can produce two extreme results:

(i) *Test using a coarse pored filter at base of sample*

Although the operator may think that he is measuring pore water pressure, because of the grade of filter the pressure measured is actually u_a and the effective stress equation, in reality, is $\sigma' = \sigma - u_a$. The strength envelope will have a large 'cohesive' intercept (Fig. 12.6).

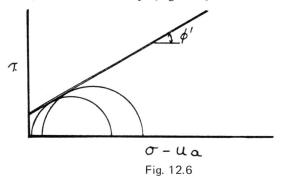

Fig. 12.6

(ii) *Test using a fine pored filter at base of sample*

Pore pressure measurements by this method will represent the pore water pressure, u_w, and the equation is $\sigma' = \sigma - u_w$. The strength envelope can have a large negative cohesive intercept (Fig. 12.7).

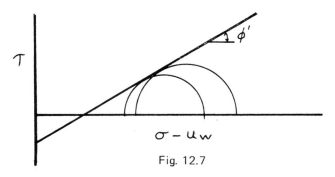

Fig. 12.7

Bishop (1960) gives an example of this type of error:

If $\chi = 0.85$ and $(u_a - u_w) = 276 \text{ kN/m}^2$ (as with a soil compacted on the dry side of optimum) then the true expression for effective stress is:

$$\sigma' = \sigma - [u_a - (u_a - u_w)\chi]$$
$$= \sigma - [u_a (1 - \chi) + \chi\, u_w]$$

$$= \sigma - [(1 - \chi)(u_a - u_w) + u_w]$$
$$= \quad - 0.15 \times 276 - u_w$$
$$= \quad - u_w - 41.4$$

This is a difference of 41.4 kN/m², which cannot be ignored in practice.

The correct result lies between there two extremes and can be obtained by measuring u_a and u_w correctly (Fig. 12.8).

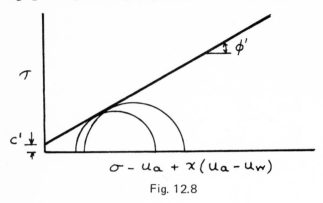

Fig. 12.8

Alternative (and safer) way to determine c' and ϕ' for a partially saturated soil

Procedure is first to fully saturate the sample and then to determine c' and ϕ'. The sample is consolidated under a back pressure which is connected to the pore water within the sample and is of sufficient intensity to cause any air present to dissolve into the water, and the sample to achieve saturation. (The calculation of this value of back pressure is discussed in the next section.) The test is carried out in the triaxial apparatus and, in order that effective stress values are unaltered during consolidation, the cell pressure may be raised by the same amount as the back pressure.

It should be noted that ϕ' is more or less correctly measured using either of the other techniques (fine or coarse discs). It is c' that is largely indeterminate if the correct procedure is not used. Bishop and Blight (1963) quote examples of this type of error in tests carried out on both boulder clay and shale. In both cases compaction had been optimum.

PORE PRESSURE CHANGES IN PARTIALLY SATURATED SOILS SUBJECTED TO CHANGES IN ALL ROUND APPLIED PRESSURE, UNDER UNDRAINED CONDITIONS

As shown in Chapter 4, the change in pore water pressure in a saturated soil, Δu, due to an all round pressure increase $\Delta \sigma$ can be expressed in the form:

$$\Delta u = B \, \Delta \sigma$$

where

$$B = \frac{1}{1 + \dfrac{nC_v}{C_c}}$$

In a saturated soil the soil compressibility, C_c, is considerably greater than the compressibility of the pore fluid, C_v, and, for all practical purposes, $B = 1$.

In a partially saturated soil the compressibility of the pore fluid becomes much larger than when the soil is saturated so that B decreases as S decreases. Pore pressure changes in a partially saturated soil must therefore be expressed by two equations:

$$\Delta u_a = B_a \, \Delta \sigma$$

$$\Delta u_w = B_w \, \Delta \sigma$$

where B_a and B_w are the parameters used to express air and water changes respectively. The effect is illustrated in Fig. 12.9.

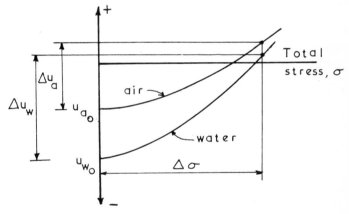

Fig. 12.9 (after Bishop 1960)

As mentioned earlier, in many practical problems S is high, from about 90 per cent upwards. In these cases the water pressure predominates in the effective stress equation and only B_w need be used. Otherwise it becomes necessary to use both B_w and B_a in the equation.

Theoretical treatment

The exact prediction of u_a and u_w changes with applied all round pressure changes is not possible. An approximate solution can be obtained using

Boyle's Gas Law and Henry's Solubility Law, provided that it is assumed that at all times during the applied pressure range $u_a = u_w$.

Henry's Law states that, at a given temperature, the weight of gas that will dissolve into a given volume of liquid is directly proportional to the pressure. It therefore follows from Boyle's Law (PV = constant) that the volume occupied by this weight of gas will be the same at all pressures.

Let V = volume of element of the partially saturated soil

      V_v = volume of voids within the element

      S = Degree of saturation

      p_0 = initial air pressure (absolute) in the voids when the sample is unconfined, i.e. $u_{a0} = u_{w0} = p_0$. The value of p_0 can vary, being atmospheric; but is generally taken as 100 kN/m^2.

      H = Henry's Coefficient of Solubility ($\doteq 0.02$ volumes of air per unit volume of water at room temperature.)

      n_0 = Initial porosity of the soil.

Consider the soil when at pressure p_0:

    Volume of water in voids   = SV_v

$\therefore$ Volume of air in voids   = $(1 - S)V_v$

    Volume of air in solution   = HSV_v

$\therefore$ Total volume of air when sample is at atmospheric pressure, p_0

$$= (1 - S)V_v + HSV_v$$

and of this $(1 - S)V_v$ is free air.

Consider the soil when the pressure within the voids is changed from p_0 to p:

then change in void pressure, $\Delta p = p - p_0$

and $u_a = u_w = p$ (assumed).

At the new pressure, p, from Boyle's Law:

$$\text{total volume of air within sample} = \frac{p_0}{p} [(1 - S)V_v + SV_vH]$$

Of this total volume HSV_v is in solution so the total free air volume is

$$\frac{p_0}{p} [(1 - S)V_v + SV_vH] - SV_vH$$

Let ΔV be the change in total volume of the element corresponding to the change in pressure, Δp. The compressibility of the soil grains and the water is negligible so that, for all practical purposes, the change in volume of the soil element is equal to the change in the volume of the free air within the elemental voids.

i.e.

$$\Delta V = \underbrace{[(1 - S)V_v + SV_vH] \frac{p_0}{p} - SV_vH}_{\text{Final free air}} - \underbrace{(1 - S)V_v}_{\text{Initial free air}}$$

or

$$\Delta V = (1 - S)V_v \left(\frac{p_0}{p} - 1\right) + SV_vH \left(\frac{p_0}{p} - 1\right)$$

$$= V_v \left(\frac{p_0}{p} - 1\right)(1 - S + SH)$$

Now $\qquad \dfrac{V_v}{V} = n_0$

$\therefore \qquad \dfrac{\Delta V}{V} = n_0 \left(\dfrac{p_0}{p} - 1\right)(1 - S + SH)$

or $\qquad \dfrac{p_0 - p}{p} = \dfrac{\Delta V}{Vn_0 (1 - S + SH)}$

Now $\dfrac{\Delta p}{p_0} = \dfrac{p - p_0}{p_0} = -\dfrac{(p_0 - p)}{p_0} = -\dfrac{(p_0 - p)}{p}\dfrac{p}{p_0} = \dfrac{p_0 - p}{p}\dfrac{p}{p_0 - p + p}$

$$= \dfrac{-\dfrac{p_0 - p}{p}}{\dfrac{p_0 - p}{p} + 1} = \dfrac{-\dfrac{\Delta V}{V}\dfrac{1}{n_0 (1 - S + SH)}}{\dfrac{\Delta V}{V}\dfrac{1}{n_0 (1 - S + SH)} + 1}$$

i.e. $\qquad \dfrac{\Delta p}{p_0} = \dfrac{-\dfrac{\Delta V}{V}}{\dfrac{\Delta V}{V} + n_0 (1 - S + SH)}$

This equation is valid only until the air in the voids has gone into solution, i.e. until the soil is saturated. This will occur when the change in the volume of the soil equals the volume of the initial free air,

i.e. when $\qquad -\dfrac{\Delta V}{V} = (1 - S)\dfrac{V_v}{V} = (1 - S)n_0$

Let the changes in the pore pressures (Δu_a and Δu_w) to bring about saturation be both equal to Δp_s.

Then $\qquad \dfrac{\Delta p_s}{p_0} = \dfrac{(1 - S)n_0}{-(1 - S)n_0 + (1 - S + SH)}$

i.e. $\qquad \Delta p_s = p_0 \dfrac{1 - S}{SH}$

From the foregoing it is now possible to plot the relationship between the pore air pressure, u_a (assumed equal to the pore water pressure u_w) and the variation of the applied total all round pressure (Fig. 12.10A).

As has been stressed, the relationship is approximate in that the suction term ($u_a - u_w$) which was assumed equal to zero, may have a value of several atmospheres and the diagram is more of the form shown in Fig. 12.9.

The theoretical relationship between the volumetric change, $\dfrac{-\Delta V}{V}$, and the applied all round effective stress, σ', is shown in Fig. 12.10B, as also is shown the variation of u_a (or u_w) with $\dfrac{-\Delta V}{V}$.

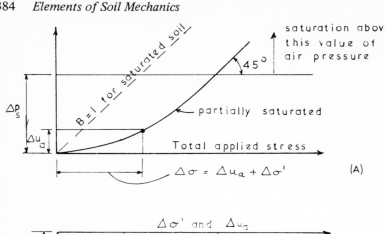

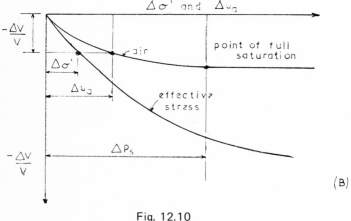

Fig. 12.10

The relationship between water and air pressure changes and the applied all round total stress illustrated in Fig. 12.10A is theoretical. To examine the actual changes a constant water test is carried out. This is not the same as an undrained test as, in the constant water test, air can be expelled from the sample. The test is usually carried out with the air in the soil at atmospheric pressure so that u_a is constant and only u_w varies. Typical results from such a test are shown in Fig. 12.11. In the figure,

s = soil suction in the unconfined state
u = negative pore water pressure
$\Delta\sigma$ = increment of total applied pressure
$\Delta u = \alpha \, \Delta\sigma$
and $u = s + \alpha \, \Delta\sigma$

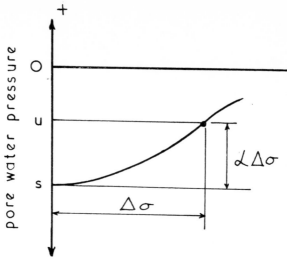

Fig. 12.11

This was the type of test for which Croney and Coleman (1960) defined the parameter α. Indeed, if p is substituted for $\Delta\sigma$ their equation is obtained:

$$u = s + \alpha\,p$$

Croney and Coleman's equation may be generalised. The change in difference between pore air and pore water pressures are equal to the change

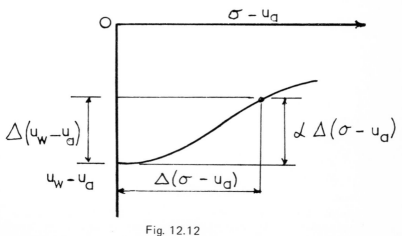

Fig. 12.12

in the difference between total applied stress and pore air pressure times α (Fig. 12.12).

In the figure it is seen that the term $u_w - u_a$ is used instead of the more usual term $u_a - u_w$. This is simply because both pressures are negative and u_w is always numerically greater than u_a.

Relationship between α and B_a and B_w

α is the parameter obtained from the constant water content test. B_a and B_w are parameters obtained from the undrained test.

Constant water test

$$\Delta (u_w - u_a) = \alpha \Delta (\sigma - u_a)$$

Undrained test

$$\Delta u_w = B_w \Delta \sigma$$

$$\Delta u_a = B_a \Delta \sigma$$

The expression obtained from the constant water content test may be expressed in the form:

$$\frac{\Delta u_w}{\Delta \sigma} - \frac{\Delta u_a}{\Delta \sigma} = \alpha \left(1 - \frac{u_a}{\Delta \sigma}\right)$$

or

$$B_w - B_a = \alpha (1 - B_a)$$

or

$$B_w = B_a + \alpha (1 - B_a)$$

From this final equation it is seen that B_w can only be equal to α when $B_a = 0$ or when there is no change in air pressure under undrained conditions, an impossible situation in a partially saturated soil.

EXAMPLES ON CHAPTER 12

Example 12.1

A roadway is to be constructed on the surface of a silty soil whose soil suction to moisture content relationship is given in Fig. 12.13A. The average bulk unit weight of the soil is 18.4 kN/m^3, liquid limit = 49 per cent, plastic limit = 20 per cent. The roadway is to consist of a 225 mm concrete slab and will be constructed during the summer months. It is expected that the water table will eventually be at a depth of 1.5 m below formation level. Determine the distribution of the equilibrium moisture content within the soil to a depth of 5 m. Unit weight of water = 9.8 kN/m^3; unit weight of concrete = 24.0 kN/m^3.

Solution

The pavement will be constructed in the summer and the soil will tend to become wetter after construction, therefore use the wetting curve, i.e. the lower part of the hysteresis loop of Fig. 12.13A. Plasticity index = 49 − 20

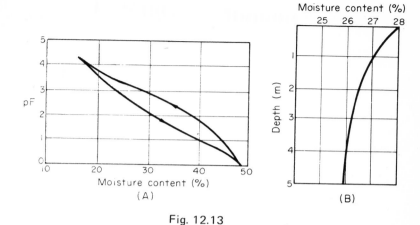

Fig. 12.13

= 29 per cent. From Fig. 12.3 α = 0.7 approx; surcharge from

slab = $\dfrac{24.0}{1000} \times 225 = 5.4 \text{ kN/m}^2$

Calculations are best set out as in Table 12.3.

The equilibrium moisture content distribution with depth is shown in Fig. 12.13. In the tabulated calculations it is assumed that the application of the uniform surcharge due to the weight of the roadway causes a uniform pressure increase (of 5.4 kN/m²) at all depths. This is so when the pavement is large and the depths examined are relatively shallow so that the spreading effect of the surface loading is insignificant.

Example 12.2

The relationship between soil suction and moisture content for a clay soil (PI = 55 per cent) is shown in Fig 12.14A. The soil will be the subgrade of a roadway which will exert a pressure of 6 kN/m² onto its surface. The saturated unit weight of the clay is 22.4 kN/m³ and the water table is expected to achieve a depth of 1 m below the formation level. Determine the equilibrium moisture content distribution to a depth of 5 m below the roadway.

Solution

From the high plasticity index (55 per cent) we see that the soil is indeed a clay and the value of α can be taken as 1.0 (see Table 12.4).

The equilibrium moisture content distribution is shown in Fig 12.14B.

Example 12.3

A sample of the clay in Example 12.2 was subjected to a consolidation test which gave the void ratio to effective pressure curve shown in Fig. 12.15. Solve Example 1.2 using Fig. 12.15 instead of Fig. 12.14A. Take G = 2.73.

Table 12.3 Example 12.1

Depth (m)	Soil overburden kN/m²	Total p (kN/m²)	Total p (m of water)	α p	u (m of water)	S = α p − u (m of water)	s (pF scale)	m (%)
0.0	0.0	5.4	0.55	0.39	−1.5	1.89	2.28	28.0
0.25	4.6	10.0	1.02	0.71	−1.25	1.96	2.29	
0.5	9.2	14.6	1.49	1.04	−1.0	2.04	2.31	27.3
0.75	13.8	19.2	1.96	1.37	−0.75	2.12	2.33	
1.0	18.4	23.8	2.43	1.70	−0.5	2.20	2.34	
1.5	27.6	33.0	3.36	2.35	0.0	2.35	2.37	
2.0	36.8	42.2	4.31	3.02	0.5	2.52	2.40	26.8
3.0	55.2	60.6	6.18	4.32	1.5	2.82	2.45	26.5
4.0	73.6	79.0	8.03	5.62	2.5	3.12	2.49	26.0
5.0	92.0	97.4	9.93	6.95	3.5	3.45	2.54	25.8

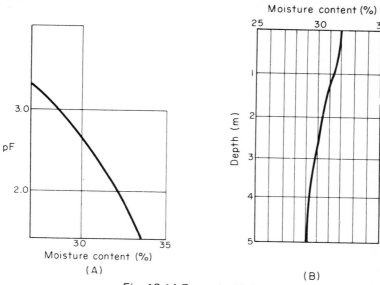

Fig. 12.14 Example 12.2

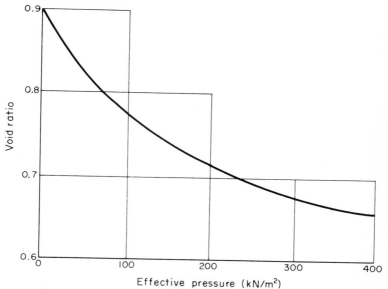

Fig. 12.15 Example 12.3

Table 12.4 Example 12.2

(Depth) (m)	Soil overburden (kN/m^2)	Total p (kN/m^2)	Total p (m of water)	u (m of water)	$S = \alpha P - u$ (m of water)	s (pF scale)	m (%)
0.0	0.0	6.0	0.61	−1.0	1.61	2.21	31.7
0.5	11.2	17.2	1.75	−0.5	2.25	2.35	31.4
1.0	22.4	28.4	2.89	0.0	2.89	2.46	31.0
1.5	33.6	39.6	4.04	0.5	3.54	2.55	30.7
2.0	44.8	50.8	5.19	1.0	4.19	2.62	30.5
3.0	67.2	73.2	7.47	2.0	5.47	2.74	29.9
4.0	89.6	95.6	9.78	3.0	6.78	2.83	29.5
5.0	112.0	118.0	12.05	4.0	8.05	2.91	29.2

Solution

As $\alpha = 1.0$ for a clay, the suction, in this case, equals the effective stress. By means of Fig. 12.15 it is possible to determine the void ratio values knowing the effective stress values. In a saturated soil the void ratio, e, is related to the moisture content, m, and the particle specific gravity, G, by the expression:

$$e = mG$$

Hence the m values can be found, as set out in Table 12.5.

Depth (m)	Void ratio	Effective stress (m of water)	Effective stress (kN/m²)	m (%)
0.0	0.864	1.61	15.8	31.5
0.5	0.853	2.25	22.0	31.2
1.0	0.846	2.89	28.3	31.0
1.5	0.834	3.54	34.7	30.5
2.0	0.825	4.19	41.0	30.2
3.0	0.812	5.47	53.6	29.7
4.0	0.802	6.78	66.5	29.4
5.0	0.790	8.05	79.0	28.9

Table 12.5 Example 12.3

Example 12.4

A set of silt samples, each with a mass of 165 g and a moisture content of 20 per cent, were compacted into a cylindrical mould of 87.0 ml volume. The particle specific gravity of the soil was 2.65. The samples were then subjected to undrained triaxial tests with the results set out below.

Cell pressure (kN/m²)	Change in volume during consolidation (ml)	Change in volume during shear (ml)	$\sigma_1 - \sigma_3$ at failure (kN/m²)	u_a at failure (kN/m²)	u_w at failure (kN/m²)
140	0.9	1.1	280	140	−103
210	2.0	1.5	420	126	−117
280	3.1	1.4	560	55	−131

(i) Determine the strength envelopes assuming (a) $\sigma' = \sigma - u_a$
(b) $\sigma' = \sigma - u_w$

(ii) Assuming that $c' = 0$, determine the values of χ that applied to each sample at its point of failure and plot the relationship between S and χ.

Solution

The two strength envelopes for part (i) are shown in Fig. 12.16.

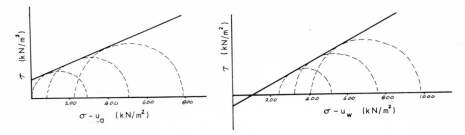

Fig. 12.16 Example 12.4(i)

The main calculations for part (ii) are set out in tabular form (Table 12.6).

Table 12.6

$\dfrac{\sigma_1 - \sigma_3}{2}$	$\dfrac{\sigma_1 + \sigma_3}{2} - u_a$	$\dfrac{\sigma_1 + \sigma_3}{2} - u_w$	χ	S(%)
140	140	383	0.76	83
210	294	537	0.79	88
280	505	691	0.82	90

The two curves of $\dfrac{\sigma_1 + \sigma_3}{2} - u_a$ and $\dfrac{\sigma_1 + \sigma_3}{2} - u_w$ against $\dfrac{\sigma_1 - \sigma_3}{2}$ are plotted and extrapolated to give an assumed point of full saturation (Fig. 12.17A). As there is no cohesion, the K_f line can be drawn through the origin up to the point of full saturation and the various 'e' and 'f' values obtained to give χ.

The degree of saturation is the one pertaining at failure. A typical determination is set out below.

Density of sample $= \dfrac{165}{87} = 1.9$ g/ml

$$M_s = \frac{165}{1.2} = 137.5 \text{ g}$$

$$V_s = \frac{137.5}{2.65} = 51.9 \text{ ml}$$

Volume of sample at failure = 87 − 2.0 = 85 ml

∴

$$V_V = 85 - 51.9 = 33.1 \text{ ml}$$

$$e = \frac{33.1}{51.9} = 0.638$$

$$S = \frac{mG}{e} = \frac{0.2 \times 2.65}{0.638} = 83 \text{ per cent}$$

The plot of variation of χ with S is shown in Fig. 12.17B.

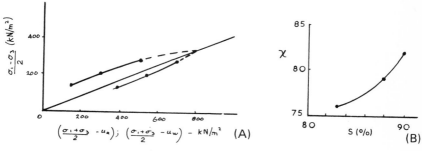

Fig. 12.17 Example 12.4(ii)

Example 12.5

The compressibility of a soil is given by the following figures:

σ' (kN/m²)	$\dfrac{-\Delta V}{V}$ (%)
0	0
17.24	1.05
34.47	1.61
68.95	2.37
137.90	3.31
275.80	4.34
551.60	5.52

The soil has a particle specific gravity of 2.66, an initial porosity of 25 per cent and an initial degree of saturation of 93.9 per cent. Determine:

(i) The dry density and moisture content.
(ii) The change in pore air pressure necessary to give full saturation. (Take Henry's coefficient of solubility as 0.02 and assume that the difference $u_a - u_w$ is negligible and that initial pore air pressure = 100 kN/m² abs.)
(iii) Determine and plot as a curve the relationship between pore pressure and change in total stress under undrained conditions.

(iv) Repeat (ii) and (iii) assuming an initial degree of saturation of 86 per cent if the compressibility of the soil is unaltered.

(v) Repeat (iv) assuming half the volume change for each increment of effective stress.

Solution

(i)
$$n_0 = 0.25 = \frac{e}{1+e} \quad \therefore e = 0.333$$

$$\rho_d = \frac{\rho_w G}{1+e} = 1000 \times \frac{2.66}{1.33} = 2000 \text{ kg/m}^3$$

$$\text{Moisture content} = \frac{M_w}{M_s} = \frac{0.25 \times 0.939 \times 1000}{0.75 \times 2.66 \times 1000} = 11.8 \text{ per cent}$$

(ii) For full saturation $\Delta p_s = \dfrac{1-S}{SH} p_0 = \dfrac{1-0.939}{0.939 \times 0.2} \times 100 = 325.0 \text{ kN/m}^2$

(iii) The pressure p_s (425 kN/m² abs., but generally referred to as the increase above initial, Δp_s, 325 kN/m²) occurs when $\dfrac{-\Delta V}{V} = (1-S)n_0$

i.e. when $\dfrac{\Delta V}{V} = (1-0.939)\,0.25 = 1.53$ per cent

As this value of compressibility is not stated in the compressibility data given at the start of the example it is now necessary to plot the values of effective stress, σ', against compressibility, $-\Delta V/V$, in order to obtain the effective stress value corresponding to $-\Delta V/V = 1.53$ per cent (32.41 kN/m²). (See Fig. 12.18A.)

The relationship

$$\Delta p = p_0 \frac{\dfrac{-\Delta V}{V}}{\dfrac{\Delta V}{V} + (1-S+SH)n_0}$$

can only hold for values of $-\Delta V/V$ up to 1.53 per cent (i.e. for air pressures up to 325 kN/m²).

The table set out opposite can now be drawn up. The calculation for Δp at $-\Delta V/V = 1.05$ per cent is as follows:

$$\Delta p = p_0 \frac{\dfrac{-\Delta V}{V}}{\dfrac{\Delta V}{V} = (1-S+SH)n_0} = \frac{100 \times 0.0105}{-0.0105 + (0.061 + 0.0188)\,0.25}$$

$$= \frac{100 \times 0.0105}{-0.0105 + 0.02} = 110.5 \text{ kN/m}^2$$

$\dfrac{-\Delta V}{V}$	$\sigma'\ (\mathrm{kN/m^2})$	$\Delta p\ (\mathrm{kN/m^2})$	$\sigma\ (\mathrm{kN/m^2})$
0	0	0	
1.05	17.24	111.70	
1.53	32.41	325	129
1.61	34.47	saturated	357
2.37	68.95		

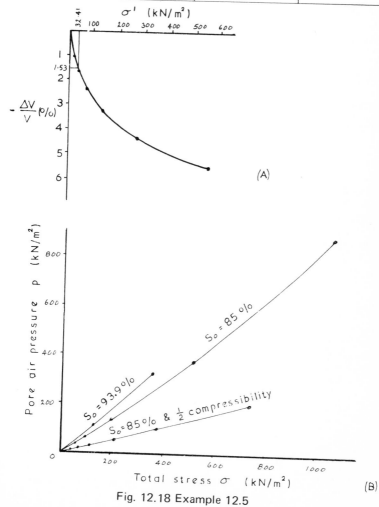

Fig. 12.18 Example 12.5

From the table on page 395 the graph of pore pressure against total stress can be plotted (Fig. 12.18B).

(iv) S   = 85 per cent

$$\Delta p_s = \frac{1 - S}{SH} p_0 = 882 \text{ kN/m}^2$$

$$\frac{-\Delta V_s}{V} = (1 - S)n_0 = 3.75 \text{ per cent}$$

Hence

$$\Delta p = p_0 \frac{\frac{-\Delta V}{V}}{\frac{\Delta V}{V} + (1 - S + SH)n_0}$$

applies when $\frac{-\Delta V}{V}$ is less than 3.75 per cent.

The values in Table 12.7 can now be completed:

Table 12.7 Example 12.5

$\frac{-\Delta V}{V}$ (%)	σ' (kN/m²)	Δp (kN/m²)	σ (kN/m²)
0	0	0	
1.05	17.24	33.6	51
1.61	34.47	62.8	97
2.37	68.95	131.3	200
3.31	137.4	383	520
3.75	186.2	882	1068
4.34	275.8	saturated	
5.52	551.6		

The plot of Δp against σ is shown in Fig. 12.18B.

(v) S = 85 per cent but half volume change, i.e. half compressibility. As before, $\Delta p_s = 882 \text{ kN/m}^2$ and $\frac{-\Delta V_s}{V} = 3.75$ per cent.

The formula for Δp holds for values of $-\Delta V/V$ less than 3.75 per cent, and a Table 12.8 can be prepared:

Table 12.8 Example 12.5

$-\dfrac{\Delta V}{V}(\%)$	$\sigma'\,(kN/m^2)$	$\Delta p\,(kN/m^2)$	$\sigma\,(kN/m^2)$
0	0	0	0
0.525	17.24	14.38	32
0.805	34.47	23.89	58
1.185	68.95	39.63	109
1.655	137.4	65.67	203
2.17	275.8	108.3	384
2.76	551.6	195.0	747

The plot of Δp against σ is shown in Fig. 12.18B.

EXERCISES ON CHAPTER 12

12.1 The soil suction and moisture content relationship of a soft clay is as follows:

Suction (kN/m^2)	80	70	60	50	40	30	20	10
Moisture content (%)	15.5	15.8	16.2	16.7	17.3	18.3	21.9	22.5

A 5 m thick layer of the clay overlies an igneous rock. Ground water level within the clay is at a depth of two metres below the surface of the clay.
(a) Determine the approximate distribution of equilibrium moisture content at every 1 m depth throughout the thickness of the clay. (Saturated unit weight of clay = 19.3 kN/m^3; particle specific gravity = 2.65.)
(b) A wide pavement is to be placed on top of the clay and will exert a pressure of 1.0 kN/m^2. By considering the average e value in the clay before the application of the pavement and after its construction and consolidation, determine the average settlement of the pavement.
Answer:

(a)	Depth (m)	0	1	2	3	4	5
	m (%)	22.0	18.8	17.7	16.9	16.4	15.9

(b) Settlement = 29 mm

12.2 Compressibility tests on a soil sample gave the following results:

σ' (kN/m^2)	$\dfrac{-\Delta V}{V}$ (%)
0	0
12.5	0.58
25.0	0.89
50.0	1.31
100.0	1.82
200.0	2.39
400.0	3.04

In the undisturbed state the soil has a porosity of 27 per cent and a degree of saturation of 93 per cent. The particle specific gravity is 2.64.

(a) Determine the pore air pressure required to give full saturation.

(b) Determine the relationship between pore air pressure and total stress under undrained conditions.

Assume that $p_0 = 100 \text{ kN/m}^2$ and that $u_a - u_w$ is negligible.

Answer

(a) $p_s = 376 \text{ kN/m}^2$

(b)

σ (kN/m^2)	35	72	146	213	275	337	398	500
u_a (kN/m^2)	25	50	100	150	200	250	300	350

REFERENCES

Barden, L.
  Consolidation of compacted and unsaturated clay, *Géotechnique*, (1965).

Bishop, A. W., Alpan, I., Blight, G. E. & Donald, I. B.
  Factors controlling the strength of partly saturated cohesive soils. *Proc. of Research Conference on Shear Strength of Cohesive Soils.* Pub. by A.S.C.E. (1960).

Bishop, A. W. & Henkel, D. J.
  The measurements of soil properties in the triaxial test. (Edward Arnold, 1962).

Croney, D. & Coleman, J. D.
  Soil moisture suction properties and their bearing on the moisture distribution in soils. *Proc. 3rd. Int. Conf. Soil Mechanics and Foundation Engineering.* (1953).
  Pore pressure and suction in soil. *Pore Pressure Conference, London, 1960.* (Butterworth) Road Research Laboratory.
  Field studies of the movement of soil moisture. Tech. paper No. 41 D.S.I.R. (1958).

Schofield, R. K.
 The pF of the water in soil. *Trans. 3rd. Int. Congr. Soil Sci.* (Oxford, 1935)

13. Site Investigation

A site investigation, or soil survey, is an essential part of the preliminary design work on any important structure in order to obtain information regarding the sequence of strata and the ground water level, and also to collect samples for identification and testing. In addition a site investigation is often necessary to assess the safety of an existing structure or to investigate a case where failure has occurred.

British Standard Code of Practice CP 2001, *Site investigations,* lists the following objects of a site investigation:

(i) To assess the general suitability of the site for the proposed works.

(ii) To enable an adequate and economic design to be prepared.

(iii) To forsee and provide against difficulties that may arise during construction due to ground and other local conditions.

(iv) To investigate the occurrence or causes of all natural or created changes of conditions and the results arising therefrom.

SOIL PROFILE

From the results of a site investigation vertical sections (soil profiles) are generally prepared, showing to scale the sequence and thickness of the strata.

Foundation engineers are mainly interested in the materials below the subsoil, and with stratified sedimentary deposits conditions may be more or less homogeneous. Boulder clay deposits can also be homogeneous although unstratified, but they often have an erratic structure in which pockets of different soils are scattered through the main deposit and make it difficult to obtain an average value for the deposit's characteristics. Furthermore, the boulder clay itself may vary considerably, and at certain levels it can even decrease in strength with increasing depth.

Secondary structure of deposits

Besides the primary structure of stratification, many clays contain a secondary structure of hair cracks, joints and slickensides. The cracks (often referred to as macroscopic fissures) and joints generally occurred with shrinkage when at some stage in its development the deposit was exposed to the atmosphere and dried out; slickensides are smooth, highly polished surfaces probably caused by movement along the joints. If the effect of these fissures is ignored in the testing programme the strength characteristics obtained may bear little relationship to the properties of the clay mass.

With the application of a foundation load there is little chance of the fissures opening up, but in cuttings (due to the expansion caused by stress relief) some fissures may open and allow the ingress of rain water which will eventually soften the upper region of the deposit and lead to local slips. Fissures are more prevalent in overconsolidated clays, where stress relief occurs, than in normally consolidated clays, but any evidence of fissuring should be reported in the boring record.

SITE EXPLORATION METHODS

Test or trial pits

A test pit is simply a hole dug in the ground that is large enough for a ladder to be inserted, thus permitting a close examination of the sides. With this method ground water conditions can be established exactly and undisturbed soil samples are obtainable relatively easily. Below a depth of about 4 m, the problems of strutting and the removal of excavated material become increasingly important and the cost of trial pits increases rapidly; in excavations below ground water level the expense may be prohibitive.

Hand auger or post-hole auger

The hand auger (attached to drill rods and turned by hand) is often used in soft soils for borings to about 6 m and is useful for site exploration work in connection with roads. In cohesive soils the clay auger shown in Fig. 13.1 is used, but for gravels a gravel (or worm) auger can be employed.

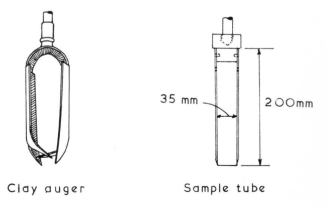

35 mm   200mm

Clay auger   Sample tube

Fig. 13.1 The post-hole auger

Boring rig

In most site investigations the boreholes are taken down by some form of well-boring equipment and can extend to considerable depths, the operation usually being carried out in the dry in Britain whereas in the United States wash boring techniques are more common.

The auger is replaced by a clay cutter—a much heavier unit weighing about 55 kg (Fig. 13.2)—and power is provided to lift and lower it. Boring

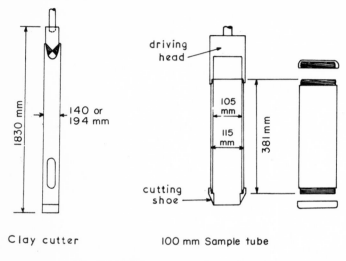

Clay cutter   100 mm Sample tube

Fig. 13.2 Clay cutter and sample tube

consists of dropping the cutter from some 1.5 to 3 m above the soil and is largely carried out by hand, although this practice is going out of fashion and when site conditions are suitable the operation is often powered. In compact sands and gravels water is generally added if the deposit is not already wet. The material is removed by means of a shell which is dropped in a similar manner to the clay cutter: it is fitted with a clack (a hinged lid) that closes as the shell is withdrawn and retains the loose particles. In extremely hard granular deposits a chisel is sometimes necessary to achieve break up of the soil.

Boreholes in sands and gravels, and most deep boreholes in clay, must be lined with steel tubes to prevent collapse of the sides, the casings (of slightly larger diameter than the cutter) being hammered or surged downwards as boring proceeds.

In order to prove bedrock a minimum penetration of 1.5 to 3 m is generally required. Penetration into soft rocks is sometimes possible with the chisel but for hard rocks a diamond drill becomes necessary, particularly if rock cores are to be obtained.

Sampling

Two types of soil sample can be obtained: disturbed sample and undisturbed sample.

Disturbed samples

The auger parings or the contents of the shell can be collected as disturbed soil samples. Such soil has been remoulded and is of no use for shear strength tests but is useful for identification tests (L.L. and P.L., particle size distribution, etc.).

Disturbed samples are usually collected in airtight tins or jars or in plastic sampling bags, and are labelled to give the bore hole number, the depth, and a description.

Undisturbed samples (cohesive soil)

In a trial pit samples can be cut out by hand if care is taken. Such a sample must be placed in an air tight container and as a further precaution should first be given at least two coats of paraffin wax.

The hand auger can be used to obtain useful samples for unconfined compression tests and employs 35 mm sampling tubes with a length of 200 mm (Fig. 13.1). The auger is first removed from the rods and the tube fitted in its place, after which the tube is driven into the soil at the bottom of the borehole, given a half turn, and withdrawn. Finally, the ends of the tube are sealed with paraffin wax.

With the boring rig, 100 mm diameter undisturbed samples are collected, the sampling tube being 105 mm diameter and usually 381 mm long (Fig. 13.2). The tube is first fitted with a special cutting shoe and then driven into the ground by a falling weight in a similar manner to the standard penetration test; during driving any entrapped water, air or slush can escape through a non-return valve fitted in the driving head at the top of the tube. After collection the sample is sealed at both ends with paraffin wax and, as a further precaution, sealing caps are screwed on to the tube.

These sampling techniques involve the removal of the boring rods from the hole, the replacement of the cutting edge with the sampler, the reinsertion of the rods, the collection of the sample, the removal of the rods, the replacement of the sampler with the cutting edge and, finally, the reinsertion of the rods so that boring may proceed. This is a most time-consuming operation and for deep bores, such as occur in site investigations for off-shore oil rigs, techniques have been developed to enable samplers to be inserted down through the drill rods so that soil samples can be collected much more quickly.

Degree of sample disturbance. No matter how careful the technique employed there will inevitably be some disturbance of the soil during its collection as an 'undisturbed' sample, the least disturbance occurring in samples cut from the floor or sides of a trial pit. With sample tubes, jacking is preferable to hammering although if the blows are applied in a regular pattern there is little difference between the two.

The degree of disturbance has been related (Hvorslev, 1949) to the area ratio of the sample tube, A_r

$$A_r = \frac{D_e^2 - D_i^2}{D_i^2}$$

where D_e and D_i are the external and internal diameters of the tube respectively. It is generally agreed that, for good undisturbed 100 mm diameter samples, A_r should not exceed 25 per cent, but in fact most cutting heads have $A_r \doteqdot 28$ per cent.

Undistributed samples (sands)

If care is taken it is possible to extract a sand sample by cutting from the bottom or sides of a trial pit. In a borehole, above ground water level, sand is damp and there is enough temporary cohesion to allow samples to be collected in sampling tubes, but below ground water level tube sampling is not possible. Various techniques employing chemicals or temporarily freezing the ground water have been tried, but they are expensive and not very satisfactory; the use of compressed air in conjunction with the sampler evolved by Bishop (1948), however, enables a reasonably undisturbed sample to be obtained.

Due to the fact that sand is easily disturbed during transportation any tests on the soil in the undisturbed state should be carried out on the site, the usual practice being to use the results of penetration tests instead of sampling.

Frequency of sampling

Samples, both disturbed and undisturbed, should be taken at every change of stratum and at least at every 1.5 m in apparently homogeneous material.

PENETRATION TESTS

The standard penetration test that was described in chapter 8 is normally used for cohesionless soils, although Terzaghi & Peck (1948) give an approximate relationship for clays:

For square footings $q_a \doteqdot 16N$ (kN/m^2)

For continuous footings $q_a \doteqdot 12N$ (kN/m^2)

where q_a = safe bearing capacity (F = 3)

   N = uncorrected test number of blows.

The Dutch cone test, also described in chapter 8, can be used for both cohesive and cohesionless soils.

PLATE LOADING TEST

Loading tests are more applicable to cohesionless soils than cohesive soils due to the time necessary for the latter to reach full consolidation. Generally two tests are carried out as a check on each other, different sized plates of the same shape being used in granular soils so that the settlement of the proposed foundation can be evolved from the relationship between the two plates. The loading is applied in increments (usually one-fifth of the proposed bearing pressure) and is increased up to two or three times the proposed loading. Additional increments should only be added when there has been no detectable settlement in the preceding 24 hours. Measurements are usually taken to 0.01 mm, and where there is no definte failure point the ultimate bearing capacity is assumed to be the pressure causing a settlement equal to 20 per cent of the plate width.

VANE TEST

In soft sensitive clays it is difficult to obtain samples that have only a slight degree of disturbance and in situ shear tests are usually carried out by means of the vane test (Fig. 13.3). The apparatus consists of a 80 mm diameter vane, with four small blades 150 mm long. The vanes are pushed into the clay 0.5 m ahead of the boring to eliminate disturbance effects, and the undrained strength of the clay is obtained from the relationship with the

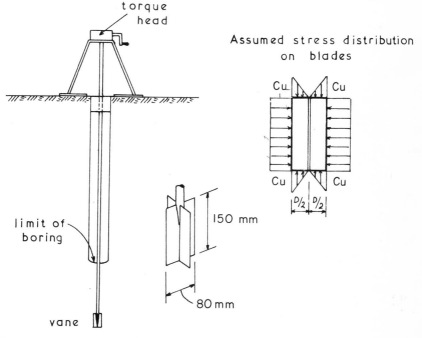

Fig. 13.3 The vane test

torque necessary to turn the vane. The rate of turning the rods, throughout the test, is kept within the range 6–12° per minute. After the soil has sheared, its remoulded strength can be determined by noting the minimum torque when the vane is rotated rapidly.

Fig. 13.3 indicates that the torque head is mounted at the top of the rods. This is standard practice for most site investigation work but, for deep bores, it is now possible to use apparatus in which the torque motor is mounted down near to the vane, in order to remove the whip in the rods.

Because of this development the vane has largely superseded the standard penetration test, for deep testing. The latter test has the disadvantage that the load must always be applied at the top of the rods so that some of the energy from a blow must be dissipated in them. This energy loss becomes more significant the deeper the bore, so that the test results become more suspect.

The assumed shear stress distribution around the vane blades is shown in Fig. 13.3. The shear stress on the perimeter is assumed uniform at c_u and, at the ends, a triangular distribution is assumed which varies from 0 at the centre of rotation to c_u at the edge.

For equilibrium the applied torque, T, = moment of resistance of vane blades,

i.e. T = surface stress × surface area × lever arm about centre + end areas × average stress × lever arm

$$= c_u \, \pi D H \times \frac{D}{2} + 2 \left[\frac{\pi D^2}{4} \times \frac{c_u}{2} \times \frac{2}{3} D \right]$$

$$= c_u \left[\frac{\pi D^2 H}{2} + \frac{\pi D^3}{6} \right]$$

$$= c_u \frac{\pi D^2 H}{2} \left(1 + \frac{D}{3H} \right)$$

where D = measured width of vane (mm)

H = measured height of vane (mm)

Example

A vane, used to test a deposit of soft alluvial clay, required a torque of 67.5 mN.

The dimensions of the vane were: D = 80 mm; H = 150 mm.

Determine a value for the undrained shear strength of the clay.

Solution

$$T = c_u \frac{\pi D^2 H}{2} \left(1 + \frac{D}{3H} \right)$$

i.e. $$67.5 = c_u \, \pi \times \frac{0.08^2 \times 1.5}{2} \left(1 + \frac{0.08}{0.45} \right) \times 1000 \ kN/m^2$$

∴ $$c_u = 38 \ kN/m^2$$

WATER LEVEL OBSERVATIONS

It is not possible to determine accurate ground water conditions during the boring and sampling operations, except possibly in granular soils.

Standpipes

In clays and silts it takes some time for water to fill in a borehole and the normal procedure for obtaining the gound water level is to insert an open-ended tube, usually 50 mm in diameter and perforated at its end, into the borehole (Fig. 13.4). The tube is packed around with gravel and sealed

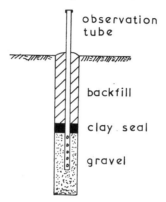

observation
tube

backfill

clay seal

gravel

Fig. 13.4 Ground water level observation in a bore hole

in position with puddle clay, the borehole then being backfilled to prevent access to rainwater. Observations must be taken for several weeks until equilibrium is achieved.

By inserting more than one tube, different strata can be cut off by puddled clay and the various water heads obtained separately. When a general water level is to be obtained, the gravel is usually extended to within a short distance of the top of the borehole and then sealed with the puddle clay.

Pore water pressure measurement

Open-ended tubes have a tendency to silt up, as well as exhibiting a slow response to rapid pore water pressure changes that can be caused by tidal variations or changes in foundation loadings. Where such measurements are necessary a closed piezometer system is used instead of an open one (see chapter 5); two main types of closed piezometer are in use, the electric vibrating wire transducer type and the hydraulic variety, both having been described by Penman (1960).

The advantages of the electrical system are that (i) pressure is measured at the tip so that piezometric levels below the gauge house level can be recorded, (ii) the ancillary equipment is compact, and (iii) the time response of these instruments to pore pressure changes is fairly rapid. Disadvantages include the fact that the readings from an electric tip depend upon an initial calibration that cannot be checked once the tip has been installed (unless it is dug out), and the risk of calibration drift (especially if the tip is to be in operation for some time). The general tendency appears to be to use the hydraulic tip whenever possible.

SOIL SURVEY PROCEDURE

Geological information
Geological survey maps and memoirs often provide useful information and should be consulted before a site exploration programme is commenced, but such information is of general application and cannot replace a soil survey.

Preliminary reconnaisance
A walk over the site can often help to give an idea of the work that will be required. Differences in vegetation often indicate changes in subsoil conditions, and any cutting, quarry or river on or near the site should be examined.

Setting out of trial pits and/or boreholes
An accurate setting out by theodolite is not necessary, since lining in with structures marked on an ordnance survey map or using a compass survey will give all the accuracy needed. For heavy structures, boreholes require to be some 15 to 30 m apart and should be taken down to about 1.5 times the width of the structure unless rock is encountered at lower depths. For roads the boreholes need not be closer than 300 m centres unless vegetation changes indicate variations in soil conditions, and need not go beyond 3 m below formation level.

Site investigation of coal spoil heaps
These investigations fall into two classes:
(i) The exploration of the site for a proposed new tip.
(ii) The investigation of an existing tip to enable a stability analysis to be carried out.
New sites
The exploration programme for a new coal spoil heap on an open site will be similar to a soils investigation for any other civil engineering structure except that it need not be on such a grand scale. Large settlements and a certain amount of bearing capacity failure will be of little consequence and therefore, even when a massive tip is envisaged, the number of borings can be kept to a minimum. In cases where the site is adjacent to existing property,

boreholes near these structures will be necessary to confirm that they will not suffer detrimental effects when the spoil heap is constructed.

Existing spoil heaps

Since bearing capacity and settlement effects will have already largely taken place in existing spoil heaps (unless they are still being worked), the only analysis necessary will be for stability, and in the case of tips in open country there is little point in proceeding with such an assessment unless a road or canal, etc., is in close proximity. Where an analysis does have to be carried out, some decision must be made as to the direction in which substantial movement could lead to damage or loss of life, because it would be economically impossible to undertake analyses in all directions.

For a stability analysis in a particular direction it should be possible to keep the number of bores down to three: one in front of the tip, one on the side of the tip through the spoil material and into the subsoil, and finally one through the top of the tip not necessarily penetrating into the subsoil. The depths to which the boreholes extend down into the subsoil need not be very great; an estimate should be made of the extent of possible slip circles and the bores should go slightly beyond these levels.

It is essential that an allowance be made for pore water pressures both in the spoil heap and in the subsoil. Spoil material is essentially granular and there is a good chance that water which has in the past found its way into the tip has also managed to find its way out, in such a case a total stress analysis may be satisfactory, but conditions will depend upon the topography of the surrounding area, and on sloping sites water may well be flowing through the tip. If water can actually be seen coming out of a tip there is a definite need for proper investigation.

Due to the cementation of the particles that will have occurred during calcination, a burnt-out tip will be much stronger than an unburnt one, but a spoil heap which is on fire is obviously a danger. Such a tip may not only develop fissures due to temperature stresses but also large voids which could lead to a loss in stability.

Sampling of spoil heap material

The evidence of the Aberfan tribunal was that satisfactory 100 mm undisturbed samples of spoil heap material can be obtained from bores through a tip with a procedure similar to that used in normal site investigations.

Whether this will apply to all coal spoil heaps, however, is doubtful. Standard penetration tests seem a logical procedure to carry out during the borings and may eventually lead to a design procedure for stability that could be applied to tips. Density tests could be undertaken in a small trial pit, possibly about half a metre below the surface to eliminate weathering effects, and these might be quite useful if the penetration tests indicated a fair degree of uniformity in the tip.

Site investigation reports

The site investigation report is the final product of an exploration programme. It consists of a summary of the ground conditions encountered,
a list of the tests carried out and recommendations as to possible foundation
arrangements.

The recipient of the report is the client, the person or company who pays
for the work done. Such people are rarely engineers and therefore appoint
an architect or consulting engineer to design any proposed development. The
person appointed is naturally concerned with the financial aspects of the
work he is supervising and this applies to the site investigation work as
well as to the later construction.

Obviously someone must keep a rein on expenditure, but if this attitude
is too strictly maintained it can have detrimental effects on the efficacy of a
site investigation. It is not unknown for a consultant to employ a soils
investigation firm to prepare a report on a development site and to specify,
in advance, the number of boreholes, the number of samples to be collected
and the number of laboratory tests that will be carried out. If relatively
homogeneous subsoil conditions are encountered, such a procedure can lead
to unnecessary costs, whereas, with variable conditions, the money allocated
may be totally inadequate if a meaningful report is to be achieved.

Ideally, the soils engineer should be allowed to modify the site investigation programme as work proceeds. Such a system could obviously be abused
but, with reputable soils firms, can prove to be both efficient and economical.

Reports are generally prepared in sections, headed as described in the
following section.

Preamble

This introductory section consists of a brief summary which gives the
location of the site, the date of the investigation and name of the client,
the types of bores put down and the equipment used.

Description of site

Here a general description of the site is given: whether it is an open field
or a redevelopment of a site where old foundations, cellars and walls, etc.,
remain. Some mention is made of the general geology of the area, whether
there are old mineral workings at depth and, if so, whether the report has
considered their possible effects or not. A map, showing the site location
and the positions of any boreholes put down, is usually included in the
report.

Description of subsoil conditions encountered

This section should consist of a short, and readable, description of the
general subsoil conditions over the site with reference to the borehole
journals. Generally the significance of any in situ testing carried out is
mentioned.

Borehole journals

A borehole journal is a list of all the materials encountered during the boring.

PROPOSED WHATSIT BRIDGE
RECORD OF BOREHOLE 109

Ref. No. 866
Ground Level 3.40 M   **O.D.**

PIT 1.0 x 1.0   TO 1.0 m
Dia. of Boring   150 mm TO 13.70m S & A
76 mm TO 17.40 m D.D.

PROGRESS			SAMPLE/TEST		STRATA			
HOLE	CASING	WATER	DEPTH	TYPE	LEGEND	DEPTH	LEVEL	DESCRIPTION
28/8/70			0.30	D1		0.30	3.10	BROWN SANDY TOPSOIL
		MET AT 2.00	1.88 – 2.13	S(29) D2				MEDIUM DENSE TO DENSE RED BROWN SILTY SAND AND FINE GRAVEL
			0.30 – 2.18	B1				
			2.20	W				
			2.50	D3		2.60	0.80	
			3.15 – 3.45	C(6)				MEDIUM DENSE BROWN SILTY SAND WITH CLAYEY LAYERS, CONTAINING OCCASIONAL GRAVEL
			3.45 – 3.75	(17) D4				
			2.70 – 3.90	B2				
			4.10 – 4.55	U–/120				
4.56	4.56	4.00	4.10	D5		4.56	-1.16	
29/8/70		1.50	5.50 – 5.95	U1/80				STIFF LIGHT BROWN LAMINATED CLAYEY SILT, WITH LAYERS OF SAND
			6.00	D6				
			6.90	D7		7.10	-3.70	
			7.45 – 7.75	S(29) D8				MEDIUM DENSE BECOMING DENSE BROWN SAND
			8.45 – 8.75	S(22) D9				
			9.45 – 9.75	S(26) D10				
			10.45 – 10.75	S(46) D11				
10.73	10.73	8.00						
30/8/70		1.50	11.20	D12		11.20	-7.80	
			11.30 – 11.75	U2/120		11.80	-8.40	COMPACT BROWN SILTY SAND WITH LAYERS OF SILTY CLAY
			11.80	D13				COMPACT BROWN SAND AND GRAVEL
13.40	12.90	9.90	12.90 – 13.35	U3/150		12.80	-9.40	HARD GREY BROWN CLAYEY SAND CONTAINING OCCASIONAL GRAVEL
31/8/70		8.00	13.35	D14				
13.70	13.44	13.00	13.70	D15		13.70	-10.30	
14/9/70		1.50	13.70 – 15.10	*1.40				HARD MOTTLED RED-BROWN, GREY AND GREEN COARSE GRAINED BASALTIC TUFF
		WATER FLUSH	15.10 – 16.34	1.24				
16.34	13.44	÷ 0.36				16.13	-12.73	
15/9/70		1.04	16.34 – 17.40	1.06		17.19	-13.79	SOFT AND MEDIUM HARD WEATHERED MOTTLED RED-BROWN, GREY-GREEN AND PURPLE BASALTIC TUFF
17.40	18.41	÷ 0.36				17.40	-14.00	HARD MOTTLED PURPLE AND GREY BASALTIC TUFF

REMARKS: **SCALE** 1/100
PENETRATION TEST CONTINUED BEYOND NORMAL DRIVE FROM 3.45M
40 MM DIAMETER PERFORATED STANDPIPE 18.00 M LONG INSERTED, SURROUNDED BY GRAVEL FILTER WITH BENTONITE SEAL AND SCREW CAP AT SURFACE.

KEY:

D	Disturbed Sample	S(30)	Standard Penetration Test	U1/70 UndisturbedSample 100mm dia
B	Bulk do do	C(27)	Cone do do	/70 No of Blows to drive sample 450mm
W	Water do	(27)	No Blows for 300mm Penetration	U–/70 Undisturbed Sample- no recovery
•	Core Recovery	V	In-situ Vane Shear Test	S&A Shell & Auger
				DD Rotary Diamond Drilled

WHATLINGS (FOUNDATIONS) LIMITED, 2410 LONDON ROAD GLASGOW E.2.

Fig. 13.5

A journal is best shown in sectional form so that the depths at which the various materials were met can be easily seen. A typical borehole journal is shown in Fig. 13.5. It should include a note of all the information that was found, ground water conditions, numbers and types of samples taken, list of in situ tests, time taken by boring, etc.

Description of laboratory soil tests

This is simply a list of the tests carried out together with a set of laboratory sheets showing particle size distribution curves, liquid limit plots, Mohr circle plots, etc.

Conclusions

It is in this section that firm recommendations as to possible foundation types and modes of construction should be given. Unless specified otherwise, it is the responsibility of the architect or consultant to decide on the actual structure and the construction. For this reason the writer of the report should endeavour to list possible alternatives: whether strip foundations are possible, if piling is a sensible proposition, etc. For each type listed an estimation of its size, working load and settlement should be included.

If the investigation has been limited by specification or finance and the conclusions have been based on scant information, it is important that the fact is mentioned so that any possible allegations of negligence may be refuted.

REFERENCES

Bishop, A. W.
>A new sampling too for use on cohesionless soils below ground water level. *Géotechnique* (1948).

Hvorslev, M. J.
>*Subsurface exploratio   and sampling of soils for civil engineering purposes* (Waterways Expt. Sta., U.S. Corps of Engineers, 1949).

Penman, A. D. M.
>*A study of the response time of various type of piezometer* (Pore Pressure Conf., London. 1960).

Terzaghi, K, & Peck, R. B.
>*Soil mechanics in engineering practice* (John Wiley, 1948).

Author Index

414 *Author Index*

Skipp, B. O. 357
Smith, G. N. 219, 291, 326
Stagg, K. G. 219
Steinbrenner, W. 221, 272
Stuart, J. G. 243
Sutherland, H. B. 246
Swartzendruber, D. 31

Talor, D. W. 136, 137, 318, 321
Terzaghi, K. 28, 43, 190, 194, 197,
    199, 240, 242–245, 270,
    283, 292, 311, 404

Thorburn, S. 275
Thorburn, T. H. 246
Timoshenko, S. P. 219

Vidal, H. 196

Whitaker, T. 259
Wilson, G. 238

Zienkiewicz, O. C. 259

Subject Index